WIND-TUNNEL TESTING

The 16-ft transonic wind tunnel of the NACA, located at Langley Field, Virginia. This tunnel, powered by two 30,000-hp motors, is the largest transonic wind tunnel in the world.

WIND-TUNNEL TESTING

ALAN POPE, M.S.

Supervisor
Experimental Aerodynamics Division
Sandia Corporation

Second Edition

JOHN WILEY & SONS, INC., NEW YORK
LONDON

COPYRIGHT, 1947, 1954
BY
JOHN WILEY & SONS, INC.

SECOND EDITION

THIRD PRINTING, OCTOBER, 1961

Library of Congress Catalog Card Number: 54-8525

PRINTED IN THE UNITED STATES OF AMERICA

To
Carol, Richy, Pattie,
and Caroline

Preface

The purpose of the second edition of *Wind-Tunnel Testing* is twofold: to revise the data and procedures given in the first edition when changes are justified in the light of new knowledge, and to extend the scope of the book to embrace new techniques not available when the first edition was prepared. Accordingly there are new chapters covering testing at nearsonic, transonic, supersonic, and hypersonic velocities; on the testing of helicopter rotors; and on suggested non-aeronautical uses of the wind tunnel. The original discussion of the design and use of the low-speed wind tunnel has been very critically examined and rewritten where it appeared that the presentation could be simplified; photographs featuring more modern airplanes and techniques have been supplied; and many numerical examples have been added. Whenever possible, the degree of correlation that could reasonably be expected between wind tunnel and flight has been included. Improvements will be noted particularly in the chapters on testing procedures and on wall corrections.

Despite the changes the second edition has been rigorously held to the purposes of the first edition: to help students taking wind-tunnel laboratory courses; to furnish a textbook for tunnel engineers; and to aid beginners in the field of wind-tunnel design.

In evaluating the material to be included in the second edition I have been singularly fortunate in having the opportunity to visit nearly every wind tunnel in the United States and Canada, to talk with the engineers using them, and to plan and conduct a wide variety of tests in many different wind tunnels. Frequently a technique presented has been selected as the best of several I have seen or tried myself.

It is hoped that the broader scope will make the second edition more useful than the first.

One of the most gratifying events connected with the first edition of *Wind-Tunnel Testing* was the letters it brought in from nearly all parts of the world—some obviously requiring several hours to write. I should be remiss indeed if I failed to thank my correspondents for their suggestions and inquiries. I hope they will write again.

Special thanks are also due to Keirn Zebb of the Cooperative Wind Tunnel, Rudolf W. Hensel of the Arnold Engineering Development Center, Robert S. Kelso and King Bird of the Cornell Aeronautical Laboratory, Edward Crofut and Elmer Ward of the Aerolab Development Corporation, and their respective staffs, and to the many engineers of the National Advisory Committee for Aeronautics who have helped out time and again. The second edition would not have been possible without their assistance.

ALAN POPE

April, 1954

NOTE

The reader should note that, in order to keep to customary undergraduate level, the treatment of transonic and supersonic testing has been omitted until the last two chapters. Thus, all statements in the first ten chapters carry the unwritten qualification "for the low subsonic Mach number range only."

A. Y. P.

Abbreviations

In view of the large number of aeronautical research centers being set up, a list such as this must be considered incomplete. However, it may be of help in identifying the source of particular publications.

Abbreviation	*Complete Meaning*
AAL	Ames Aeronautical Laboratory (NACA), Moffett Field, California
ACA	Australian Council for Aeronautics, CSIR
AEDC	Arnold Engineering Development Center (Air Force), Tullahoma, Tennessee
AFAC	Air Force Armament Center, Eglin Field, Florida
AFCRC	Air Force Cambridge Research Center, Cambridge, Massachusetts
AFFTC	Air Force Flight Test Center, Muroc, California
AFMTC	Air Force Missile Test Center, Cocoa, Florida
AFSWC	Air Force Special Weapons Center, Albuquerque, New Mexico
APL	Applied Physics Laboratory, Johns Hopkins University, Silver Spring, Maryland
ARC	Air Research Committee (British)
ARIS	Aeronautical Research Institute of Sweden, Ulsvunda, Sweden
ARI, TIU	Air Research Institute, Tokyo Imperial University (Japanese)
AVA	Aerodynamische Versuchsanstalt (Göttingen Institute for Aerodynamics), Göttingen, Germany
BRL	Ballistic Research Laboratory, Aberdeen Proving Ground, Maryland
CAI	Central Aerohydrodynamic Institute, Moscow, U.S.S.R.
CSIR	Council for Scientific and Industrial Research, Australia
CNRC	Canadian National Research Council, Ottawa, Canada

Abbreviation	*Complete Meaning*
DTMB	David Taylor Model Basin (Navy), Carderock, Maryland
DVL	Deutsche Versuchsanstalt für Luftfahrtforschung (German Institute for Aeronautical Research), Berlin and Göttingen, Germany
ETH	Eidgenossische Technische Hochschule (Swiss Institute of Technology)
GALCIT	Guggenheim Aeronautical Laboratory of the California Institute of Technology, Pasadena, California
IAeS	Institute of Aeronautical Sciences (United States)
JAM	Journal of Applied Mechanics
JAS	Journal of the Aeronautical Sciences (United States)
JPL	Jet Propulsion Laboratory, California Institute of Technology, Pasadena, California
JRAS	Journal of the Royal Aeronautical Society (British)
LAL	Langley Aeronautical Laboratory (NACA), Langley Field, Virginia
LFA	Luftfahrtforschungsanstalt Hermann Göring (Hermann Göring Institute for Aeronautics), Braunschweig, Germany
LFPL	Lewis Flight Propulsion Laboratory (NACA), Cleveland, Ohio
LRPG	Long Range Proving Ground (of the AFMTC)
MIT	Massachusetts Institute of Technology, Cambridge, Massachusetts
NACA	National Advisory Committee for Aeronautics (United States)
NAMTC	Naval Air Missile Test Center, Point Mugu, California
NOL	Naval Ordnance Laboratory, White Oaks, Maryland
NPL	National Physical Laboratory, Teddington, Middlesex, England
NRTS	National Reactor Testing Station, Arco, Idaho
NSL	Naval Supersonic Laboratory, Cambridge, Massachusetts
OAL	Ordnance Aerophysics Laboratory, Daingerfield, Texas

Abbreviation	*Complete Meaning*
ONERA	Office National d'Études et de Recherches Aeronautiques (National Bureau of Aeronautical Research), Paris, France
ONR	Office of Naval Research, Washington, D. C.
ORNL	Oak Ridge National Laboratory, Oak Ridge, Tennessee
PRS	Proceedings of the Royal Society of London (British)
QAM	Quarterly of Applied Mechanics
R&M	Reports and Memoranda (of the Air Research Committee)
RAE	Royal Aeronautical Establishment, Farnborough, Hants, England
RM	Research Memorandum of the NACA
SAE	Society of Automotive Engineers (United States)
TM	Technical Memorandum of the NACA
TN	Technical Note of the NACA
TR	Technical Report of the NACA
WADC	Wright Air Development Center, Wright-Patterson Air Force Base, Ohio

Contents

Chapter 1

THE WIND TUNNEL

Information useful for aerodynamic design may be obtained in a number of ways: from wind tunnels, rocket sleds, water tunnels, drops from aircraft, flying scale models, whirling arms, shock tubes, water tables, plunge barrels, rocket flights, and ballistic ranges. Each device has its own sphere of superiority, and no one can be called "best." This textbook, however, considers only the design and use of the wind tunnel.

The wind tunnel is a device for testing aircraft and their components in a controlled airstream under laboratory conditions. Through use of the tunnel it may be assured that the first flight of a new aircraft will not be its last. Accordingly, the wind tunnel has been supported by those in aeronautical development since the first tunnels were built several years before the Wright brothers' flight.

There are today about two hundred tunnels in the United States. Half of these are for subsonic work, both commercial and in schools, and the remainder for testing at high speed. After all, the development of a new aircraft requires a vast amount of research, and any process that can reduce the cost of this work should be vigorously pursued. Wind tunnels through the use of models and twenty-four-hour availability offer a rapid, economical, and accurate means for aerodynamic research. By this means both dollars and lives are saved.

The various nations of the world support the whole field of aeronautical research, of which wind-tunnel testing is a major item, according to their abilities and desires. Usually each nation sets up a separate organization that augments the activities of the armed services, and further work is farmed out to the engineering universities. In the United States this central agency is the National Advisory Committee for Aeronautics (NACA), whose offices are in Washington, D. C., and laboratories at

1

Langley Field, Virginia; Cleveland, Ohio; Moffett Field, California; and Edwards Air Force Base, California.

The armed services have tunnels of their own, also. The Air Force has several at Wright Field, Ohio, and at Tullahoma, Tennessee. The Navy has tunnels at the David Taylor Model Basin in Carderock, Maryland; the Naval Air Missile Test Center at Point Mugu, California; the Naval Ordnance Laboratory at White Oaks, Maryland; the Ordnance Aerophysics Laboratory at Daingerfield, Texas; and the Naval Supersonic Laboratory in Cambridge, Massachusetts. The Army has tunnels at the Aberdeen Proving Grounds, Maryland. In addition, nearly every aircraft corporation has at least one wind tunnel.

Since the wind tunnel is a device primarily intended for scale-model testing, it is proper that we pause now and consider how scale tests can best be conducted so that the results may be most effectively applied to full-scale craft.

1:1. Important Testing Parameters. When a body moves through a medium, forces arise that are due to the viscosity of the medium, its inertia, its elasticity, and gravity. The inertia force is proportional to the mass of air affected and the acceleration given that mass. Thus, while it is true that a very large amount of air is affected by a moving body (and each particle of air a different amount), we may logically say that the inertia force is the result of giving a constant acceleration to some "effective" volume of air. Let this effective volume of air be kl^3, where l is a characteristic length of the body and k a constant for the particular body shape. Then we may write

$$\text{Inertia force} \sim \rho l^3 V/t$$

where ρ = the air density, slug per cu ft; V = velocity of the body, ft per sec; t = time, sec.

Substituting l/V for t, we get

$$\text{Inertia force} \sim \frac{\rho l^3 V}{l/V} \sim \rho l^2 V^2 \qquad (1:1)$$

The viscous force, according to its definition, may be written

$$\text{Viscous force} \sim \mu V l \qquad (1:2)$$

where μ = coefficient of viscosity, slug per ft-sec.

The gravity force is simply

$$\text{Gravity force} = \rho l^3 g \tag{1:3}$$

where g = acceleration of gravity.

By definition, the bulk modulus of elasticity of a gas is the stress needed to develop a unit change in volume. It is given the symbol E and has the units of pounds per square foot. We have then

$$\text{Elastic force} \sim E l^2 \tag{1:4}$$

The speed of sound in air a is related to its elasticity according to

$$E = \rho a^2$$

so that we may write

$$\text{Elastic force} \sim \rho a^2 l^2$$

The important force ratios (as identified with the men who first drew attention to their importance) then become

$$\text{Reynolds number} = \frac{\text{Inertia force}}{\text{Viscous force}} = \frac{\rho}{\mu} V l \tag{1:5}$$

$$\text{Mach number} = \frac{\text{Inertia force}}{\text{Elastic force}} = \frac{V}{a} \tag{1:6}$$

$$\text{Froude number} = \frac{\text{Inertia force}}{\text{Gravity force}} = \sqrt{\frac{V^2}{lg}} \tag{1:7}$$

The last two equations, it will be noted, use the square root of the ratio rather than the ratio itself.

A model under such conditions that it has the same Reynolds and Mach numbers as its full-scale counterpart will have forces and moments on it that can be directly scaled. Flow patterns of the two bodies will be exactly similar. If the body in question is in free flight (a spin or dynamic model) the model should in addition be maintained at the same Froude number as its full-scale counterpart, and its mass density should be governed by eq. 5:39. Further discussion on testing parameters may be found in Sects. 5:17 and 5:24.

Fortunately, all three of the similarity conditions rarely need be applied simultaneously. For models held rigidly in a wind tunnel the Froude number loses its significance. Below a value of 0.4, Mach-number effects are rarely important; and above a value of 1,500,000 the Reynolds-number effects are frequently predictable. Thus, for a great majority of problems, models are adequate for high-quality research; and frequently, when they are not, some devious means can be employed to make them work. Increased pressure can be used directly to build the Reynolds number; gases having qualities different from those of air

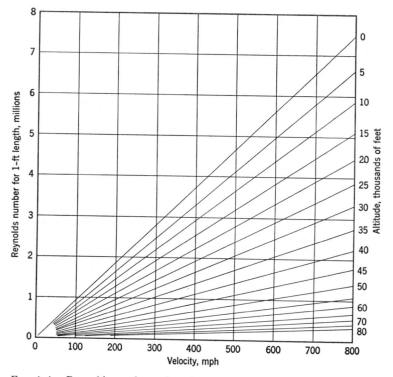

FIG. 1:1. Reynolds-number values for a range of velocities and altitudes, standard atmosphere. Also see Fig. 12:6.

can reduce the speed of sound in the medium and save tunnel power,* and, when Froude number must be matched, the squared term enables small speed increases to produce great improvements. It may be safely stated that an overwhelming percentage of aerodynamic problems can be helped or solved by wind-tunnel model tests.

* For a given power input to a wind tunnel, the substitution of Freon 12 for air enables the Mach number of the stream to be increased by a factor of 2.5, and the Reynolds number to be increased by a factor of 3.6. Added complexity in operation and data analysis is the price to be paid for the gain.

For convenience the values of Reynolds number per foot are presented for standard air up to 80,000 ft altitude in Fig. 1:1. Values of ρ/μ for a range of tunnel conditions are given in Fig. 1:2. Standard sea-level $\rho/\mu = 6380$.

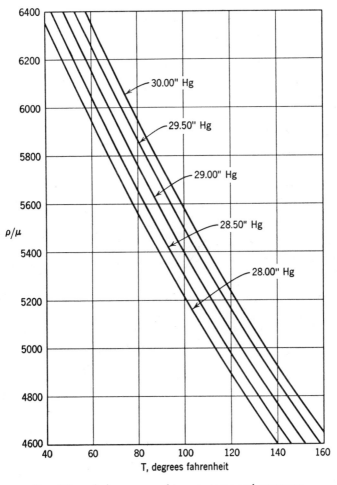

FIG. 1:2. ρ/μ for a range of temperatures and pressures.

The following paragraphs discuss the nomenclature and types of wind tunnels, and examples of each are given. It is regrettable that some of the new and more advanced tunnels are at present on the restricted list.

1:2. Nomenclature. A conventional single-return wind tunnel with the component parts marked with their common names is outlined in Fig. 1:3. Other terms are frequently encountered since full agreement in terminology has not yet been reached. The tunnel itself is often called a "wind channel." The contracting cone may be called an "entrance cone" or a "nozzle." The wind-tunnel fan may also be referred to as a "propeller." The testing section may be called the "working section," "throat,"

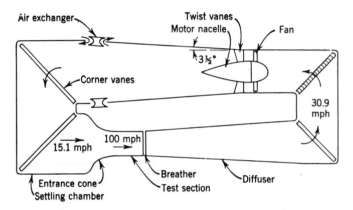

Fig. 1:3. A conventional single-return wind tunnel.*

"channel," or "jet." Sometimes the word "jet" means "open jet" (no solid boundaries). The uncertainty of the nomenclature is rarely confusing, however, for the sense of the context usually removes any doubts as to the meaning intended.

1:3. Types of Wind Tunnels. There are two basic types of wind tunnels. The first, called an open-circuit (or "Eiffel" or, "NPL") † tunnel, has no guided return of the air (see Fig. 1:4). After the air leaves the diffuser, it circulates by devious paths back to the intake. If the tunnel draws its air directly from the atmosphere, entirely fresh air is used.

The second type, called a closed-circuit or "Prandtl," "Göttingen," or "return-flow" tunnel, has, as the last name implies, a continuous path for the air (see Fig. 1:3).

* This figure is actually a little oversimplified since a tunnel with an air exchanger would in all probability not have a breather.

† Strictly speaking, the Eiffel-type tunnel has an open jet, whereas the NPL type has a closed jet. Both are open-circuit tunnels.

Except for the induction-type high-speed tunnel and a few special-purpose tunnels, such as the NACA Free-Flight tunnel, the open-circuit arrangement is rarely employed.

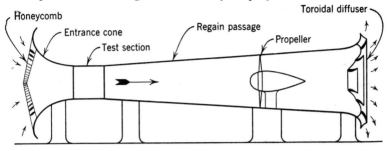

Fig. 1:4.   Open-circuit wind tunnel.   Modern practice usually includes entrance and exit towers to reduce the effects of atmospheric winds.

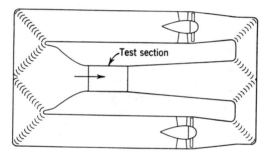

Fig. 1:5.   Double-return wind tunnel.

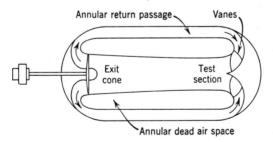

Fig. 1:6.   Annular-return wind tunnel.

The closed circuit may be one of three types: single- (Fig. 1:3), double- (Fig. 1:5), or annular- (Fig. 1:6) return.   Of these, only the first is in general acceptance at present.   In the double- and annular-return arrangements, the particular air that scrapes along the walls of the return passage forms the center of the jet and hence passes directly over the model. Unless the contraction ratio is large, this air is extremely turbulent and tends to make the interpretation of the test data difficult. A further disadvantage of the double-return tunnel is that a variation in velocity distribution may be caused by yawing a large model. In the single-return tunnel, the general mixing and stabilizing effect of the fan tends to reestablish any flow variation due to the model, but in the double-return type the flow deflected to one side can remain there, impairing the roll and yaw data.

Further identification of wind tunnels may be made through the cross-sectional form of the test section. It may be square, rectangular, rectangular with tempered corners, octagonal, circular, or elliptic. The test section may be completely walled in (closed jet) or consist simply of an open space with the air streaming from the entrance cone to the exit cone. Whether the test section is open or closed, the boundaries affect the flow about the model, and the test data must be corrected to agree with free-air results. The nature and magnitude of these corrections are discussed in Chapter 6.

Tunnels whose jet speeds exceed about 400 mph are called "high-speed" tunnels, and those whose jet speeds exceed the velocity of sound are called "supersonic." Both these types require refined calculations both in design and in operation. It will be noted that most supersonic tunnels are quite small.

A few specialized tunnels exist wherein the models fly freely and moving-picture cameras record their movements for later consideration. These include the NACA Spinning tunnels and the NACA Free-Flight tunnel.

1:4. Single-Return Tunnel. Several of the schools in this country have wind tunnels generally similar to the design outlined in Fig. 1:3. The test section of these tunnels is about 65 sq ft in area, and about 300 hp is employed. This size makes a good low-speed (about 125-mph) set-up, economical to build and operate, and fully capable of the majority of tests required. Some of the tunnels can be operated with either open or closed jet.

Typical equipment for this type of tunnel includes a three-point suspension system for the models and a turntable for panel tests.

1:5. Single-Return Pressure Tunnel. The Wright Brothers Wind tunnel at the Massachusetts Institute of Technology is a step above the lower-power tunnel mentioned in Sect. 1:4. Using

2000 hp, the tunnel is capable of 250 mph with the test section at standard pressure, 396 mph with it at 0.23 atmosphere, or 145 mph at 3.5 atmospheres. The low pressure yields the highest Mach number, and the high pressure yields the highest Reynolds number. It takes about 2 hours to obtain either of the nonstandard pressures.

The Wright Brothers tunnel is one of the few with an elliptic jet, having one of that form 10 ft by 7.5 ft. The major portion of the tunnel is of metal; the test section is wood. Cooling for the 2000 hp is obtained by running water over the metal shell. (See also Ref. 1:1.)

1:6. High-Speed Pressure Tunnel. An example of the high-power, high-speed tunnel is found in the Southern California Co-op tunnel in Pasadena, California. Here 12,000 hp are used in a single-return-type tunnel, with facilities available for pressure changes from 0.25 to 4.0 atmospheres. The working section is rectangular, 8.5 ft by 12 ft, with tempered corners which reduce the test section area to about 95 sq ft. The maximum performance may be summed up as follows:

1. At 0.25 atmosphere, $V_{max.} = 700$ mph and $q = (\rho/2) V^2 = 375$ lb/ft^2.

2. At atmospheric pressure, $V_{max.} = 475$ mph and $q = 700$ lb/ft^2.

3. At 4 atmospheres, $V_{max.} = 260$ mph and $q = 930$ lb/ft^2.

A discussion of this tunnel and others of similar capacity is given in Chapter 11.

1:7. Variable-Density Tunnel. The Variable-Density tunnel of the NACA (Ref. 1:2) was the pioneer high-pressure tunnel, being capable of 20 atmospheres. For structural reasons it had an unusual annular return passage, with the 5-ft-diameter working section at the tunnel center. This arrangement yields the minimum steel requirement but is poor as regards model visibility, room for an optical system, and general accessibility.

The advantage of the pressure tunnel lies in the possibility of attaining high Reynolds numbers without either very large models or very high speeds. For example, the full-scale Reynolds number of a quarter-scale model of a 200-mph airplane would require 800 mph under normal pressure conditions. This is far beyond the compressibility burble and might be unreasonable from a power standpoint. With a pressure of 8 atmospheres, the full-scale Reynolds number is attained with only 100 mph.

Though the Variable-Density tunnel is no longer used for testing because of its extremely high turbulence, it did provide early clues to the effect of the Reynolds number on airfoil characteristics. The VDT now serves as a pressure reservoir for several small high-speed tunnels.

The British "Compressed-Air Tunnel" is a second tunnel similar in size and capacity to the American "VDT." The newer 7 by 10 ft tunnel of the RAE also has an annular return.

It might well be mentioned in passing that high pressure is no cure-all for getting a high Reynolds number, as model strength may be a limiting factor.

1:8. Full-Scale Tunnel. The Full-Scale tunnel at Langley Field (Ref. 1:3) is capable of testing actual airplanes of moderate

Official Photograph, National Advisory Committee for Aeronautics.

FIG. 1:7. Full-scale Tigercat in the Moffett Field full-scale wind tunnel. The mounting system shown is special for this test.

size under near-flight conditions. Housed in a large building whose walls form part of the double-return passages, this remarkable tunnel attains wind velocities up to 118 mph with an open jet 60 ft wide and 30 ft high.

A full-scale tunnel serves several purposes impossible to attain in any tunnel accommodating models only:

1. Full-scale prototypes may be "cleaned up."

2. Alterations to actual airplanes may be made without regard to weight or airworthiness.

3. Flying scale models of very large planes may be tested.

4. Actual engine installations may be run under near-flight conditions. (See Fig. 1:7.)

5. A correlation between flight and small model tests may be obtained.

In addition to the well-known tunnel at Langley Field, two other full-scale tunnels are in existence: the large wind tunnel at Chalais-Meudon, France, whose jet is 26 ft by 52 ft; and the Full-Scale tunnel at Moffett Field, California, whose jet is 40 ft by 80 ft. (See Fig. 1:7.)

1:9. Smoke Tunnel. A different approach to the problem of studying air flow is made possible by a smoke tunnel (Ref. 1:4).

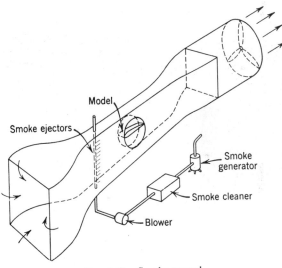

FIG. 1:8. Smoke tunnel.

In this type of apparatus, nozzles just ahead of the model emit cleaned smoke in streamer form. This smoke follows the air flow and makes the flow patterns visible. Smoke tunnels are usually low-velocity tunnels (about 40 mph) and have test sections of the two-dimensional type. Examples of smoke pictures are shown in Figs. 1:9 and 1:10.

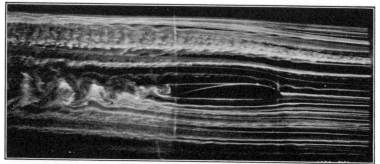

Official Photograph, National Advisory Committee for Aeronautics.

FIG. 1:9.   Smoke picture, low α, low Reynolds number.

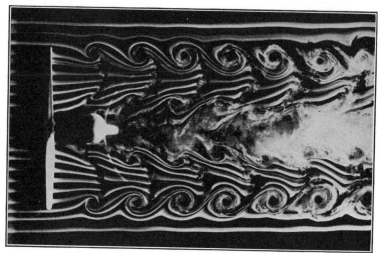

Courtesy F. N. M. Brown, University of Notre Dame.

FIG. 1:10.   Smoke picture of propeller operating near design advance ratio.

1:10. Free-Flight Tunnels. The NACA has several free-flight tunnels in which no balance * is utilized. In these tunnels, models dynamically as well as dimensionally similar to their full-scale counterparts fly under the influence of gravitational, aerodynamic, and inertia forces, and motion pictures are made of their flight (Figs. 1:11 and 1:12).

* A balance is a device to measure the forces and moments that the airstream puts on the model.

Official Photograph, National Advisory Committee for Aeronautics.

FIG. 1:11.   NACA 5-ft Free-Flight tunnel in operation.

In the NACA Free-Flight tunnel the model is kept in a steady-state glide, balanced between gravitational forces and the slightly inclined airstream. The model controls are remotely movable. Various glide paths can be simulated by changing the tilt of the tunnel and its airspeed. Two operators are thus required, one for the model controls and one for the tunnel. The free-flight tunnel yields information on stability and controllability.

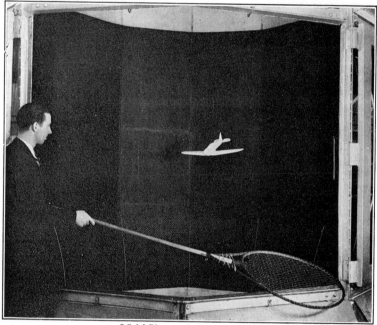

Official Photograph, National Advisory Committee for Aeronautics.
FIG. 1:12.   NACA free-spinning wind tunnel.

The Gust tunnel comprises a model catapulting rig and a vertical airstream. The model is catapulted through the vertical airstream, and motion pictures are made of its path. A small recording accelerometer in the model furnishes data on its behavior. By varying control screens in the vertical duct, nearly any gradient can be made to appear in the gust. This tunnel furnishes valuable data for structural design.

The NACA also has a 20-ft free-spinning tunnel in which models are spun in an airstream that blows vertically upwards. The flow has a lower velocity at the center to keep the models from sliding over to the walls. The speed of the airstream may be rapidly altered and is usually kept equal to the rate of descent of the model, causing it to remain in one location relative to the observers. After a specified period, a mechanism changes the control surfaces to make the model recover; moving pictures then record the number of turns necessary to attain a diving condition. A net at the base of the tunnel prevents damage to the model. Correlation between recovery time of properly constructed models and of actual airplanes is good. In general the spin tunnel yields the angle of sideslip, rate of rotation, and angle of attack during a spin. A satisfactory model spins at an angle of attack steeper than 45 degrees and recovers from the spin in less than two turns after the controls are moved.

Another type of test found quite useful is the determination of whether the pilot will clear the tail surfaces if forced to bail out during a spin. For this a dummy pilot is released while the airplane is spinning and the path of the dummy relative to the airplane is observed.

It might be mentioned that the vertical tunnels for testing parachutes differ from the spin tunnels in that they require an even velocity front instead of the dish-shaped front required for a spin tunnel.

1:11. Supersonic Tunnels. Quite early in the study of aerodynamics, it became apparent that there might be serious changes in the flow patterns about bodies when at any point over the body the local velocity exceeded the local speed of sound. It was a long time, however, before any testing apparatus was available to investigate this field.

The first high-speed tests were made in the direct exhaust of high-pressure tanks, but such arrangements were unsatisfactory, owing to turbulence and general unsteadiness of flow. (This was before the science of damping screens (Sect. 3:14) had been developed.)

Next the induction type of tunnel was tried. This type employs an annular slot downstream of the test section from which high-pressure air is emitted. In turn this draft creates a low-pressure region into which atmospheric air rushes. An example of an induction drive is shown in Fig. 1:13, where four jet engines are used instead of a high-pressure tank. This tunnel, erected by the Saab Aircraft Company of Linkoping, Sweden, returns about 10 per cent of the hot air to prevent condensation in the test section, an effect discussed in Chapters 11 and 12.

But all the early induction-type tunnels received their air from storage tanks and hence had limited time for running. To make available continuous operation and to increase the tunnel speed well into the supersonic range, a very high-speed tunnel was constructed in Zürich, Switzerland. Later a similar but more

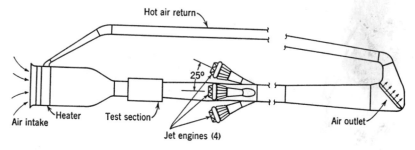

FIG. 1:13.   The Saab induction wind tunnel.

powerful wind tunnel was built at the Guidonia Laboratories in Milan, Italy (Ref. 1:7). Both were of the single-return type and had larger test sections than the previously constructed tunnels.

The United States has now become active in this field, and a large number of supersonic wind tunnels have been built.

A new and very promising form of supersonic wind tunnel was disclosed at the end of World War II when inspection of the German wind tunnels became possible. This consisted of a large

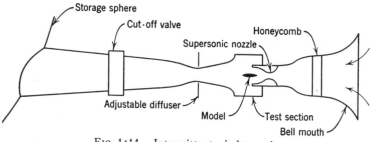

FIG. 1:14.   Intermittent wind tunnel.

evacuated sphere connected to the atmosphere by a valve-controlled passage. This passage had a convergent-divergent nozzle such as that shown in Fig. 1:14 so that, when the valve was opened and air rushed into the sphere, a test section downstream of the nozzle was at a speed above that of sound.

Further, until the tank reached a specific pressure, the speed in the test section remained constant owing to a phenomenon of supersonic flow that makes the velocity dependent on the nozzle shape, not on the back pressure. Though such a tank would again limit a run to a few seconds, the automatic speed control of the design made it much more satisfactory than earlier induction types. Several tunnels of this type have been built in this country.

Before closing this section on supersonic tunnels, it seems in order to mention some of their design fundamentals and to draw attention to the many difficulties. In the first place, supersonic speeds are obtained not by pressures alone, but by pressures plus specially designed convergent-divergent passages. This means that a supersonic tunnel must have either a separate nozzle for each speed, or an adjustable one. The power required is considerable, too. One design having a test section 12 in. by 18 in. requires 14,000 hp to reach a speed two and a half times that of sound.

Above the speed of sound a diverging passage increases the speed of the stream as opposed to the action when the speed is below that of sound. Further, the jump back to subsonic speed occurs abruptly. Unless this jump occurs very close to sonic speed, large losses will result. Hence it will be seen that the combination of directly opposing laws of flow and the possibility of large losses due to a compressibility shock makes the design of a supersonic regain passage extremely difficult.

A more complete treatment of supersonic tunnels may be found in Chapter 12. Design features of induction tunnels are covered in Ref. 1:14.

1:12. Open-Circuit Tunnel. Very few open-circuit wind tunnels exist in the world today, owing largely to their dependence on weather conditions. They are, however, ideal for engine tests, since 100 per cent of the air may be replenished by fresh outside air. An example of an open-circuit tunnel that controls the vagaries of weather by an immense air-drying system is the 6 by 8 ft supersonic tunnel of the NACA, shown in Fig. 1:15. It differs from that of Fig. 1:4 in that the drive system is upstream of the test section.

1:13. Low-Turbulence Tunnel. In 1946 the NACA announced the completion of the first very low-turbulence tunnel capable of testing three-dimensional models at high Reynolds numbers.

The important features of this tunnel include (besides pressurization similar to the Southern California Co-op tunnel) an extraordinarily high contraction ratio (25 to 1) and the use of eight stages of mesh screen across the settling chamber.

All these artifices contribute towards reducing the turbulence in the test section. (For additional information see Ref. 2:24.)

Official Photograph, National Advisory Committee for Aeronautics.

Fig. 1:15.   The Lewis Flight Propulsion Laboratory 8 by 6 ft supersonic wind tunnel, the most powerful open-circuit wind tunnel in the world.   The air is dried in the white building at the upper right, flows into the tunnel downstream of the drive motors, is cooled, enters the domed test section region, and exits through the long diffuser.   Since this photograph was made, an elbow has been added to the diffuser and sound-absorption apparatus has been included in the dogleg.

1:14. Stability Tunnel.   The only tunnel directly designed for dynamic stability work is located at the Langley Field branch of the NACA.   Its most vital feature is its ability to subject the models to curving airstreams that simulate those actually encountered when an airplane rolls, pitches, or yaws.   The rotating airstream for simulating roll is produced by a motor-driven paddle just ahead of the test section.   Curved air of properly varying velocity for simulating pitch and yaw is produced by a combination of a curved test section and velocity screens.   The proper use of this apparatus makes possible the determination of the stability derivatives.

1:15. Two-Dimensional Tunnel. The NACA has several two-dimensional tunnels designed and devoted entirely to section tests. For this type of airfoil research the test section is quite flat, and the model spans the shorter axis from one wall to another. Such a tunnel is shown in Fig. 5:14. This tunnel has a test section 3 ft by 7½ ft, and, like the Low-Turbulence tunnel at Moffett Field, achieves extremely low turbulence through the use of screens in the settling chamber.

Many tunnels of varying jet shapes have alternate two-dimensional jets that may be installed when needed. Some of these special jets consist merely of large endplates for the airfoil models; others contract the entire stream to a narrow jet and have an additional diffuser downstream. Properly designed, a two-dimensional jet insert can increase the maximum speed of a tunnel by 70 per cent. See Sect. 2:13.

1:16. Ice Tunnel. A great deal of very important work has been done in the NACA ice tunnel at the Lewis Flight Propulsion Laboratory in Cleveland. Here, in a 6 by 9 ft test section, models are subjected to icing conditions and the formation and methods of removal of ice are studied (Fig. 1:16).

The tunnel itself is worthy of comment since it entails the usual wind-tunnel aerodynamic difficulties plus the addition of ice. This leads to a large-capacity cooler just before the settling chamber, water spray nozzles (heated to prevent their freezing and to assure proper cloud formation) in the settling chamber, and steam-heated guide vanes to prevent ice accretion from plugging the first and second turns. The fan is protected by a 1-in.-mesh wire screen but even so suffers from the high humidity and from ice pieces that get by the screen.

All exposed instrumentation must be specially designed to remain ice-free. Total head tubes are electrically heated and have a water blow-out provision between readings.

The effects of ice are in general to increase the drag and reduce the maximum lift of the wings, to reduce the propeller efficiency, and to increase the drag of the fuselage. Successful solutions to the icing of airframe and instruments have been attained through the efforts of flight test and ice-tunnel work. Work on jet engine icing is currently proceeding.

The importance of ice-tunnel work makes it imperative that a much larger and faster ice tunnel be provided in the near future.

Official Photograph, National Advisory Committee for Aeronautics.

FIG. 1:16. Inspecting two types of icing-rate meter after comparative icing tests in the Icing Research Tunnel at Lewis Flight Propulsion Laboratory of the National Advisory Committee for Aeronautics. The lower device is a rotating-disk continuous-indicating meter. The upper U-tube device is an NACA pressure-type ice detector and meter now in quantity use on worldwide air routes to gather statistics of the duration and severity of icing encounters for aid in designing protection for all-weather aircraft.

1:17. All-Purpose Tunnel. There are several tunnels which may be run with both open and closed test sections, and a few which vary their test-section sizes. The Rhodes St. Genese tunnel in Brussels does even more than this and deserves special mention for remarkable utility in the low-speed range. Fundamentally, it has a closed test section. A second tunnel is made by replacing the diffuser with a larger one and leaving the test

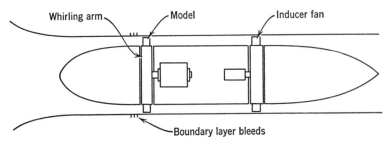

FIG. 1:17. Whirling-arm wind tunnel.

section open. This yields an open-throat tunnel 9.8 ft in diameter. Still a third tunnel is made by rotating the entrance cone into a vertical position to form an open-circuit tunnel with a vertical test section. Thus, the same power plant and return passage are made to serve three purposes.

1:18. Whirling-Arm Tunnel. A type of wind tunnel which has been used for airfoil tests in the transonic range is the NACA Annular Tunnel shown in Fig. 1:17 (Ref. 1:15). Basically it

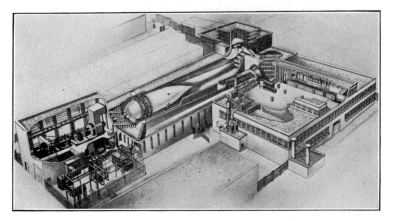

FIG. 1:18. Tunnel and laboratory of the Boeing Airplane Co.

consists of a whirling arm placed in a controlled airstream whose velocity is parallel to the axis of the whirling arm. The speed of the stream is used to change the angle of attack of the whirling model and to provide clean air by moving the model's wake downstream.   A particular advantage of this type of tunnel should be its freedom from wave reflection (see Chapter 11) in the sonic range.   However, it is understood that instrument difficulties are very great with this arrangement.

1:19. Table of Low-Speed Wind Tunnels.   Table 1:1 furnishes a brief description of a number of wind tunnels. It is admittedly not complete, since the disposition of the German and Japanese wind tunnels is not available, and, deliberately, a large number of small classroom-type wind tunnels in this country have been omitted.

A table of transonic wind tunnels is in Chapter 11, and separate tables of supersonic and hypersonic tunnels are in Chapter 12.

TABLE 1:1. LOW-SPEED WIND TUNNELS
1. The National Advisory Committee for Aeronautics

Tunnel	Located at	Type	Jet Open or Closed	V max. mph	Energy Ratio	Turbulence Factor	Jet Shape	Jet Length	Contraction Ratio	Hp	Reference or Remarks
Full-Scale	Langley Field, Va.	Double return	Open	120	2.84	1.1	60 x 30 ft, elliptic	0.93B	4.93	8,000	TR 459, 1933
19-ft, Pressure	Langley Field, Va.	Single return	Closed	260			19 ft, round	1.5D		8,000	2.3 atmospheres maximum
Variable-Density	Langley Field, Va.	Annular return	Closed		1.6	2.6	5 ft, round				TR 416, 1932
20-ft, Free-Spinning	Langley Field, Va.	Annular return	Closed	60	0.35		12-sided polygon	1.25D	2.9	400	
Free-Flight	Langley Field, Va.	Open circuit	Closed	60			12-sided polygon	1.25D		280	
Two-Dimensional Pressure, LTT	Langley Field, Va.	Single return	Closed	350	1.4		3 x 7½, rectangular	1.0h	20	2,000	TN 1283, 1944 10 atmospheres maximum
4 x 6 ft, Vertical	Langley Field, Va.	Single return	Closed	76		1.93	4 x 6 ft, rectangular	0.75B	3.37	50	TN 387, 1931
Stability	Langley Field, Va.	Single return	Closed	360		1.08	6 ft, square	3.7D	10	600	TN 734, 1939
7 x 10 ft No. 1	Langley Field, Va.	Single return	Closed	300	6.8	1.01	7 x 10 ft, rectangular	1.5B	13	1,600	
6 x 9 ft, Ice Tunnel	Cleveland, Ohio	Single return	Closed	350	7.0		6 x 9 ft, rectangular	2.2B	10	4,160	
High-Altitude	Cleveland, Ohio	Single return	Closed	500	4.6		20 ft, round	2.0D	6.25	18,000	Aero Digest, Jan. 15, 1944
7 x 10 ft No. 1	Moffett Field, Calif.	Single return	Closed	300	6.8		7 x 10 ft, rectangular	1.4B	13.0	1,600	
7 x 10 ft No. 2	Moffett Field, Calif.	Single return	Closed	300	6.8		7 x 10 ft, rectangular	1.4B	13.0	1,600	
Full-Scale	Moffett Field, Calif.	Single return	Closed	250	8.5		40 x 80 ft, elliptic			36,000	

(Many new high-speed and supersonic wind tunnels are under construction at the NACA.)

TABLE 1:1. LOW-SPEED WIND TUNNELS (*Continued*)

2. *Colleges and Industry of the United States*

Tunnel	Located at	Type	Jet Open or Closed	V_{max} mph	Energy Ratio	Turbulence Factor	Jet Shape	Jet Length	Contraction Ratio	Hp	Reference or Remarks
U. of Akron	Akron, Ohio	Single return	Open	124	3.56	1.1	6.5 ft Diam.				
California Institute of Tech.	Pasadena, Calif.	Single return	Closed	250	7.0		10 ft, round	0.8D	4.0	800	
Consolidated-Vultee Aircraft	San Diego, Calif.	Single return	Closed	200	2.0		8 x 12 ft, rectangular	1.25B	6.55	2,250	*Aero Digest,* Jan. 15, 1944
U. of Detroit	Detroit, Mich.	Single return	Both	150	3.7	1.5	7 x 10 ft, rectangular			275	*Aircraft Engineering,* Oct. 1931
Georgia Institute of Technology, 9 ft	Atlanta, Ga.	Single return	Both	150		1.7	9 ft, round	1.1D	4.9	375	
Grumman Aircraft, 7 x 10	Bethpage, L. I.	Open circuit	Closed	160	1.0		7 x 10 ft, rectangular			1,275	
Guggenheim Airship Inst.	Akron, Ohio			34			12 ft, round	2.0D			
Lockheed Aircraft Co.	Burbank, Calif.	Single return	Closed	314	7.0		8 x 12 ft, rectangular	1.25B	6.55	2,250	
U. of Maryland	College Park, Md.	Single return	Closed	280	3.5	1.05	7.75 x 11 ft, rectangular	1.27B	7.31	2,200	
MIT Wright Bros.	Cambridge, Mass.	Single return	Closed	250		1.08	10 x 7.5 ft, elliptic	1.5D		2,000	*SAE Journal,* Sept. 1941
U. of Michigan	Ann Arbor, Mich.	Single return	Open	100	1.00	1.22	8 ft, octagonal	2.1D	4.0	1,200	*Aircraft Engineering,* June 1931
Nat. Bur. Stds., 6 ft	Washington, D. C.	Single return	Closed	175			6 ft, octagonal		7.0	750	
Nat. Bur. Stds., 4½ ft	Washington, D. C.	Single return	Closed	100			4.5 ft, octagonal	4.2D	7.1	75	
New York University	New York, N. Y.	Double return	Closed	125	3.5	1.4	7 x 10 ft, rectangular	1.0B	4.5	250	
North American Aircraft	Inglewood, Calif.	Single return	Closed	325	6.5	1.1	7.75 x 11 ft, rectangular	1.09B	8.0	3,000	*Aero Digest,* Aug. 1942

Institution	Location	Circuit		Power (hp)			Test section				Reference
Northrop Aviation	Hawthorne, Calif.	Single return	Closed	165	3.8	1.1	10 ft, round (est.)	1.0D	5.0	1,000	
Rensselaer Polytechnic Institute	Troy, N. Y.		Both	90			8 x 12 ft, rectangular				
U. of Stanford	Stanford, Calif.	Open circuit	Closed	100	1.85	2.4	7.5 ft, round		6.7	125	
Texas A. and M.	College Station, Tex.	Open circuit	Closed				7 x 10 ft, rectangular				
U. of Washington	Seattle, Wash.	Double return	Closed	250	6.2	1.2	8 x 12 ft, rectangular	0.83B	6.0	1,500	JAS, Oct. 1939
U. of Wichita	Wichita, Kan.	Single return	Closed	150		1.21	7 x 10 ft, rectangular	1.2B	6.0	700	
3. Armed Services of the United States											
WADC, 5 ft	Wright Field, Ohio	Open circuit	Closed	300	3.5	1.5	5 ft, round	3.6D	3.7	1,600	
WADC, 20 ft	Wright Field, Ohio	Single return	Closed	425	1.61		20 ft, round		5.05	40,000	Aero Digest, April 1941
WADC, Vertical, 12 ft	Wright Field, Ohio	Annular return	Open	80	2.52	1.67	12 ft, round	1.25D	4.0	1,000	
Wash. Navy Yard, 6 ft	Washington, D. C.	Single return	Open	120	0.3	2.67	6.33 ft, round	1.03D	5.15	200	TN 536, 1935
Wash. Navy Yard, 8 x 8 ft	Washington, D. C.	Single return	Closed	70	4.0	1.01	8 x 8 ft, square	2.5B		500	
DTMB,* 8 x 10 No. 1	Carderock, Md.	Single return	Closed	200	4.0	1.01	8 x 10 ft, rectangular	1.3B	4.5	1,000	
DTMB,* 8 x 10 No. 2	Carderock, Md.	Single return	Closed	180			8 x 10 ft, rectangular	1.3B	4.5	700	
4. Other Nations											
AUSTRALIA											
9 x 7	Melbourne	Single return	Closed	195	5.08	1.15	7 x 9 ft, octagonal	1.51D	4.0	550	Aircraft Engineering, Nov. 1943

*David Taylor Model Basin.

TABLE 1:1. LOW-SPEED WIND TUNNELS (*Continued*)

4. *Other Nations* (*Continued*)

Tunnel	Located at	Type	Jet Open or Closed	V max. mph	Energy Ratio	Turbulence Factor	Jet Shape	Jet Length	Contraction Ratio	Hp	Reference or Remarks
BELGIUM											
Rhode St. Genese †	Brussels	Single return	Open	176	1.9	1.4	9.8 ft, round	1.5D	4.0	1,155	
Rhode St. Genese †	Brussels	Single return	Closed	313	6.0	1.4	6.6 ft, round	1.25D	9.0	1,155	
Rhode St. Genese †	Brussels	Open circuit	Open	90	0.6		9.8 ft, round		4.0	1,155	
CANADA											
John Street	Ottawa, Ont.	Double return	Open	160	2.7	1.24	9 ft, round	1.52D	4.0	600	
New Horizontal	Ottawa, Ont.	Single return	Closed	325	6.0	1.28	6 x 10 ft, ellipse	1.25D	9.0	2,000	
Spinning	Ottawa, Ont.	Annular return	Open	50	1.85	1.92	15 ft, round	0.67D	4.0	275	
CHINA											
Tsing Hua University	Nanchang	Single return	Both	130	5.8		12 to 18 ft, round			450	*Aircraft Engineering,* Sept. 1939
ENGLAND											
Fairey Aircraft	Hayes	Single return	Closed	174			10 x 12 ft, elliptic		4.14	350	*Aircraft Engineering,* Jan. 1939
Handley-Page Aircraft	Radlett	Single return	Closed	132	3.4		7 x 5.3 ft, octagonal	1.28D	4.0	220	*Aircraft Engineering,* July 1940
NPL Open-Jet #1	Teddington	Double return	Open	130	2.7		7 x 9 ft, elliptic	1.5D	3.9	300	*Aircraft Engineering,* June 1935

NPL Open-Jet #2	Teddington	Double return	Open	130	2.7		7 x 9 ft, elliptic	1.5D	3.9	300	
NPL 7 ft	Teddington	Open circuit	Closed	67	0.48		7 ft, square	6D		200	
NPL 13 ft x 9 ft	Teddington	Single return	Closed	164	4.2		13 x 9 ft, octagonal	1.8D	4.0	750	
NPL 9 ft x 7 ft	Teddington	Single return	Closed	136	4.5		9 x 7 ft, octagonal	1.5D	4.0	250	
NPL Compressed-Air	Teddington	Annular return	Open	60	2.3	2.0	6 ft, round	1.2D	3.6	400	Flight, June 1, 1932
NPL Low-Turbulence	Teddington	Single return	Closed	110	3.6		7 ft, octagonal	6.3D	8.2	100	R&M 1843
NPL Duplex	Teddington	Open circuit	Closed	67	0.53		14 x 7 ft, rectangular			400	Flight, June 1, 1932
RAE, 5 ft, Low-Speed	Farnborough	Single return	Open	215	2.4	1.5	5 ft, round	1.8D	2.78		R&M 1364, 1930
RAE, 11 ft	Farnborough	Single return	Closed	294	4.0		11.5 x 8.5 ft, octagonal	1.75B	6.0	4,000	
RAE, Free-Spinning	Farnborough	Open circuit	Closed	37.5	0.6		12 ft, round	2.3D		120	
RAE, 24 ft	Farnborough	Single return	Open	115	2.57		24 ft, round	1.83D	3.53	2,000	R&M 1720, 1936
Vickers-Armstrong	Weybridge, Surrey	Single return	Closed	200	3.3		13 x 9 ft, rectangular		10	2,000	
FRANCE											
Hispano-Suiza	Paris	Open circuit	Open	205	2.94		16.4 ft, round	1.61D		4,000	Aircraft Production, April 1941
Alger #1	Alger	Open circuit	Open or Closed	227	4.0		5.9 x 7.2 ft, rectangular	1.5B	4.0	860	
CH #1 Full-Scale	Chalais-Meudon	Open circuit	Open	111	2.14		26 x 52 ft, elliptic	1.4D	3.5	6,000	
Cannes #1	Cannes	Open circuit	Closed	111	5.8		9.8 ft, round	1.53D	6.1	160	

† These tunnels are variations of a single tunnel.

TABLE 1:1. LOW-SPEED WIND TUNNELS (Continued)

4. Other Nations (Continued)

FRANCE (Continued)

Tunnel	Located at	Type	Jet Open or Closed	V max, mph	Energy Ratio	Turbulence Factor	Jet Shape	Jet Length	Contraction Ratio	Hp	Reference or Remarks
ML Ice-Tunnel	Mont-Lachat	Open circuit	Closed	200	3.1		4.6 x 10.5 ft, rectangular	1.4h	6.1	1,260	
TO #4	Toulouse	Open circuit	Open	94			6.6 x 9.8 ft, elliptic			240	
TO #5	Toulouse	Single return	Open	94			13.9 ft, round			430	
Lille #1	Lille	Single return	Closed	192			11.1 ft, round			200	
Lille #2 Spin-Tunnel	Lille	Single return	Closed	78			6.6 ft, round			52	
CH #2 Spin-Tunnel	Chalais-Meudon	Open circuit					16.4 ft, round			475	

GERMANY

Nearly all the German wind tunnels were removed to England, France, and the United States for study, evaluation, and use. Those for which information is available are listed under their new locations.

ITALY

Tunnel	Located at	Type	Jet Open or Closed	V max, mph	Energy Ratio	Turbulence Factor	Jet Shape	Jet Length	Contraction Ratio	Hp	Reference or Remarks
Breda	Milan	Single return	Open	205	2.3		6.56 ft, round	1.65D	5.0	800	TM 922, 1939
Caproni	Milan Taliedo	Double return	Open	121	2.4	1.945	4.92 ft, round	1.2D		190	
Piaggio	Finale-Ligure	Open circuit	Closed	90	2.2		6.56 ft, round	2.0D		100	

Name	Location	Circuit	Type				Test section				Reference
RUMANIA											
Bucharest Polytech	Bucharest	Annular return	Closed	93	3.35		4.9 ft, round	1.67D	7.85	50	TM 651, 1931
RUSSIA											
Adamtchik	Moscow	Open circuit	Closed	80.5	1.53		4.9 ft, round			47	TM 386, 1926
Joukowski	Moscow	Open circuit	Closed	112.0	3.1		9.8 ft, round			350	TM 386, 1926
Moscow Technical School	Moscow	Open circuit	Closed	107.3	3.5		4.9 ft, round				
SPAIN											
Cuatro Vientos	Cuatro Vientos	Single return	Open				9.8 ft, round			700	TM 414, 1926
SWEDEN											
CARI				225			12 ft, round			1,300	
SWITZERLAND											
Zürich ETH, 3 x 2 meter	Zürich	Single return	Both	195	6.4		9.8 x 6.7 ft, rectangular			700	Aircraft Engineering, Aug. 1935
Swiss Fed. Mil. Dept.	Emmen	Single return	Open	134		1.24	5.7 x 14.6 ft, rectangular				
Swiss Fed. Mil. Dept.	Emmen	Single return	Both	180		1.08	19.7 x 26.2 ft, rectangular				

PROBLEMS

1:1. What difficulties are encountered when testing in a pressure tunnel that are not met in other types?

1:2. What disadvantages would there be in utilizing natural wind velocities for testing?

1:3. Look up the available references on three similar tunnels, and prepare a short paper discussing them.

1:4. For what type of work is a full-scale tunnel most suited? not suited?

1:5. Discuss some of the necessary features of a smoke tunnel.

1:6. Explain the difference between an Eiffel- and a Prandtl-type tunnel.

REFERENCES

1:1. John R. Markham, The M.I.T. Wright Brothers Wind Tunnel, *SAE Journal*, September, 1941.

1:2. Eastman N. Jacobs, The Variable-Density Tunnel, *TR* 416, 1932.

1:3. Smith J. DeFrance, The NACA Full-Scale Wind Tunnel, *TR* 459, 1933.

1:4. C. Townsend Ludington, *Smoke Streams*, Coward-McCann, New York.

1:5. C. H. Zimmerman, Preliminary Tests in the NACA Free-Spinning Tunnel, *TR* 557, 1936.

1:6. John Stack, The NACA High Speed Wind Tunnel and Tests of Six Propeller Sections, *TR* 463, 1933.

1:7. Antonio Ferri, Investigations and Experiments in the Guidonia Supersonic Wind Tunnel, *TM* 901, 1939.

1:8. Mario Pittoni, The Breda Wind Tunnel, *TM* 922, 1939.

1:9. J. Ackeret, High-Speed Wind Tunnels, *TM* 808, 1936.

1:10. W. S. Farrer, Smoke Investigation of Air Flow, *JAS*, July, 1932.

1:11. A. Bailey, Development of High-Speed Induction Wind Tunnel, *R&M* 1468, 1932.

1:12. A. Bailey, The Development of a High-Speed Induction Wind Tunnel of Rectangular Cross Section, *R&M* 1791, 1937.

1:13. A. Bailey, Further Development of a High-Speed Wind Tunnel of Rectangular Cross Section, *R&M* 1853, 1938.

1:14. W. F. Lindsey, Choking of a Subsonic Induction Tunnel by the Flow from an Induction Nozzle, *TN* 2730, 1952.

1:15. Louis W. Habel, The Langley Annular Transonic Tunnel and Preliminary Tests of an NACA 66–006 Airfoil, NACA *RM* L8A23 (Declassified), 1948.

Chapter 2

WIND-TUNNEL DESIGN

It should be borne in mind that no one tunnel will be adequate for the complete testing program of a new type of airplane. Such a program demands not only the conventional fixed model tunnel

Courtesy Boeing Airplane Co.

FIG. 2:1. The handy control panel of the Boeing wind tunnel, showing the gate open and a model of the XC-97 Stratocruiser ready for testing. The tail strut windshield is unusually close to the model.

but also facilities for testing spin and stability models. The design of these special tunnels, some of which are so rare as to be almost unique, is well beyond the scope of this book. Here the subject is simply the general-utility tunnel.

The requirements of general utility are perhaps most completely met by the single-return tunnel. The ability to operate with open or closed throat is advantageous too. The wind-tunnel engineer would probably set as a desirable minimum the ability to attain a testing Reynolds number of at least 1,500,000 to 2,500,000. Indeed, it may be seen from Chapter 7 that there is little need to have more than 2,500,000 unless about 9,000,000 is attained. The 1,500,000 to 2,500,000 criterion requires roughly a 1-ft wing chord at 150 mph. Yet, with such conditions for the wing, the tail surfaces of a complete model are at an undesirably low Reynolds number. This consideration points to a larger, higher-speed tunnel, and so the circle goes. Somewhere, unless the cost of tunnel construction, tunnel operation, model construction, and testing is of no consequence, a limit must be set. Many tunnels with rectangular test sections 7 ft by 10 ft or 8 ft by 12 ft have been constructed, usually having a tunnel speed of about 250 mph. This seems to be a very satisfactory tunnel size for the determination of drag, stability, and hinge moments.

Ideally, at least, the wind-tunnel design engineer starts a new tunnel by determining its purpose and hence the required jet shape and airspeed. From the testing requirements he also determines whether the tunnel shall have an atmospheric or closed return. The estimated number of hours of operation and local power costs then dictate the optimum tunnel efficiency. This involves the principle frequently applicable in engineering that added first cost can result in high efficiency and lower operating costs. As will be seen later, in wind-tunnel design added efficiency is achieved by increased tunnel length and hence increased cost of construction.

As a final step in the design, the losses in the test section, corners, diffusers, and entrance cone are calculated and summed up to get the input power.

From a practical standpoint, the design may take the amount of money available as the starting point. Various designs in the proper bracket are then considered until the optimum is selected. The physical location may also be a decisive factor. If the tunnel is to be located in a certain building, or on a specific plot of ground, the designer must consider this factor in the layout.

Additional problems arise if the tunnel is of special design. For instance, the pressure-type tunnels may be initially tested by being filled with water under pressure to avoid the danger that would arise if they failed under a compressed-air load. The weight of the water may indeed alter the normal foundation design. Tunnels with atmospheric return require additional studies of their physical surroundings.

The general layout for a tunnel, supposing that no extraneous factors seriously enter into the design, has reached a form generally agreed upon for reasons of construction economy and tunnel efficiency. This usually embraces a diffuser of three or four test section lengths, and two sets of similar corners to save a little engineering and construction cost. The plane of the return passage is almost always horizontal, to save cost and make the return passage easier to get to. The vertical return is justified only when space is at a premium. No rule or general procedure has been agreed upon as regards the shape of the return passage —round or rectangular. Factors governing the choice are given in the appropriate paragraphs.

Factors influencing the design of the test section, corners, return passage, and contraction cone are discussed on the following pages. The actual power losses are covered in Sect. 2:11.

2:1. The Test Section. As has been mentioned previously, most wind-tunnel designs are started with two criteria in mind: (1) the type of testing to be performed; and (2) the tunnel necessary to do the job. The "tunnel necessary" includes considerations of jet dimensions (size and shape), and the desired tunnel wind speed. These items in turn determine (within broad limits) the power that will be needed and largely determine the entire design. In a way, the jet size and wind speed could be interpreted as one criterion: desirable test Reynolds number. In theory, at least, a larger jet using a larger model could operate satisfactorily at a lower speed. But although the same Reynolds number could be obtained in a tunnel of twice a given size at half the power, the original cost of the larger tunnel would be (roughly) four times that of the smaller. In practice the jet speeds in the larger tunnels are as high as, if not higher than, those in the smaller ones.

In the past engineers have used many different reasons for selecting test section shapes. Round, elliptical, square, rectangular, duplex, octagonal, rectangular with tempered corners, round with flats on the sides and floor, elliptical with a floor flat, and many other shapes have been adopted. The most fundamental consideration is the test section area, for it determines the tunnel power requirements directly, the difference in skin friction between the various shapes being negligible. The second consideration is a combination of aerodynamics and utility. For a given test section area, the greatest width section could test the largest span model, but beyond about a 7 by 10 height-width ratio the tunnel wall effects vary so widely across the model span that the accuracy of the data is questionable. It is also difficult to turn a large model over for inverted tests in a wide, flat tunnel. Still further, a 7 by 10 test section preserves reasonable conditions for propeller testing should the need arise, and it does not grow ridiculously wide and flat when a wall-mounted panel model is tested.

The curved test sections (round and elliptic) rarely end up being all curved. For one thing a flat floor is a very handy thing to stand on during model changes, and, for another, it is almost a must for a yawing three-strut support system. Such a system also virtually dictates a flat ceiling. The side walls come in for their flats, too; for better windows, for attaching wingtip models and sometimes for attaching reflection plane models. With flats involved, the accurate computation of wall effects becomes a very difficult job. For all these reasons, plus the ease of installing a ground board in a rectangular tunnel and the added cost of construction of compound curves, the round and elliptical test sections are dropping out of favor. Indeed a tunnel with an octagonal test section has been constructed by a propeller manufacturer even though the research primarily required a round one.

For general test work added impetus has been given to the 7 by 10 configuration since the NACA has prepared detailed wall correction charts for that size.

The length of the test section in common practice varies from one to two times the major dimension of the jet. Although the power losses in the jet are sizable (see Sect. 2:11) owing to the high speed, and a power advantage would accrue from keeping the length down, special set-ups inevitably arise that make a long jet very handy.

As the air proceeds along the test section the boundary layer thickens. This action reduces the effective area of the jet and causes an increase of velocity. The velocity increase in turn produces a drop in local static pressure, tending to draw the model downstream. This added drag, called "horizontal buoyancy," is discussed in Chapter 6, where corrections may be found.

If the cross-sectional area of the jet is increased enough to allow for the thickening boundary layer, a constant value of the static pressure may be maintained throughout the test section. Unfortunately no exact design method is available that assures the development of a constant static pressure. For a first approximation the walls of a closed jet should diverge about $\frac{1}{2}$ degree each; finer adjustments may be necessary after the tunnel is built and the longitudinal static pressure is measured. Some tunnels whose test sections have corner fillets have these fillets altered until a constant static pressure is obtained. The advantages of such a flow are enough to justify a moderate amount of work in obtaining it.

A practical detail in jet design rarely satisfactorily attained is the installation of sufficient windows for viewing the model. In the course of testing it will become necessary to see all parts of the model: top, sides, bottom, and as much of the front as is reasonably practical. If powered model tests are to be considered, bullet-proof glass is in order.

Adequate lighting is also needed, and separate switches for lights below eye level should be provided. Permanent floodlights to be used in photographical work should also be installed.

The above paragraphs have been written for the customary closed test section because that type is most generally in use. For propeller and rotor tests, however, the open jet offers considerable advantage, as can be seen by reference to Sects. 6:10, 6:11, and 6:28, where the corrections for propeller and nacelles are seen to be much smaller if an open jet is employed.

The objections to an open jet are twofold:

1. The wind-tunnel balance usually requires so much shielding for operating with an open jet that approximately one solid boundary is simulated. This confuses the boundary corrections to be applied and raises doubt that the jet is truly open.

2. The power required for a given tunnel with an open jet may easily exceed three times the power required by the same tunnel at the same speed with a closed jet. Further data on this factor may be obtained by comparing energy ratios (see Sect 3:16) for tunnels with open and closed test sections from Table 1:1.

If an open jet is employed the exit cone should be larger than the entrance cone. Darrius (Ref. 2:12) suggests a 6-degree expansion, and indeed 10 degrees would not be unreasonable. Some engineers keep the diffuser at constant diameter for about a half jet length to allow the flow to stabilize.

It will easily be seen that an open jet used with an open-circuit return is a virtual impossibility unless the open jet is surrounded by a sealed-off chamber, as air would flow into the jet as much as into the entrance cone. Indeed, a sealed-off area around a closed jet is a beneficial item for both open-circuit and closed-return tunnels, reducing leakage, the entry of dust, and outside noise.

2:2. The Return Passage. As the power losses in a wind tunnel vary with the cube of the airspeed, it is desirable to increase the cross-sectional area of the return passage and hence reduce the local tunnel speed as rapidly as possible. This is particularly important in the region before the first corner because (as will be demonstrated) a large percentage of the total power loss occurs therein. The rate of this area increase is limited by the amount of expansion the air will stand without separating from the walls with accompanying large losses. Tests have shown that a reasonable expansion of a round passage is about 5 to 8 degrees between opposite walls. When a rectangular passage is expanded in one direction only, an angle of 12 degrees between opposite walls is permissible.

The smaller expansion angles make for a longer, more expensive tunnel whose flow is the optimum and whose cost of operation slightly lower than that of a large-expansion-angle tunnel. Crowding the upper limit of expansion to save construction cost has its disadvantages. In the usual three-dimensional test section the model is mounted in the middle of the airstream, and its wake proceeds downstream without seriously impairing the flow in the tunnel. Only a small increase in power is required with increasing angle of attack of the model. In the two-dimensional jet a more serious effect appears. As the model stalls, the turbulent flow, being at the walls (as well as at the middle of the airstream), may start a separated region that can spread downstream along the tunnel sides, stalling the diffuser. The power required for this large separated region may exceed 150 per cent of that required for the tunnel with the model at a low angle. Hence, either a reserve of power must be maintained, or this flow must be controlled through slots in the diffuser emitting air at high velocity. Such an arrangement is called "boundary-layer control." A tunnel whose diffuser is below atmospheric pressure may sometimes obtain boundary-layer control with simple guided slots open to the atmosphere.

One item in the return passage that deserves mention is a strong wire "safety" screen between the test section and the propeller to serve as a catch-all when failure of a model occurs. Though such failures can be reduced by careful design of the model, and the leaving of tools, pieces of material, and model parts in the test section can be reduced by an alert crew, somehow, sooner or later, some objects will join the slipstream and go hurrying towards the propeller with calamitous intent. Whether

Courtesy Georgia Institute of Technology.

Fig. 2:2.   Corner vanes and safety screen.

the janitor then sweeps up the propeller along with the now fragmentary model parts is a function of the grid efficiency only. Obviously, the power losses suffered from the addition of such an obstacle may be reduced by having the screen in the lowest-velocity section possible. Additional power may be saved by selecting the largest mesh compatible with the desired degree of protection, and designing the screen to cover only the lower area of the tunnel where any foreign objects are most likely to occur. Placing the screen at the trailing edges of the second set of guide vanes is advantageous because the vanes may act as buffers, and the drag of the screen is reduced by being in the wake of the vanes. The strength of a safety screen is greatly increased by brazing each wire crossing.

If the tests to be run include extensive smoke-flow studies or the operation of internal-combustion engines, an atmospheric return may be the optimum design. Even so, a considerable diffusion passage is needed to drop the local airspeed to such a value that the energy contained in the air "dumped" out the end is small.

Any return passage should have sufficient airtight doors and windows so that accessibility and visibility are well provided for, particularly near the propeller-power plant unit and the entrance cone. Special hatchways for removing a propeller blade or even the drive motor should be provided for. A drain at the lowest place in the tunnel is also a good idea.

2:3. The Breather. If the tunnel is to be operated with an open jet, due consideration must be given to the possibility of pulsations arising similar to the vibrations in an organ pipe. This phenomenon, believed to be a function of jet length, can be quite serious.

The simplest solution, usually successful, consists of putting a slot (about 0.05 diameter wide) in the diffuser which connects it to the atmosphere. Such an arrangement is called a "breather." If the slot is properly made and adjusted so that it is just large enough to prevent organ-piping, the losses can be kept low. In some open-jet tunnels alterations to the exit cone proved sufficient to prevent the vibration, but in others no satisfactory exit cones or breathers have been found that would permit operation above 200 mph.

Closed-jet tunnels usually require breathers too, because the entire return passage is above atmospheric pressure, and some air may leak out. In turn the loss of air would drop the jet pressure below atmospheric unless it were replenished. The proper place for a closed-jet tunnel breather is at the downstream end of the test section (see Fig. 1:3), and like that for an open-jet tunnel a slot about 0.05 diameter wide usually suffices. It should be covered with a fine screen to reduce the amount of dust that enters the tunnel.

Since vibration of parts of the wind tunnel contributes to noise, discomfort of the tunnel crew, and possible fatigue failures, and usually adds to the turbulence in the wind stream, it is good practice to have the natural frequencies of all tunnel parts well above any exciting frequencies. Many of these parts of the tunnel are directly amenable to basic vibration theory; others must wait for treatment after the tunnel is built. At that time, for the small tunnels at least, flat panels can be checked with a simple shaker motor, and by means of a vibrometer or a similar

Courtesy Consolidated Vultee Aircraft Corp.

FIG. 2:3. The long nacelle in the Convair wind tunnel. Also clearly visible are the fan blades and anti-twist vanes.

device the natural frequencies can be determined. Any below the maximum fan rpm should be increased by stiffening the part. A special effort should be made to keep vibration out of the test section and balance supports.

2:4. The Fan-Flow Straightener System. Although a large number of wind tunnels have the fan just downstream from the second corner, there is ample evidence that this may not be the best location. First, however, let us rule out the positions that we may say are definitely undesirable. The fan develops its highest efficiency if it is located in a stream of a fairly high velocity, and its cost is at least partially proportional to its diameter. These two items rule out a fan in a very large part of the return passage or in the settling chamber. On the other hand, damage from a failing model and poor flow distribution make a position in the diffuser moderately risky. The argument for a position just downstream of the second turn is that the flow has by then been in a section of constant area for a considerable time and from that fact should be relatively smooth when it meets the fan; also, of course, at this location the velocity is desirably high. However, in reality the flow is not too good after two turns.

The location that seems most promising is between the first and second corners. Here the fan has the protection of the first set of corner vanes, and has the same speed as in the more popular location. The poor flow in the diffuser has to some extent smoothed out by now, and any aberrations that the fan puts in the stream have the maximum chance to damp out. However, this location is unattractive if sufficient room for a long nacelle cannot be provided.

The wind-tunnel fan, seemingly similar to the propeller of an airplane, operates under peculiar conditions that put it in a class by itself. For one thing, unlike the airplane propeller, the wind-tunnel fan is prevented by the familiar law of continuity * from producing an increase of velocity in the slipstream; and, for another, rotation imparted to the flow is of paramount importance instead of being considered a loss to be removed by a second propeller only when high torque is prohibited.

Three basic fan-straightener systems are in current use: (1) a fan with straightener vanes behind it; (2) a fan with prerotating vanes ahead of it, probably also having straightener vanes behind it; (3) counterrotating fans in which the second fan removes the rotation imparted by the first.

The counterrotating fan can remove all the twist for all tunnel speeds and power inputs. Since two fans can obviously be designed to develop more thrust than one, the counterrotating fans may become essential in high-power installations. The drive is more complicated, however, as equal torque should be applied to both fans.

Fans with prerotating vanes can develop more thrust for a given blade area because the initial rotation increases the total velocity of the airstream. Also the increased fan-blade angle

* See p. 42.

used with prerotating vanes may increase the efficiency. If a model should break and parts fly through the tunnel, the prerotating vanes offer a measure of protection to the tunnel fan. They have the disadvantage that they cannot impart the proper prerotation for different power conditions and hence must be made adjustable or have straightener vanes added behind the fan.

For tunnels of moderate size and power a single fan is usually quite satisfactory. If it is properly designed, a straightener system can be devised that will remove the twist for all power inputs and speeds. Such straighteners are discussed in the following paragraphs.

A variable-pitch fan is of great value even when a variable-rpm drive is available since it gives much quicker speed control than varying the drive rpm. In tunnels with large contraction ratios the change in velocity distribution in the test section with change in fan-blade angle does not seem to be measurable. Also, when the drive motor is of the synchronous type the fan can be put in flat pitch for low pull-in torque and then opened out to develop the tunnel speed. This action may lead to greater power outputs from this type of motor as the pull-in torque is often the limiting factor.

The design of wind-tunnel fans has had considerable discussion (Ref. 2:14), but a method proposed by Patterson (Ref. 2:13) is presented here because it considers the fan-straightener system as a unit and does not concern itself merely with the fan. As rotation must be kept low if a fixed straightener system is to remove the twist for all conditions, consideration of the vanes becomes important, and their design will frequently necessitate a fan vastly different from what the ordinary criteria indicate. The fact that each section of this type of fan operates at constant efficiency, though of small merit as far as the fan is concerned, makes the usual graphical integration of the thrust and torque loading curves unnecessary, and hence the design is facilitated.

This theory, however, neglects the loss associated with the necessary tip clearance at the tunnel wall and the radial flow at the fan encountered due to the centrifugal action. The large boss recommended for use with a wind-tunnel fan tends to lessen the latter effect. The tip-clearance loss will result in efficiencies slightly lower than indicated by this theory. The loss due to tip clearance adds to both the friction and expansion losses that occur at the walls of a wind tunnel and indicates that instead of constant thrust the wind-tunnel fan should perhaps have a graded thrust loading curve, greatest at the walls in order to best develop a uniform velocity front. This refinement is beyond the scope of this presentation.

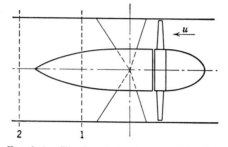

FIG. 2:4.   The fan-straightener combination.

First let us consider the flow in a duct so that the terms and factors encountered later in the fan theory may be understood when applied.

A. Flow in a Duct

When Bernoulli's equation

$$p + \tfrac{1}{2}\rho V^2 = \text{constant}$$

is written between two locations in a duct, it applies only if the losses between the sections are zero. Naturally, in practice, they never are, and one or the other of the two terms at the second section must show a diminution corresponding to the loss in head. The law of continuity for an incompressible fluid, $A_1 V_1 = A_2 V_2$, where A and V are areas and velocities at two stations, makes it impossible for the velocity to fail to follow Bernoulli's rule, and hence the velocity head at the second location will be as predicted. But there will be a drop in static head Δp corresponding to the friction loss. This loss in pounds per square foot appears over the area A_2, so that the product of the two yields the drag of the section between 1 and 2. Multiplying the drag by the velocity yields the power lost. According to familiar experience, the drag of a surface varies with the dynamic pressure q, and it is customary to express the loss of the section in coefficient form, defining

$$k = \frac{\Delta p A}{\tfrac{1}{2}\rho A V^2} = \frac{\Delta p}{q} \qquad (2:1)$$

It will be seen that the coefficient k compares with C_D in wing-drag calculations.

Throughout the wind tunnel the losses that occur appear as successive static-pressure drops to be balanced by the static-pressure rise through the fan. The total pressure drop Δh must be known for the design of the fan. If a model of the tunnel is available, the necessary pressure rise may be measured across the fan and extrapolated to full-scale Reynolds number. An alternative method is to calculate the energy ratio (see Sects. 2:11 and 3:16) and find the fan pressure rise coefficient $k = \Delta h / (\frac{1}{2}\rho u^2)$, where u is the velocity through the propeller. It is now in order to consider several design features of the fan-straightener system.

B. Factors Influencing the General Layout

It will be seen from Fig. 2:5 that high fan efficiencies are largely determined by proper selection of the advance ratio (see p. 46) and utilization of L/D ratios of the order of 50. It remains to demonstrate the best methods for satisfying these criteria.

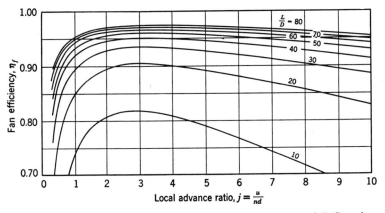

Fig. 2:5. Approximate fan efficiencies for various advance and L/D ratios.

Large advance ratios imply lowered speeds of fan rotation, necessitating a drive motor of low rpm or a geared driving system. The desire for higher rpm for the driving motor indicates that the higher-speed regions of the wind tunnel are best suited for the location of the fan. Balancing that against the increase of nacelle drag as the local speed is increased, the best compromise usually locates the fan downstream of the first or second corner after the test section. If the fan is to be driven by a motor outside the tunnel, the corner location offers a short shaft length.

L/D ratios as high as 50 and higher are obtainable only with "infinite" aspect ratio and moderately thin airfoils. Infinite aspect ratio can be simulated by effectively endplating both the fan blade root and the tip, endplating being accomplished by providing a large nacelle or "boss" for the root and maintaining a small tip clearance so that the tunnel wall becomes the tip endplate. The large nacelle is advantageous from other considerations, too.* By decreasing the tunnel cross-sectional area at the propeller a higher velocity is achieved, and higher motor

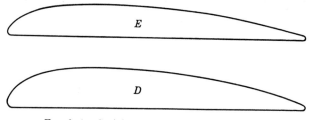

Fig. 2:6.   Satisfactory airfoils for fan sections.

speeds are possible at the same advance ratio. The large boss also encloses the fan root sections that must be thicker for structural reasons, leaving only the thin, highly efficient sections exposed to the airstream. Frequently it is possible to use an airfoil of constant thickness in the exposed portion, thus facilitating the design. Small gains are to be found from utilizing an L/D greater than 50, so that the actual airfoil selected is of secondary importance from an aerodynamic standpoint and structural considerations can be entertained. Type E of the RAF propeller sections is satisfactory, as is the slightly thicker Type D (see Fig. 2:6). The ordinates of these airfoils are shown in Table 2:1.

Although the optimum boss diameter is from 0.6 to $0.7D_f$, where D_f = diameter of the tunnel at the fan, a smaller value of 0.3 to 0.5 is more practical for wind-tunnel use. The very large boss requires a large and long nacelle for proper streamlining, which, in turn, involves costly construction difficulties and greater power losses from the diffusing action as the area of the air passage is increased. It would be possible to prevent the

* See Sect. 2:6.

diffusing losses by shaping the tunnel so that the area throughout the fan-nacelle region remained constant, but such irregularity would also entail expensive construction.

TABLE 2:1. ORDINATES OF FAN PROFILES D AND E

Distance from Leading Edge	Height above Flat Undersurface D	E
0	0.0135	0.0115
0.0125	0.0370	0.0319
0.025	0.0538	0.0442
0.05	0.0780	0.0610
0.075	0.0925	0.0724
0.10	0.1030	0.0809
0.15	0.1174	0.0928
0.20	0.1250	0.0990
0.30	0.1290	0.1030
0.40	0.1269	0.1022
0.50	0.1220	0.0980
0.60	0.1120	0.0898
0.70	0.0960	0.0770
0.80	0.0740	0.0591
0.90	0.0470	0.0379
0.95	0.0326	0.0258
1.00	0.0100	0.0076
L.E. rad.	0.0135	0.0115
T.E. rad.	0.0100	0.0076

The number of blades on the fan is somewhat arbitrary, for the product of the number of blades and their chord represents the total area and must be aligned with the thrust requirements. Several factors influence the selection of the number of blades. The minimum number probably is four; at least that number is needed to assure little pulsation in the airstream. The maximum number of blades will doubtless be limited by strength considerations. The maximum value of the sum of the blade chords Nc must not exceed the local circumference at the root if excessive interference is to be avoided. The Reynolds number of the blade chord should be above 700,000 in order to keep the section drag low. Since the number of blades is not critical, a reasonable procedure is to estimate the number needed and examine the final design to see whether alterations are in order.

C. THE FAN ADVANCE RATIO, j

In the simple blade element theory (Ref. 2:15), the angle of attack of a local section of the blade is simply the local blade angle minus the advance angle $\phi = V/(2\pi n r)$, where V = forward speed, n = rps, and r = section radius. This definition, which neglects both the induced indraft and rotation, is permissible only because a second assumption (that the airfoil coefficients should be based on an aspect ratio of 6.0) is made. With a wind-tunnel fan, no indraft is possible, but rotation exists and the simple blade-element advance angle is seriously changed. Figure 2:8 and eqs. 2:24 and 2:25 demonstrate the proper interpretation of the advance angle for a fan in a duct.

D. THE ROTATION, e

It has already been demonstrated that in order to meet the requirements of the law of continuity there can be no increase of axial velocity in a duct of constant area. However, the fan imparts twist or rotation to the airstream and hence increases its absolute velocity. This added speed is removed, not turned, by the straightener vanes, and its energy appears as a rise in static pressure.

Increasing the diameter of the fan boss will decrease the amount of rotation for a given installation, as will increasing the fan rpm.

The rotation $e = \omega r/u$ will be largest at the fan boss.

E. THE STRAIGHTENER VANES

Experiments at the NPL have shown that satisfactory antitwist or straightener vanes can be made by using the NACA symmetrical airfoils set with their chords parallel to the tunnel centerline provided that the amount of twist to be removed is small compared with the axial velocity. The limiting twist is that required to stall the vanes; i.e., $e = \omega r/u = \tan \tau$ (where τ = angle of twist in the slipstream and ω = angular velocity in the slipstream at radius r) must correspond to an angle less than α_{stall} of a symmetrical section at infinite aspect ratio including multiplane interference. The interference is an advantage here as with the type of straighteners to be employed it decreases the lift curve slope by a factor of 0.75. That is, α_{stall} with interference is 33 per cent above the free-air stall angle. (See Fig. 2:9.)

The chord for the proposed straightener may be found from

$$c_s = 2\pi r/N_s \qquad (2:2)$$

where N_s = number of straightener vanes; c_s = chord of vane at radius r.

If a constant thickness ratio is assumed for the straightener vanes, the actual thickness at the wall would be large owing to the large chord. Hence it is advantageous to select a constant thickness (not thickness ratio). A reasonable value is that $t_s/c_s = 0.15$ at $x = r/R = 0.8$. (R = tunnel radius at propeller section.) Hence from eq. 2:2.

$$t_s/c_s = N_s t_s/2\pi R x \qquad (2:3)$$

A value of 7 comes to mind for N_s, as in order to avoid periodic interference with the fan the straightener should have a number of blades that is no multiple of the even number of fan blades.

There will be a loss through the straightener, of course, and this loss will be greater than the skin friction of the vanes in free air as the straightener is a diffuser, changing the rotational velocity ωr to static head. The pressure loss coefficient of a straightener composed of symmetrical NACA airfoil sections has been empirically determined as

$$k_s = 0.045(t_s/c_s) + 0.003 \qquad (2:4)$$

Substituting from eq. 2:2 we have

$$k_s = (0.045/2\pi r)t_s N_s + 0.003 \qquad (2:5)$$

F. Fan-Straightener Theory

The theory for the design of a wind-tunnel fan-straightener system is as follows:

Letting the total cross-sectional area at the plane of the fan be A_f and the area of the fan boss be A_b, the power output becomes (Fig. 2:4)

$$\text{Power out} = \Delta h \cdot (A_f - A_b) \cdot u = \eta_t \, \text{bhp} \cdot 550$$

where η_t = total efficiency of fan and straightener system.

Hence

$$k = \frac{\eta_t \, \text{bhp} \cdot 550}{\frac{1}{2}\rho u^3 (A_f - A_b)} = \frac{\eta_t \, \text{bhp} \cdot 550}{\frac{1}{2}\rho V_t^3 A_t} \frac{V_t^2}{u^2}$$

where A_t and V_t are the test section area and velocity, respectively.

Applying the definition of the energy ratio (p. 115) and the law of continuity,

$$k = \eta_t \frac{1}{ER_1} \frac{(A_f - A_b)^2}{A_t^2} \qquad (2:6)$$

The efficiency of the fan-straightener unit is derived from the basic relation

$$\eta_t = \frac{\text{Power out}}{\text{Power in}}$$

$$\text{Power in} = 2\pi n Q$$

where Q = torque, n = revolutions per second.

It will be convenient to consider the efficiency of a blade element in the development later, so rewriting η_t for an annulus of width dr at radius r we have:

$$\eta_t = \frac{\Delta h \cdot 2\pi r \cdot dr \cdot u}{2\pi n \, dQ}$$

This procedure is possible since this method employs a constant efficiency over the entire cross-section, as explained on p. 41.

The elemental torque is

$$dQ = 2\pi r \cdot dr \cdot \rho u \cdot \omega r^2 \qquad (2:7)$$

and, as $\Delta h = k \cdot \frac{1}{2}\rho u^2$, and $\Omega = 2\pi n$,

$$\eta_t = k u^2 / 2\Omega r^2 \omega$$

Defining the local advance ratio

$$j = u/nd = u\pi/2\pi n r = u\pi/\Omega r \qquad (2:8)$$

and expressing the rotation of the flow e as a fraction of the axial velocity,

$$e = \omega r / u \qquad (2:9)$$

and

$$\eta_t = k j / 2\pi e \qquad (2:10)$$

Writing the loss in head due to the straightener as Δp_s and proceeding as in the derivation of eq. 2:10, we find

$$\eta_s = k_s j / 2\pi e \qquad (2{:}10a)$$

We may determine e from

$$e = kj / 2\pi \eta_t$$

And hence η_f becomes determined through

Fan efficiency = Total efficiency + Straightener efficiency loss

or, in symbols,

$$\eta_f = \eta_t + \eta_s \qquad (2{:}10b)$$

Writing the elemental thrust as the pressure rise times the elemental area, we have

$$dT = \Delta p \cdot 2\pi r \cdot dr \qquad (2{:}11)$$

Expressing the local radius as a fraction of the tip radius R by the relation $x = r/R$, and dividing the expression for the elemental thrust by $\frac{1}{2}\rho u^2 \cdot \pi R^2$ to reduce it to coefficient form, we have

$$\frac{dT_c}{dx} = \frac{\Delta p \cdot 2\pi r \cdot R}{\frac{1}{2}\rho u^2 \pi R^2} = \frac{2\,\Delta p \cdot x}{\frac{1}{2}\rho u^2} \qquad (2{:}12)$$

The total pressure rise required of the fan and straightener is

$$\Delta h = k \cdot \tfrac{1}{2}\rho u^2$$

$$= \text{Fan rise} + \text{Rotation} - \text{Straightener loss}$$

$$= \Delta p + \tfrac{1}{2}\rho \omega^2 r^2 - k_s \cdot \tfrac{1}{2}\rho u^2$$

Solving, the necessary rise through the fan is

$$\Delta p / \tfrac{1}{2}\rho u^2 = k + k_s - e^2 \qquad (2{:}13)$$

And eq. 2:12 becomes

$$dT_c / dx = (k + k_s - e^2) \cdot 2x \qquad (2{:}14)$$

The elemental torque in coefficient form becomes

$$dQ_c = \frac{dQ}{\frac{1}{2}\rho u^2 \cdot \pi R^2 \cdot R} \qquad (2{:}15)$$

$$dQ_c / dx = 4x^2 e \qquad (2{:}16)$$

So that

$$Q_c = \int_{x_0}^{1.0} \frac{dQc}{dx} \, dx$$

and, finally,

$$Q_c = (kJ/\pi\eta_t)(1 - x_0{}^2) \qquad (2{:}17)$$

where x_0 = radius ratio at the root section; J = advance ratio of fan tip.

Equation 2:17 determines the input torque necessary and hence the power required to realize the total pressure rise Δh.

By approaching the problem in a slightly different manner it is possible to get a relation between j, η_f, and e such that the local L/D is determined.

We proceed as follows: The total pressure rise due to the fan is

$$\Delta h_f = \text{Static rise} + \text{Rotational dynamic head}$$

and

$$\Delta h_f = \Delta p + \tfrac{1}{2}\rho\omega^2 r^2 \qquad (2{:}18)$$

Power output $= \Delta h_f \cdot 2\pi r \, dr \cdot u$

$$= 2\pi r \, dr \cdot u \, \Delta p + \tfrac{1}{2}\rho\omega^2 r^2 \cdot 2\pi r \, dr \cdot u$$

$$= u \cdot dT + \tfrac{1}{2}\omega \, dQ$$

The fan efficiency $\eta_f = \dfrac{u \, dT + \tfrac{1}{2}\omega \, dQ}{2\pi n \, dQ}$, or, in coefficient form,

$$\eta_f = \frac{u \, dT_c}{2\pi n \cdot dQ_c \cdot R} + \frac{1}{2}\frac{\omega}{2\pi n}$$

$$= \frac{J}{\pi}\frac{dT_c}{dQ_c} + \frac{1}{2}\frac{ej}{\pi} \qquad (2{:}19)$$

Substituting from 2:14 and 2:16,

$$\eta_f = \frac{j}{2\pi e}(k + k_s)$$

Expressing the elemental thrust in a form similar to conventional wing coefficients we have

$$dT = \tfrac{1}{2}\rho W^2 \cdot c \, dr \cdot N C_t \qquad (2{:}20)$$

where $W = u/\sin\phi$ (twist neglected), N = number of blades and

$$C_t = \text{thrust coefficient} = c_l \cos\phi - c_{d0}\sin\phi$$

$$C_x = \text{torque force coefficient} = c_l \sin\phi + c_{d0}\cos\phi$$

$$(2{:}21)$$

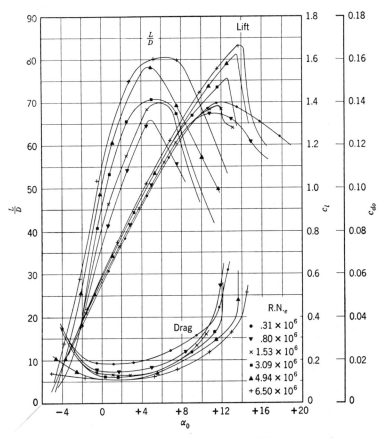

FIG. 2:7. Characteristics of fan airfoil D, infinite aspect ratio.

Reducing Eq. 2:20 to the T_c form, we have

$$\frac{dT_c}{dx} = \frac{NC_t \frac{1}{2}\rho u^2 \cdot cR}{\frac{1}{2}\rho u^2 \sin^2 \phi \pi R^2} = \frac{NC_t \cdot c}{\pi R \sin^2 \phi}$$

$$\frac{dT_c}{dx} = \frac{yC_t}{\sin^2 \phi} \qquad (2:21a)$$

where $y = Nc/\pi R$ by definition.

The corresponding elemental torque is

$$dQ = NC_x \cdot \frac{1}{2}\rho W^2 \cdot c \, dr \cdot r$$

$$\frac{dQ_c}{dx} = \frac{yxC_x}{\sin^2 \phi} \qquad (2:22)$$

Substituting in 2:19, the fan efficiency

$$\eta_f = \frac{j}{\pi}\frac{C_t}{C_x} + \frac{1}{2}\frac{ej}{\pi} \tag{2:23}$$

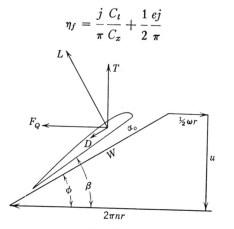

Fig. 2:8.

From Fig. 2:8,

$$\tan\phi = \frac{u}{2\pi nr - \frac{1}{2}\omega r}$$

$$= \frac{u}{\pi nd - \frac{1}{2}\frac{\omega r}{u}\frac{u}{nd}\frac{\pi}{\pi}nd} \tag{2:24}$$

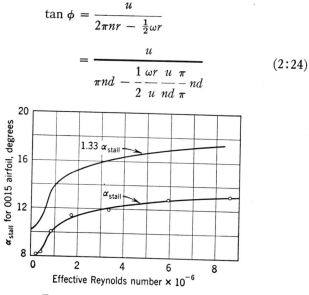

Fig. 2:9.   Effect of interference.

Hence from eqs. 2:8 and 2:9

$$\tan\phi = \frac{j}{\pi}\frac{1}{1 - \frac{1}{2}ej/\pi} \tag{2:25}$$

Hence from eqs. 2:21, 2:23, and 2:25

$$\eta_f = \frac{\dfrac{j}{\pi}\left(\dfrac{L}{D} - \dfrac{j}{\pi}\right) + \dfrac{1}{2}\dfrac{ej}{\pi}\left(1 - \dfrac{1}{2}\dfrac{ej}{\pi}\right)}{\dfrac{L}{D}\dfrac{j}{\pi} + 1 - \dfrac{1}{2}\dfrac{ej}{\pi}} \qquad (2:26)$$

With η_f and j known, eq. 2:26 can be employed to yield the L/D desired at each corresponding radius, but the values of c_l, c_{d0}, and α_0 cannot be determined accurately until the local Reynolds number is known. Hence it is necessary to determine an approximate Reynolds number as follows:

1. Using calculated L/D, read approximate lift coefficient $c_{l\,\text{approx.}}$ in Fig. 2:7.

2. From $dT_c/dx = 2x(k + k_s - e^2)$ find dT_c/dx.

3. Calculate yC_t from

$$\frac{dT_c}{dx} = \frac{yC_t}{\sin^2 \phi} \qquad (2:27)$$

4. Calculate $y_{\text{approx.}}$ from

$$y \cong \frac{yC_t}{c_{l\,\text{approx.}}\cos\phi} \qquad (2:28)$$

5. Get approximate c from

$$c_{\text{approx.}} = \frac{\pi R y_{\text{approx.}}}{N} \qquad (2:29)$$

6. $$RN = (\rho/\mu)cW \qquad (2:30)$$

where μ = viscosity of the air. Having the Reynolds number, we now use the characteristic curves of the selected airfoil section to determine c_l, c_{d0}, and α_0.

The values of the advance angle ϕ may be determined from eq. 2:25. The blade angle is determined from

$$\beta = \phi + \alpha_0 \qquad (2:31)$$

Since dT_c/dx is known for each value of x from eq. 2:14, C_t may be found from eq. 2:21, sin ϕ from eq. 2:25, and y from eq. 2:21a. From

$$c = \pi R y / N \qquad (2:32)$$

the local chord may be computed.

G. Design Procedure

1. Select a desired overall efficiency η_t, and add to it the estimated straightener loss (2 to 4 per cent) to get the required fan efficiency η_f.

2. From the plot of approximate fan efficiencies vs. advance ratios (Fig. 2:5) determine the required L/D and j range to attain η_f. If the available range is excessive, select the advance ratio for the tip speed as low as possible, as this will yield maximum rpm and minimum rotation. Determine n from

$$n = u/jd$$

Check to see that a tip speed of 550 ft/sec is not exceeded so that compressibility losses will not be encountered.

3. Calculate k from eq. 2:6, and e from eq. 2:10. Check that e at the root is less than $1.33\alpha_{stall}$ from Fig. 2:9.

4. Calculate t_s/c_s and k_s from eqs. 2:3 and 2:4.

5. Calculate η_s from eq. 2:10a and η_f from eq. 2:10b.

6. Determine L/D from eq. 2:26.

7. Calculate ϕ from eq. 2:25.

8. Read approximate c_l from Fig. 2:7.

9. Find dT_c/dx from eq. 2:14.

10. Calculate yC_t, y, c, and RN from eqs. 2:27, 2:28, 2:29, and 2:30.

11. Using approximate RN, read accurate c_l, c_{d0}, and α_0 from Fig. 2:7, and get C_t from eq. 2:21.

12. Calculate y from eq. 2:21a.

13. Calculate c from eq. 2:32.

14. Determine β from eq. 2:31.

15. Determine Q from eq. 2:17.

Example 2:1

A fan is required for a wind tunnel whose energy ratio is 5.0. The area of the test section is 56.4 ft², and the testing velocity is 193 mph = 283 ft/sec. The wind-tunnel diameter at the fan is 13 ft.

A boss diameter of $0.6D$ and 12 blades are values selected for preliminary calculations. Hence $A_f - A_b = 133 - 47.8 = 85.2 \text{ ft}^2$, and $u = 284 \times 56.4/85.2 = 188$. Let $\eta_t = 0.93$, and $\rho/\mu = 5800$.

Step 1. Estimating the straightener loss at 3 per cent, it is seen that the fan efficiency must therefore be 96 per cent.

Step 2. From Fig. 2:5 it is seen that $\eta_f = 96$ per cent may be reached from $j = 2.2$ to $j = 4.8$, using $L/D = 50.0$, which is a reasonable value.

$$n = \frac{u}{JD} = \frac{188}{2.2 \times 13} = 6.58$$

$$\Omega = 2\pi n = 41.4 \text{ rad/sec}$$

$$V_{\text{tip}} = 2\pi nR = 2\pi \times 6.58 \times 6.5 = 269 \text{ ft/sec}$$

which is well below 550 ft/sec, the approximate limit to avoid compressibility.

Step 3.

$$k = \frac{\eta_t}{ER}\left(\frac{A_f - A_b}{A_t}\right)^2 = \frac{0.93}{5.00}\left(\frac{85.2}{56.4}\right)^2 = 0.425$$

$$e = \frac{kj}{2\pi\eta_t} = \frac{0.425}{2\pi(0.93)}j = 0.0729j$$

$$j = \frac{u}{nd} = \frac{u}{nDx} = \frac{188}{(6.58)(13.0)x} = \frac{2.20}{x}$$

$$e_{\text{root}} = \frac{2.20}{0.6} \times 0.0729 = 0.267$$

$$\tau = \tan^{-1} 0.267 = 14.9°$$

This is below $1.33\alpha_{\text{stall}}$ from Fig. 2:9, using an estimated $RN = 3,000,000$.

Step 4. The thickness of the straightener vanes (to be held constant) is $t_s/c_s = 0.15$ at $x = 0.8$. From eq. 2:2 we have

$$c_{s(x=0.8)} = \frac{2\pi Rx}{N_s} = \frac{2\pi(6.5)(0.8)}{7.0} = 4.67 \text{ ft}$$

which makes $t_s = 0.15 \times 4.67 = 0.70$ ft. Hence from eq. 2:3

$$\frac{t_s}{c_s} = \frac{N_s t_s}{2\pi Rx} = \frac{7 \times 0.70}{2\pi(6.5)x} = \frac{0.12}{x}$$

$$k_s = 0.045(t_s/c_s) + 0.003 \qquad (2:4)$$

$$= (0.0054/x) + 0.003$$

The remaining steps are indicated and tabulated below.

x	0.6	0.7	0.8	0.9	1.0
j	3.67	3.14	2.75	2.44	2.20
e	0.267	0.229	0.200	0.178	0.160
t_s/c_s	0.20	0.171	0.15	0.133	0.12
k_s	0.0120	0.0107	0.0098	0.0090	0.0084
$\eta_s = \dfrac{k_s j}{2\pi e}$	0.026	0.023	0.021	0.020	0.018
η_t	0.930	0.930	0.930	0.930	0.930
η_f (eq. 2:10b)	0.956	0.955	0.951	0.950	0.948
j/π	1.17	1.00	0.875	0.777	0.700
$\frac{1}{2}ej/\pi$	0.156	0.1145	0.0875	0.0692	0.056
L/D (eq. 2:26)	40.6	38.8	36.1	36.5	37.0
$\tan \phi$	1.39	1.13	0.960	0.835	0.742
ϕ, degrees	54.3	48.5	43.8	39.8	36.6
c_l approx.	0.53	0.51	0.50	0.52	0.51
$k + k_s - e^2$	0.366	0.384	0.395	0.402	0.406
$\dfrac{dT_c}{dx}$	0.440	0.538	0.633	0.724	0.812
$\sin^2 \phi$	0.660	0.560	0.475	0.410	0.360
yC_t	0.290	0.301	0.301	0.296	0.292
$\cos \phi$	0.584	0.663	0.725	0.769	0.800
$y_{approx.}$	0.937	0.890	0.755	0.742	0.715
$c_{approx.}$	1.59	1.52	1.285	1.264	1.21
$W = u/\sin \phi$	231	251	273	293	313
$RN_{approx.}$	2.13×10^6	2.22×10^6	2.04×10^6	2.08×10^6	2.21×10^6
c_l	0.55	0.53	0.51	0.51	0.51
c_{d0}	0.0140	0.0140	0.0150	0.0140	0.0130
α_0	−0.2	−0.2	−0.6	−0.5	−0.5
β, degrees	54.1	48.3	43.2	39.6	35.8
C_t (eq. 2:21)	0.32	0.352	0.369	0.432	0.408
y	0.873	0.834	0.795	0.738	0.700
c	1.483	1.418	1.350	1.250	1.190

The usual requirement that the propeller blade section be thin (especially at the tips) does not rigidly hold in wind-tunnel fans. The reasons are two: the airspeed at the fan is rarely very high and compressibility effects are not serious; and high enough L/D ratios are obtained so easily that straining for small increments through the use of thin sections is unnecessary. The thicker sections are stronger, too, but peculiar high-frequency vibrations that occur in many wind-tunnel fans and the possibility of the propeller's being struck by airborne objects make it advisable to incorporate margins of safety of the order of 5.0 into their design. An advantage accrues from having removable blades, as a damaged blade may then be replaced without re-building the entire fan.

Fan vibrations are often caused by an asymmetrical velocity front reaching the fan, due to improper turning in the corners and/or flow detachment from the walls. Surveys ahead of the fan can determine whether this condition exists, and adjustments of the corner vanes or any abrupt places in the tunnel can be made. For large installations a jacking gear which enables the fan to be slowly rotated for inspection purposes is good practice.

Tests of fans designed by the above method indicate that actual efficiencies will be from 3 to 5 per cent less than theoretical, owing to tip clearance and boundary-layer effects at boss and tip.

If changes are made to the tunnel after it has been built, it may be necessary to make a fan revision. Though an entirely new fan would be best, flaps have been installed in several tun-nels with satisfactory results and, of course, at much less cost than a whole new fan. The procedure is to rivet or screw flat sheet at the desired flap angle until the chord is satisfactory to meet the new condition.

2:5. The Drive Motor. Since the thrust of the fan and the drag of the various tunnel components vary with the square of the fan rpm it would appear that to maintain an even velocity front in the test section speed adjustments should be made by varying fan rpm rather than fan pitch. Although this conclu-sion is justified in short tunnels of low contraction ratio, in the larger tunnels, particularly those with dust screens and internal coolers to act as flow dampers, it is certainly not true. Indeed, many of the larger tunnels which are equipped with both rpm and pitch change use the latter as quicker and simpler. It does seem as though provision of both types of control is a good de-sign procedure.

Considering the drives capable of variable-speed control, we have the following:

1. Generator and d-c motor. A direct-current generator run by a synchronous motor and used to electrically drive a direct-current motor in the tunnel is a satisfactory system below 200 hp, the cost becoming excessive above that figure. It offers excellent speed control.

2. Tandem drive. The combination of a d-c motor for low powers and a single-speed induction motor for high powers is satisfactory for the range of 300 to 20,000 hp. With this arrange-

ment the d-c motor is used for low-power operation and for bringing the induction motor up to running speed.

3. Variable frequency. A set-up similar to the model motors
described in Chapter 5 also may be used as a tunnel drive, normally below 3000 hp. This set-up embraces a synchronous
motor driving a d-c generator whose output is used to run a d-c
motor which drives an alternator. The output of the alternator is
used to drive the fan motor, which can be either a synchronous or
an induction motor. This is a good system but quite expensive.

4. Magnetic coupling. A synchronous motor can be used to
drive a fan through a variable-speed magnetic coupling. This
is one of the least expensive set-ups as far as first cost is concerned, but possibly it is also the least attractive from an operational standpoint. This type of set-up is rarely over 5000 hp.

5. Multispeed squirrel cage. An induction motor arranged to
have several operating speeds may be used in conjunction with
a variable-pitch fan to get a satisfactory drive. However, the
upper power limit—around 2500 hp—and the high starting loads
reduce its appeal.

6. Wound-rotor induction motor. In general one cannot
expect wide rpm changes, good control, or high efficiency from a
wound-rotor induction motor, although such a motor has been
used with reasonable success in combination with a variable-
pitch fan. It does offer a low first cost and moderately small
motor for tunnel installations.

7. Doubly fed induction motor. This arrangement requires
a variable-frequency power source which is fed into the rotor of
an induction motor. Its first cost is high, but it is probably the
most widely used drive for very high-power installations where
efficiency is important.

8. Internal-combustion drive. The use of an internal-combustion engine is undesirable both from the standpoint of operating cost and lack of long-time reliability. In the few tunnels
where they have been used the engineers invariably look forward
to the day when the gasoline engine can be replaced by an electric drive. For reasons almost unknown (but surmised to be
connected with the lack of a cooling airstream over the station-
ary engine and unskilled maintenance) reciprocating engines
rarely deliver the life in tunnel use that they do on aircraft, 300
hours being a fairly typical figure per engine. When an aircraft
engine must be used, special care should be taken that the ex-

haust manifold be water jacketed or otherwise cooled. An annoying trouble with these engines (as if the above is not sufficient) is that their spark plugs foul up under the low-load operation frequently needed in a tunnel.

2:6. The Nacelle. In a previous section it has been shown that the nacelle must be from 0.3 to 0.7 diameter in order to give the best flow conditions for the fan. In turn, however, this large nacelle makes a lot of trouble that must receive special attention if the best flow is to result. Normally, the nacelle is located in the return passage, which in all probability has a diffusion angle of 6 or 7 degrees. Nacelles that look excellent from free air standards are far too short for use in a duct; a check of the effective duct areas over the afterbody of most nacelles reveals that they raise the local diffusion angle to around 12 to 14 degrees, and frequently separation takes place.

The cure is to use a very long nacelle (see Fig. 2:3), which reduces the local expansion angles to not over 7 degrees, and, if needed, add some boundary-layer control devices such as suction slots. The net result will be a reduction of both scale and intensity of turbulence, and possibly a reduction of tunnel surging, if it has occurred.

2:7. The Corners. It is not practical in wind-tunnel design to make the corners of the return passage so gradual that the air can follow the curve with but small loss. Such corners would require more space than is usually allotted to a tunnel and also would increase the costs of construction. Abrupt corners are therefore usually in order, and their losses are kept to a minimum by means of proper turning vanes.

The nature of losses in a straight duct have been discussed on p. 42, and the corners of a duct behave in a similar manner: the law of continuity assures the same airstream velocity after the turn as before it if no area change has occurred, while the drag of the corner due to both skin friction and separation losses appears as a drop in static pressure Δp. Again this loss is usually referred to the velocity in the duct by

$$\eta = \Delta p / q$$

where η = corner loss coefficient and q = dynamic head in the corner.

An abrupt corner without vanes may show a loss of 100 per cent of the velocity head ($\eta = 1.00$). With carefully designed vanes an η of 0.15 is reasonable. The basic idea is to divide the corner into many turns of high aspect ratio. In this application, then, the rectangle formed by any two vanes should have a width-height ratio of at least 6. In general, this criterion defines the vane gap since the height is known. The vane chord should then be about 2½ times the gap. Where a choice remains, allowance should be made for the fact that the vane drag goes down as the Reynolds number goes up. Here the Reynolds number is based on the vane chord, and larger chords are hence preferable.

Several vane profiles are shown in Fig. 2:10, and each is labeled with the loss experienced under test conditions by the various

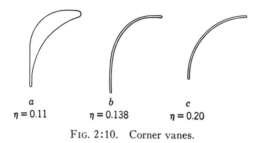

a
$\eta = 0.11$
b
$\eta = 0.138$
c
$\eta = 0.20$

FIG. 2:10.   Corner vanes.

experimenters (Refs. 2:6, 2:7, 2:8, and 2:9) at Reynolds numbers of about 40,000. Equation 2:39 yields values slightly higher than Fig. 2:10 would indicate, but it is felt that the increase is justified for the usual installations.

The hollow vanes offer the opportunity of contributing to the tunnel cooling as they have room for a coolant to be circulated internally. Any of these guide vanes can be used in conjunction with horizontal vanes to form a honeycomb.

As the velocity is highest at the guide vanes just downstream of the tunnel test section, they are the most critical and should receive the most careful workmanship. All vanes should have adjustable trailing edges for minor corrections to the flow angle.

New information (Ref. 2:25) indicates that type (b) in Fig. 2:10 probably has less loss than the value given and very probably is the most advantageous type to use.

2:8. Honeycombs. A number of the older wind tunnels have honeycombs in the settling chamber in order to improve the flow in the test section and to reduce tunnel surge. Usually they are made of octagonal cells with their length 5 to 10 times their width. Newer tunnels of high contraction ratio rarely need or

benefit by honeycombs, and in one that has come to the author's
attention, a honeycomb proved worthless for reducing surge.
The use of screens for improving the flow is discussed in Sects.
3:11 and 3:14.

2:9. The Entrance Cone.   The shape of the entrance cone
should be selected to give a continuously increasing velocity from

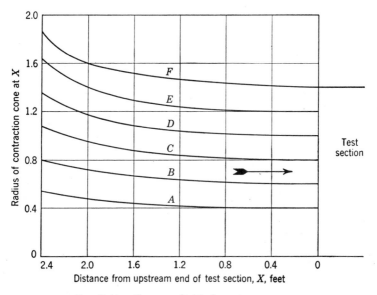

Fig. 2:11.   Curves suitable for entrance cones.

settling chamber to test section.   Usually this requirement results in an entrance cone about 1 diameter long, faired rapidly at
first and then very gradually as the test section is neared.   Curves
suitable for entrance cones in round wind tunnels have been given
by Tsien (Ref. 2:4), and several are shown in Fig. 2:11.

A settling chamber about 0.5 diameter long ahead of the entrance cone seems to aid materially in improving the flow in the
test section.

The contraction ratio of the entrance cone determines the
overall size and hence the cost of a closed-circuit wind tunnel so
that consideration of the cone entirely by itself is not rational.
However, an important item to consider when selecting the contraction ratio is the effect that it has in decreasing the velocity
variation in the test section.

Let us suppose that the variation of the velocity ahead of the contraction is v_n from the average velocity V_n, and in the test section it is v_0 from the mean value V_0. Writing Bernoulli's equation between the two sections we have

$$p_n + \tfrac{1}{2}\rho(V_n + v_n)^2 = p_0 + \tfrac{1}{2}\rho(V_0 + v_0)^2$$

Expanding, and making the good approximation that there is little loss of head between the two stations so that

$$p_n + \tfrac{1}{2}\rho V_n{}^2 = p_0 + \tfrac{1}{2}\rho V_0{}^2$$

we have

$$v_n{}^2 + 2v_n V_n = v_0{}^2 + 2v_0 V_0$$

Dividing through by $V_n{}^2 V_0{}^2$ and neglecting $(v/V)^2$ as small

$$\frac{v_0}{V_0} = \frac{V_n{}^2 v_n}{V_0{}^2 V_n}$$

But $V_n{}^2 / V_0{}^2 = 1/n^2$, where n = area contraction ratio. Hence

$$\frac{v_0}{V_0} = \frac{1}{n^2} \frac{v_n}{V_n} \qquad (2:33)$$

or the variation in velocity varies inversely as the square of the contraction ratio. It is seen that a large contraction ratio, say from 7 to 14, is a great help in obtaining good jet flow.

2:10. Materials of Construction. Wind tunnels are usually constructed of wood, metal, or concrete, the individual design dictating the choice.

The smaller tunnels (about 3-ft throat) are commonly of plywood, which makes for easy construction and, if need be, easy alteration. Adequate fire precautions should be observed.

Pressure tunnels are usually metal, which is advantageous if surface cooling is to be employed. The greater expansion of the metal tunnel may cause small flow variations as the temperature changes. The immense cranes needed during the construction of a metal tunnel are shown in Fig. 2:12.

Concrete construction may be either conventional poured forms or sprayed Gunite. Usually a structural steel ring and stringer base are required for strength. A concrete tunnel must have the inside walls painted or hardened to lock in the dust.

Official Photograph, National Advisory Committee for Aeronautics.

FIG. 2:12. Erection of the all-metal 12-ft pressure tunnel at the Ames Aeronautical Laboratory.

The construction of a poured-concrete tunnel is shown in Fig. 2:13.

2:11. Power Losses. Wattendorf (Ref. 2:10) has pointed the way towards a logical approach to the losses in a return-type wind tunnel. The procedure is to break the tunnel down into (1) cylindrical sections, (2) corners, (3) expanding sections, and (4) contracting sections, and calculate the loss for each.

In each of the sections a loss of energy occurs, usually written as a drop in static pressure, Δp, or as a coefficient of loss, $K = \Delta p / q$. Wattendorf refers these local losses to the jet dynamic pressure, defining the coefficient of loss as

$$K_0 = \frac{\Delta p}{q} \frac{q}{q_0} = K \frac{q}{q_0} \qquad (2:34)$$

or, since the dynamic head varies inversely as the fourth power of the tunnel diameter,

$$K_0 = K D_0^4 / D^4 \qquad (2:34a)$$

where D_0 = jet diameter; D = local tunnel diameter.

Courtesy of United Aircraft Corp.

Fig. 2:13. Construction of a poured-concrete wind tunnel. Steel rings and wood forms.

Using the above definitions, the section energy loss $\Delta E = K\frac{1}{2}\rho A V^3$ may be referred to the jet energy by

$$\Delta E = K\frac{1}{2}\rho A V^3 \frac{A_0 V_0 \cdot V_0^2}{A_0 V_0 \cdot V_0^2}$$

$$= K\frac{1}{2}\rho A_0 V_0^3 \frac{D_0^4}{D^4}$$

and, finally,

$$\Delta E = K_0 \cdot \tfrac{1}{2}\rho A_0 V_0^3$$

where A_0 = test section area; A = local area.

$$\text{Energy ratio} = \frac{\text{Jet energy}}{\Sigma \text{ circuit losses}} = ER_t$$

(See Sect. 3:16.)

$$ER_t = \frac{\frac{1}{2}\rho A_0 V_0^3}{\Sigma K_0 \frac{1}{2}\rho A_0 V_0^3} = \frac{1}{\Sigma K_0} \qquad (2:35)$$

It will be noted that the above definition of the energy ratio excludes the fan and motor efficiency.

The magnitude of the losses in a circular wind tunnel may be computed as follows:

In the *cylindrical sections* the pressure drop in length L is $\Delta p/L = (\lambda/D)(\rho/2)V^2$, and $K = \Delta p/q = \lambda(L/D)$. Therefore

$$K_0 = \lambda(L/D)(D_0^4/D^4) \qquad (2:36)$$

For smooth pipes at high Reynolds numbers von Kármán gives (Ref. 2:11)

$$1/\sqrt{\lambda} = 2\log_{10} R\sqrt{\lambda} - 0.8 \qquad (2:37)$$

where D = local tunnel diameter, ft; V = local velocity, ft/sec; $RN = (\rho/\mu)VD$.

As eq. 2:37 is tedious of solution, a plot is shown in Fig. 2:14.

For open cylindrical sections such as an open jet, a reasonable value for skin-friction coefficient is

$$\lambda = 0.08$$

For an open jet of $\dfrac{\text{length}}{\text{diameter}} = 1.5$, the loss becomes $0.08 \times 1.5 = 12$ per cent as compared to about one-tenth that value for a closed jet.

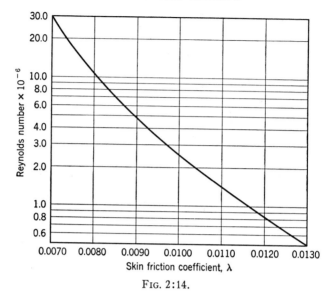

FIG. 2:14.

In the *divergent sections*, both wall friction and expansion losses occur. The combined loss of the two is summed up by

$$K_0 = \left(\frac{\lambda}{8 \tan (\alpha/2)} + 0.6 \tan \frac{\alpha}{2}\right)\left(1 - \frac{D_1^4}{D_2^4}\right)\frac{D_0^4}{D_1^4} \quad (2:38)$$

where α = divergence between opposite walls (not over 10 degrees); D_1 = smaller diameter; D_2 = larger diameter.

It will be seen that the smaller expansions yield smaller losses up to the point where the skin friction of the added area becomes excessive. This, it will be seen by differentiating eq. 2:38, occurs when

$$\tan (\alpha/2) = \sqrt{\lambda/4.8}$$

For reasonable values of λ the most efficient divergence is therefore about 5 degrees. However, available space limitations for the tunnel as well as the cost of construction usually dictate that a slightly larger divergence be employed at a small increase in cost of operation.

It will be noted that the losses in a divergent section are two to three times greater than the corresponding losses in a cylindrical tube, although the progressively decreasing velocity would seem to indicate losses between that of a cylindrical section with the diameter of the smaller section and that of one with the diameter of the larger section. The reason for the added loss is that the energy exchange near the walls is of such a nature that the thrust expected from the walls is not fully realized. Effectively, a pressure force is thereby added to the skin-friction forces.

It should also be noted that the angle between opposite walls of a diffuser is a very poor diffuser parameter, the point being that the rate of pressure rise in two diffusers having equal wall angles but different entrance diameters is quite different, and rate of pressure rise is probably a much better criterion. Following this logic a number of wind tunnels have a wider wall angle in the return passage than in the diffuser. An additional argument for this type of design is that the disturbance caused by a model in the test section may limit satisfactory diffuser angles below smooth flow values.

In the *corners*, friction in the guide vanes accounts for about one-third of the loss, and rotation losses for the other two-thirds. For corners of the type shown in Fig. 2:10 the following partly empirical relation is reasonable, being based on a corner pressure drop of $\Delta p/q = 0.15$ at $RN = 500,000$.

$$K_0 = \left(0.10 + \frac{4.55}{(\log_{10} RN)^{2.58}} \right) \frac{D_0{}^4}{D^4} \qquad (2{:}39)$$

In the *contraction cone* the losses are friction only, and the pressure drop is

$$\Delta p_f = \int_0^L \lambda \frac{\rho}{2} V^2 \frac{dL}{D}$$

where L = length of contraction cone.

$$K_0 = K \frac{D_0{}^4}{D^4} = \frac{\Delta p_f}{q} \frac{D_0{}^4}{D^4} = \int_0^L \lambda \frac{dL}{D} \frac{D_0{}^4}{D^4} \frac{D_0}{D_0}$$

$$= \lambda \frac{L}{D_0} \int_0^L \frac{D_0{}^5}{D^5} \frac{dL}{L} \qquad (2{:}40)$$

Assuming a mean value for λ,

$$K_0 = 0.32 \lambda L/D_0 \qquad (2{:}41)$$

As the total loss in the contraction cone usually runs below 3 per cent of the total tunnel loss, any errors due to approximations in the cone losses become of small importance.

Losses in *honeycombs* have been reported by Roberts (Ref. 2:17). Values of K suitable for use in eq. 2:34a are given in Fig. 2:15 for honeycombs with a $\dfrac{\text{length}}{\text{diameter}} = 6.0$, and equal tube areas. Roughly speaking, the loss in a honeycomb is usually less than 5 per cent of the total tunnel loss.

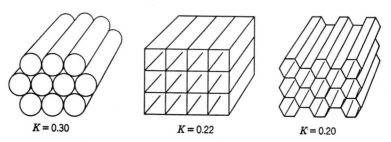

$K = 0.30$　　　　　　$K = 0.22$　　　　　　$K = 0.20$

FIG. 2:15.　Some honeycombs and their losses.

The losses incurred in the single-return tunnel of Fig. 2:16 based on a tunnel temperature of 100° F ($\rho/\mu = 5560$) and a test section velocity of 100 mph are as tabulated.

SECTION	K_0	% TOTAL LOSS
1. The jet	0.0093	5.1
2. Divergence	0.0391	21.3
3. Corner	0.046	25.0
4. Cylinder	0.0026	1.4
5. Corner	0.046	25.0
6. Cylinder	0.002	1.1
7. Divergence	0.016	8.9
8. Corner	0.0087	4.7
9. Corner	0.0087	4.7
10. Cylinder	0.0002	0.1
11. Cone	0.0048	2.7
	0.1834	100.0

Energy ratio, $ER_t = 1/\Sigma K_0 = 1/0.1834 = 5.45$

Probably this figure should be reduced about 10 per cent for leaks and joints.

The effect of varying the angle of divergence or the contraction ratio for a tunnel similar to the one of Fig. 2:16 may be seen in Figs. 2:17 and 2:18.

The possibility of attaining higher energy ratios has several promising leads. One fundamental is the increase of efficiency that accompanies larger Reynolds numbers. That is, a large tunnel similar to a small tunnel will have the greater efficiency of the two.

Reduction of the losses in the divergent passage is limited, as previously stated, to a certain minimum angle between opposite walls. The use of this minimum angle would, however, yield smaller losses than are customarily encountered. Corner losses

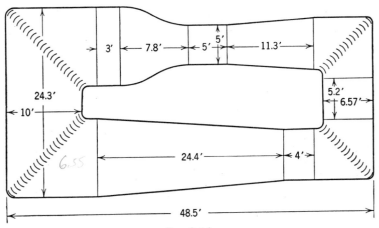

Fig. 2:16.

may be reduced through the use of two relatively untried innovations. The first is to break the four 90-degree turns into several vaned turns of less than 90 degrees (Ref. 2:12). The second is to employ potential elbows (Ref. 2:3) for the turns. Increasing the contraction ratio through a longer return passage will also increase the energy ratio but at an added cost in tunnel construction. Increased length before the first turn is particularly effective.

An entirely different approach, particularly useful for high-speed tunnels, is to reduce the power required for a given speed by reducing the air density through partly evacuating the entire tunnel. This procedure greatly complicates model changes as the tunnel pressure must be relieved before the tunnel crew can enter. (Some of the newer tunnels overcome this difficulty by having pressure doors that seal off the test section from the rest of the tunnel and greatly reduce the pumping between runs.)

As the power required is a function of ρV^3, by reducing the pressure to one-fourth its former value the speed may be increased by the ratio $\sqrt[3]{4}$ to 1 for the same power input. Stated differ-

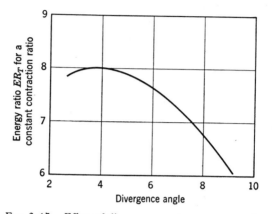

FIG. 2:17.   Effect of divergence angle on energy ratio.

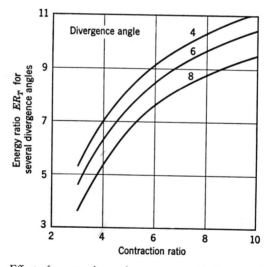

FIG. 2:18.   Effect of contraction ratio on energy ratio for several divergence angles.

ently, a 59 per cent higher Mach number will be attained with the lower pressure.

When figuring power requirements for a proposed design, consideration must also be given to (a) the power required to overcome model drag under the most extreme cases and (*b*) the power required to overcome the increased tunnel losses due to parts of the diffuser stalling from the model effects.

For (*a*) the power required to fly a model whose span is 0.8 tunnel diameter, $AR = 5$, and $C_D = 0.5000$ is probably sufficient.

Item (*b*) for conventional tests is covered in (*a*) above, but for wingtip mounting or section tests as much as 150 per cent *more* power may be needed if the diffuser is seriously stalled and large rotational and diffusion losses are created.

2:12. Cooling. All the energy supplied to the propeller driving a wind tunnel finally emerges as an increase of heat energy

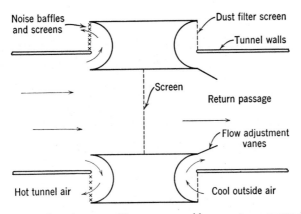

Fig. 2:19. An air exchanger. The screen provides an extra pressure drop for additional flow through the air exchanger.

in the windstream. This increases the temperature of the tunnel air until the heat losses finally balance the input. For low-power tunnels (and particularly those with open jets) this balance is realized at reasonable temperatures, the heat transfer through surface cooling and air exchange being sufficient. For tunnels with high power inputs and high jet velocities this low-temperature balance no longer occurs. For example, the heat rise incurred by bringing air to rest at 450 mph is about 36° F. With an energy ratio of 8.0, the heat rise in the airstream would be 4.5° F per circuit, leading in a very short while to prohibitive temperatures. Obviously, tunnels in this class require cooling arrangements to augment the inherent heat losses.

Additional cooling may be accomplished by four means: (1) an increase of surface cooling by running water over the tunnel ex-

terior; (2) interior cooling by the addition of water-cooled turning vanes or (3) a water-cooled radiator in the largest tunnel
section; (4) a continual replacement of the heated tunnel air with
cool outside air by means of an air exchanger.

Some high-speed tunnels use an air exchanger (Figs. 2:19 and
2:20) to replace the lower-energy boundary layer with cool out-

Fig. 2:20.   View of air exchangers from inside the return passage.

side air, having exchange towers to assure adequate dispersion
of the heated air and fresh air that is free from surface contamination.   Assuming the previously mentioned rise of 4.5° F per
circuit, a 10 per cent exchange would limit the rise to 45° F,
excluding heat losses elsewhere.   (Ten per cent is a lower than
average amount of exchange.)

One difficulty associated with an air exchanger is that it puts
the highest-pressure section of the tunnel at atmospheric pressure, and hence the jet pressure is below atmospheric.   This
leads to troublesome but by no means insoluble problems of
sealing off the balance room.   (The same low jet static pressure
is present in open-circuit tunnels.)   Another difficulty that must

be considered is the possible effects of weather conditions on a tunnel with a large amount of air exchanged.

It should be mentioned that a breather slot at the downstream end of the test section can be used in conjunction with the air exchanger to get the jet up to atmospheric pressure and hence avoid balance sealing troubles. However, this arrangement

Official Photograph, National Advisory Committee for Aeronautics.

FIG. 2:21. Wingtip mounting of a full-scale F-80 in the high-altitude wind tunnel at the Lewis Flight Propulsion Laboratory.

with the air going in the breather and out the exchanger requires as much as 20 per cent of the total power input.

The internal heat exchangers needed for high-powered wind tunnels require an immense amount of surface, a great deal more than is offered by all four sets of guide vanes. Accordingly, a special installation is needed, and there is almost no way around a very large amount of drag. In a preliminary study reported by Steinle (Ref. 2:20) pressure drops of 8 to $18q$ were measured across exchangers; another design, unreported, had $4q$. Thus the heat exchanger must be placed in the largest section of the tunnel where the q is lowest; incidentally this helps because at this point the temperature of the stream is highest and heat exchange consequently simplest.

In view of its power cost a great deal of thought should go into the design of a heat exchanger, and it should be remembered that normal streamlining should be used here as well as elsewhere. Unfortunately no information is available as to the optimum design, although work is being done on the problem at several laboratories. Engineers employing dry air in low-pressure tunnels have found that rubber hose used in cooler connections had to be removed to keep dryness satisfactory.

The unknowns of internal and external boundary-layer thicknesses make the problem of cooling through the walls quite difficult. In discussing internal cooling, Tifford (Ref. 2:5) states that a radiator has possible advantages over cooled turning vanes.

The obvious disadvantages of high temperatures in the wind tunnel include added trouble cooling the drive motor (if it is in the tunnel and does not have separate cooling), the rapid softening of the model temporary fillets, and increased personnel difficulties. Another deleterious effect is the drop in Reynolds number that occurs with increasing temperatures whether the tunnel is run at constant speed or at constant dynamic pressure. Figure 2:22 illustrates this effect.

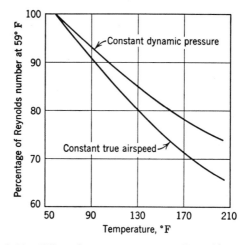

Fig. 2:22.   Effect of temperature on test Reynolds number.

As most electric motors have high efficiencies, placing the motor outside the tunnel is probably not justified by the small amount of tunnel heating saved thereby, but the ease of tunnel repowering without a nacelle change is a strong argument for the external drive motor.

2:13. Jet Inserts. Many tunnels have an auxiliary two-dimensional test sections which fit inside the normal test section in order to provide testing facilities for shorter-span models at considerable savings in model cost. These jets are usually either endplate or contraction types.

The endplate jet insert consists of two flat plates sealed at tunnel floor or ceiling (Fig. 2:23) with a space between them for

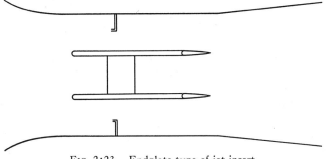

FIG. 2:23.   Endplate type of jet insert.

mounting and testing a constant-chord two-dimensional airfoil model. In some installations the model supports come up inside the endplates, and the rear pitch strut is used to hold and move the wake survey rake. Since the drag of the model changes with many factors, and since drag changes can make more air pass *around* instead of through the test section, special provision must be made to control the test dynamic pressure. One procedure is to use the customary double piezometer to hold the quantity of air constant that enters the original test section, and ascertain that a constant fraction of *that* air passes through the new test section by reading pitot-static tubes placed outside it. Variations can be made by remotely movable trailing edge flaps on the endplates.

A second approach is to contract the whole tunnel test section by an additional contraction section (Fig. 2:24). This has the advantages of greatly increasing the contraction ratio and making the installation of turbulence screens easy, and of providing sure and positive two-dimensional conditions. On the other hand, a much smaller quantity of air now passes through the tunnel for a particular test speed since the test section area is reduced, and in many cases the performance of the tunnel fan is greatly impaired.* Still another source of trouble is the problem of diffusing the overcontracted passage. Somewhere some extremely rapid diffusion is going to have to take place, and the task is exceedingly difficult to do with even passable efficiency.

Several other items are of interest when inserts are under consideration. One of these is the question whether to mount the insert horizontal so that the model is vertical, or vice versa.

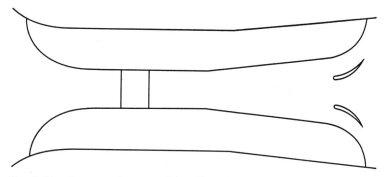

Fig. 2:24.   A contraction type of two-dimensional jet insert.   An abrupt expansion is often preferred over the vane type shown.

The horizontal insert offers the opportunity of using liquid seals around the model mounting endplates, but on the other hand the model is somewhat more difficult to get to for adjustments. Force measuring is also made more difficult by the large and indeterminable tares of the model mounting endplates, so much so that it is sometimes preferable to obtain the lift by pressure distributions on the model or on the floor and ceiling, and drag by a momentum rake; or to leave a small gap between model and walls.

In conclusion, it does not appear possible to recommend one type of two-dimensional jet insert as superior, with the final note that, aerodynamics laid aside for a moment, the endplate type of insert is far easier to install and remove.

2:14. Safety.   Though it may seem strange to bring the question of safety into a discussion of wind tunnels, the long

---

* A convenient way to think of the operation of the fan is to discuss the pressure rise it can produce in the units of the dynamic pressure approaching it. The reduction of quantity mentioned above will hence reduce the amount of power the fan can absorb.

roster of injured indicates it is not to be overlooked. Accidents in tunnel use include fires, falls, injuries from sharp-edged models, and personnel being locked in a tunnel when it is started.

Starting with the last, anybody who enters a part of a wind tunnel not readily visible to the tunnel operators without firm understanding regarding the restarting time is an idiot. But since it is not the practice to injure idiots, many tunnels preface a start with a blast on a horn, and a 5-second wait for incumbents to punch stop switches installed in test sections, return passages, and near the fan blades. When it is necessary for someone to be in the tunnel while it is running, very clear signals or understanding must again be obtained.

Falls are unfortunately frequent in wind tunnels. Their rounded surface, often coated with oil or ice, and the precipitous slope of entrance cones have resulted in bruises and even broken arms and legs. The author speaks feelingly at this point. In view of the danger associated with the entrance cone and settling chamber, pitot-static tubes, thermocouples, and the like should be wall mounted.

Fires in wind tunnels seem to be almost the rule rather than the exception: a broken propeller can spark a dust screen into fire; a trouble light can make plenty of trouble; or even building forms can in some way become ignited. Since the tunnel is closed, special care should be taken in selecting fire extinguishers. And special care should be taken also to see that fire extinguishers emitting poisonous vapors are not easily tripped. It may well be that the world's record for the hundred yard dash rightfully belongs to a tunnel engineer who inadvertently activated the carbon dioxide system in one of the largest east-coast tunnels.

The advent of the sharp edges on metal models is a new and potent hazard; the author does not know a tunnel engineer who has not suffered from this source. It is only good sense to protect the tunnel crew from these sharp edges, either by tape or wood slats.

Safety may seem like a puerile subject, but it loses that appearance *afterwards*.

PROBLEMS

2:1. What percentage of the power supplied to a wind-tunnel motor appears as heat energy in the air? (The motor itself is in the tunnel.)

2:2. State four methods of cooling a tunnel.

2:3. In what sections of the tunnel do the largest losses occur?

2:4. Explain why there is no increase of axial speed across the propeller disk.

2:5. What are the objections to a double-return tunnel?

2:6. Discuss materials that could be used in the construction of a wind tunnel.

2:7. Check the loss calculations for the tunnel of Fig. 2:16.

2:8. Which end of the test section is the larger? Why? What angle of divergence is reasonable?

2:9. Why is straightener vane loss greater than skin friction alone?

2:10. About how much power would be required for a 450-mph tunnel having atmospheric pressure in the 20-ft-diameter test section? Assume a reasonable energy ratio.

2:11. Name four different propulsion systems used for wind tunnels.

2:12. State reasonable amounts of air exchanged by an air exchanger.

2:13. State advantages and disadvantages incurred by using an air exchanger.

2:14. Air at 2117 lb per sq ft static pressure and 100 lb per sq ft dynamic pressure enters a 90-degree cascaded corner. State probable static and dynamic pressure after the turn.

2:15. State two methods that enable a crew to work on a model in a pressure tunnel without blowing down the entire tunnel.

2:16. Why are thin propeller blades necessary on an airplane but not in a wind tunnel?

REFERENCES

2:1. Felix Nagel, Static and Dynamic Model Similarity, *JAS*, September, 1939.

2:2. Ivan A. Rubinsky, The Use of Heavy Gases or Vapors for High Speed Wind Tunnels, *JAS*, September, 1939.

2:3. Boleslaw Szczeniowski, Design of Elbows in Potential Motion, *JAS*, January, 1944.

2:4. Tsien, Hsue-Shen, On the Design of a Contraction Cone for a Wind Tunnel, *JAS*, February, 1943.

2:5. Arthur N. Tifford, Wind Tunnel Cooling, *JAS*, March, 1943.

2:6. G. Krober, Guide Vanes for Deflecting Fluid Currents with Small Loss of Energy, *TM* 722, 1932.

2:7. A. R. Collar, Some Experiments with Cascades of Airfoils, *R&M* 1768, 1937.

2:8. G. N. Patterson, Note on the Design of Corners in Duct Systems, *R&M* 1773, 1937.

2:9. D. C. McPhail, Experiments on Turning Vanes at an Expansion, *R&M* 1876, 1939.

2:10. F. L. Wattendorf, Factors Influencing the Energy Ratio of Return Flow Wind Tunnels, p. 526, 5th International Congress for Applied Mechanics, Cambridge, 1938.

2:11. T. von Kármán, Turbulence and Skin Friction, *JAS*, January, 1934.

2:12. G. Darrius, Some Factors Influencing the Design of Wind Tunnels, *Brown-Boveri Review*, July-August, 1943.

2:13. G. N. Patterson, Ducted Fans: Design for High Efficiency, *ACA* 7, July, 1944.

2:14. A. R. Collar, The Design of Wind Tunnel Fans, *R&M* 1889, August, 1940.

2:15. W. C. Nelson, *Airplane Propeller Principles*, John Wiley & Sons, New York, p. 9.

2:16. G. N. Patterson, Ducted Fans: High Efficiency with Contra-Rotation, ACA 10, October, 1944.

2:17. H. E. Roberts, Considerations in the Design of a Low Cost Wind Tunnel, Paper presented at 14th Annual Meeting of the Institute of Aeronautical Sciences, January, 1946.

2:18. Paul A. Libby and Howard R. Reiss, The Design of Two-Dimensional Contraction Sections, *QAM*, Vol. IX, April, 1951.

2:19. W. A. Mair, The Design of Fans and Guide Vanes for High Speed Wind Tunnels, *R&M* 2435, 1951.

2:20. Warren C. Steinle, The Experimental Determination of Aerodynamic Total-Pressure Losses for Heat Exchanger Surfaces Considered for the 7 x 10 Foot Transonic Wind Tunnel, *DTMB Aero Report* 807, 1951.

2:21. G. T. Strailman, New Wind Tunnel Drive Control, *Electrical Engineering*, July, 1952.

2:22. Paul A. Libby and Howard R. Reiss, The Design of Two-Dimensional Contraction Sections, *QAM*, Vol. IX, No. 1, April, 1951.

2:23. B. Thwaites, On the Design of Contractions for Wind Tunnels, *R&M* 2278, 1946.

2:24. Hugh L. Dryden and Ira H. Abbott, The Design of Low-Turbulence Wind Tunnels, *TR* 940, 1949.

2:25. K. G. Winters, Comparative Tests of Thin Turning Vanes in the RAE 4 x 3 Foot Wind Tunnel, *R&M* 2589, 1947.

Chapter 3

INSTRUMENTATION AND CALIBRATION
OF THE TEST SECTION

After a tunnel is constructed, the next step is to determine its flow characteristics and, of course, to change any that are not satisfactory. Before we can go into this, however, it is necessary to discuss the quantities that we shall be measuring and the instruments that experience has shown are the best to do the job. Besides those instruments needed for calibration we will also discuss others needed for testing.

The low-speed airstream is defined when we know its distribution of dynamic pressure, static pressure, total pressure, and its temperature and turbulence. We may then compute its velocity and the Reynolds number for a particular model. Much of our interest then is centered on determining pressures, and for this procedure it is hard to beat simple fluid columns. The device by which the height of the fluid is measured is called a manometer, and we will first look into fluids that are suitable for manometer use.

3:1. Fluids and Manometers. The most commonly used fluid is alcohol. It is popular because it is cheap, is easy to obtain, and has low viscosity. Its low specific gravity is productive of a higher fluid column than is obtained with water.

The specific gravity of alcohol varies moderately with temperature. Corrections for this effect may be found from Fig. 3:1. It follows, for example, that if alcohol is labeled either by its specific gravity at some temperature ("sp. gr. = 0.801 at 80° F") or by its water content ("94.0 per cent alcohol") it will be completely defined and its proper curve for temperature correction may be determined. It also follows that the temperature of the manometer fluid should be read along with the various fluid heights.

The method of correcting the specific gravity of alcohol for changes in temperature is explained in the following example.

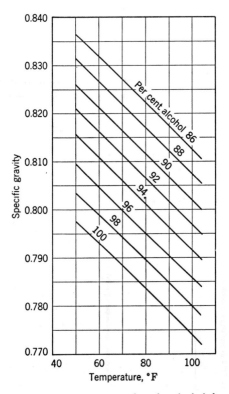

Fig. 3:1. Temperature corrections for alcohol density.

Example 3:1

An alcohol-water mixture has a specific gravity of 0.805 at 68° F. What is the percentage of alcohol, and what will be the specific gravity at 77° F?

1. Locate the point (0.805, 68° F) in Fig. 3:1, and draw a line through it parallel to the other lines of the figure. Estimate the distance between the lines 94 and 96 per cent, and read 94.6 per cent alcohol.

2. Follow down the newly constructed 94.6 per cent line until it intersects 77° F. Read sp. gr. = 0.802.

Sometimes the pressures to be measured require that fluids heavier than alcohol be utilized; several of these are listed in Table 3:1. Only pure liquids should be employed, for the heavy portions will settle out of a mixture.

TABLE 3:1

Liquid	Specific Gravity (approx.)	Remarks
Alcohol	0.80	All around the most satisfactory.
Silicone DC 200	0.902	Has a very low boiling point.
Water	1.00 *	Makes a poor meniscus due to excessive surface tension.†
Methylene chloride	1.30	Attacks rubber.
Bromobenzene	1.50	Quite volatile.
Ethyl bromide	1.50	Too volatile to use.
Carbon tetrachloride	1.59	Attacks rubber, but is cheap and otherwise good. Hard to color.
Acetylene tetrachloride	1.59	Attacks rubber.
Ethylene dibromide	2.13	Quite volatile; low surface tension and meniscus poor.
Tetrabrome-ethane ‡	2.97	Attacks rubber.
Mercury ‡	13.56	Oil the meniscus for best results. Mercury attacks brass and solder.

* 0.998 at 70° F.

† The surface tension may be made acceptable through the addition of a wetting agent such as used in photographic processes.

‡ Also see Fig. 12:17.

The liquids that attack rubber may sometimes be used with synthetic rubber tubing or most of the plastic tubing now available.

For photographic work it is usually necessary to color the fluid to make the detail in the films easier to read. Ordinary ink will work for water and alcohol, as will any of a great number of textile dyes, but inasmuch as many dyes will fade if iron is present it is usually advisable to make all metal parts of the manometer of brass. Black is a very suitable color, and alcohol may be so dyed with a commercial dye called Nigrosine 12525; Buffalo Chrome Black, 2 BN; or Direct Black, E concentration.

The heights of the fluid columns are measured in a great variety of ways, depending on the accuracy desired. The simplest is to fasten a glass or clear plastic tube to a meter stick, and read the fluid height directly; readings to about 0.5 mm may be obtained thus. Precision manometers are better. Some of them entail a hairline to which the fluid meniscus is made tangent by raising or lowering it on a lead screw; others have a float on the fluid which has a tiny mirror on it for optical magnification; still others read remotely by means of an electrically driven pointer which just maintains contact with the fluid.   Any of the above instruments may be built to yield accuracies of ±0.002 in. or better.

A simple manometer is shown in Fig. 3:2.   Its main features include: (1) a rotatable indicator piece so that arbitrary slopes

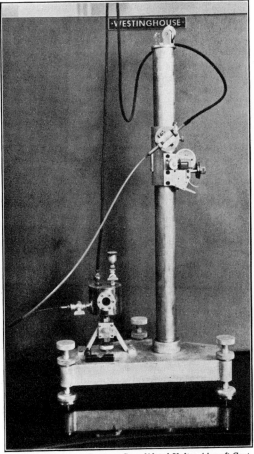

Courtesy Consolidated-Vultee Aircraft Corp.

Fig. 3:2.   A vernier manometer.

can be used on the fluid meniscus to increase accuracy; (2) a vernier scale for precise reading; (3) a suitable damping arrangement; (4) a variable-height indicator or a variable-height reservoir so that the system is null and no error is incurred by having a variation in reservoir level as the fluid column changes.

If fluid heights to be measured are large, it would be better to move the reservoir and keep the indicator at eye level, rather than vice versa as shown in Fig. 3:2.

3:2. Multiple Manometers. Very frequently it is necessary to measure a large number of pressures simultaneously. Normally the accuracy needed does not require precision equip-

Courtesy Consolidated-Vultee Aircraft Corp.

FIG. 3:3. An adjustable-angle multiple manometer. Sometimes a dial-type thermometer is mounted directly on the manometer for fluid temperature data.

ment, and it is sufficient to mount a large number of glass tubes (25 to 30) on a lined plate, forming what is called a multiple manometer. The tube readings are customarily recorded photographically, and except for a few important tubes read visually the values are read after the test.

There are two types of multiple manometers: those with the tubes in front of a lined glass plate with rear illumination, and those having a solid plate, and illumination from the front. By far the great majority of multiple manometers are of the glass-plate type, but having built and used five, the author feels constrained to go against the majority and point out the advantages, particularly for low-speed and class work, of the solid-plate type.

For low-speed work the manometer must be lowered until it is from 30 to 45 degrees with the horizontal in order to get useful fluid heights. In this position glass plates sag appreciably and let the tubes bend with a surprisingly large error resulting. (Additional bracing usually interferes with the lights.) The internally illuminated manometer is much heavier. Special ink must be obtained to make good lines on glass. When the lights are in the back, darker dyes must be used with a resultant staining of the tubes. And, finally, anything that must be moved about and is largely glass always runs the risk of being broken.

It will be noticed that most of the above arguments disappear for a permanent installation used for high-speed work.

At any rate, some design hints that will tend towards getting a good manometer are proffered herewith.

1. Avoid the use of iron anywhere where fluid can touch; iron causes many dyes to precipitate out.

2. Use the commercially available brass sylphon tubing to connect the reservoir to the manometer foot. This tubing is permanent, and far superior to rubber or any of the plastic hoses with which the author is acquainted.

3. Provide manometer tilting such that one man can do the job.

4. Provide an adjustable reservoir so that the wind off fluid heights may be set anywhere on the manometer.

5. Provide a straight-line path for cleaning the tubes.

6. The maximum fluid height (i.e., the tube length) should allow for a maximum of $8q$.

7. Reference marks every 0.2 in. with heavy lines at the inches seem to be satisfactory.

The connections of the multiple manometer should be checked frequently by letting a low pressure at the orifice raise a fluid column and hold it when the orifice is sealed. The simple "response" check is not sufficient, for leaking tubes respond readily to a sudden increase of pressure. Whenever possible it is advisable to have at least one atmospheric reference tube to permit obtaining absolute pressure values.

Not infrequently a manometer tube will fail to level properly owing to either dirt in the glass tube or a bubble in the line. Care is necessary if accurate readings are desired. If the reservoir is dropped down except when the manometer is in active use, minimum glass stain will result.

Various complicated methods are used to read films made of multiple manometer readings, but one of the simplest is to prepare a special scale for each program, as follows:

Project the film onto a ground-glass screen and measure the manometer inch markings to determine the film scale. Translate this scale, including fluid density, into $\Delta p/q$, ending with, say, $\Delta p/q = 1.0$ is 2.31 in. on the ground glass. Make a paper scale divided into tenths of $\Delta p/q$, and glue it on a wood backing. Provide a red offset for tunnel static pressure for negative pressures and a blue mark for positive pressures. Direct $\Delta p/q$ readings may then be made as fast as a person can read.

The quality of the film data will be improved if the camera used to take it holds the film flat against the plate by a vacuum arrangement, as in an aerial camera.

3:3. The Pitot-Static Tube. The most common device for determining the total head and the static pressure of a stream is

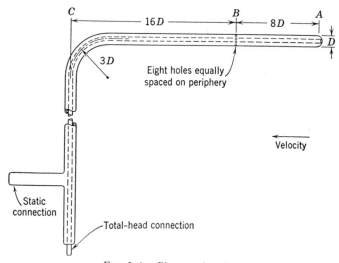

FIG. 3:4. Pitot-static tube.

the pitot-static tube, an instrument that yields both the total head and static pressure. A "standard" pitot-static tube is shown in Fig. 3:4. The orifice at A reads total head $(p + \frac{1}{2}\rho V^2)$, and those at B read the static pressure, p. If the pressures from the two orifices are connected across a manometer, the pressure differential will, of course, be $\frac{1}{2}\rho V^2$, from which the velocity may be calculated. (For determining ρ see Example 3:4.)

The pitot-static tube is easy to construct, but it has some inherent errors. If due allowance is made for these errors, a true reading of the dynamic pressure within about 0.1 per cent may be obtained.

It has been amply demonstrated that a total head tube with a hemispherical tip will read the total head accurately independent of the size of the orifice opening as long as the yaw is less than 3 degrees.* Hence the total head reading introduces no difficulties.

The static holes suffer from two effects: (1) The crowding of the streamlines near the tip reduces the pressure along the shank of the pitot-static tube so that the static pressure at the static orifices will be low. The amount of error is seen in Fig. 3:5.

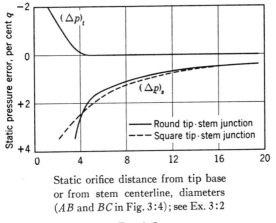

Static orifice distance from tip base
or from stem centerline, diameters
(AB and BC in Fig. 3:4); see Ex. 3:2

FIG. 3:5.

(2) A high-pressure region exists ahead of the stem that tends to make the indicated static pressure too high.

The two effects may block each other out if the static holes are properly located. The "standard" pitot-static tube does not employ this principle as it would require the static holes to be so close to the tip that small deviations in tip construction or damage to the tip could make a relatively large error in the static reading.

* A squared-off tip has even less angle error and is to be preferred when only total head is needed.

Hence: (1) If a new pitot-static tube is to be built it may either be designed as per Fig. 3:4 and its static pressure readings corrected as per Fig. 3:5, or a 2.5D tip length and 9D stem length may be used. The 2.5-9D arrangement should require no correction but should be checked for accuracy. (2) Existing pitot-static tubes should be examined for tip and stem errors so that their constants may be found.

Example 3:2

A pitot-static tube whose static orifices are 3.2D from the base of the tip and 8.0D from the centerline of the stem reads 12.05 in. of water on a manometer for a particular setting of the tunnel. If the test section is at standard pressure and 113° F, find (1) the dynamic pressure, (2) the indicated airspeed, and (3) the true airspeed.

First of all, the pitot-static tube error must be found.

(a) *Tip error.* From Fig. 3:5 it is seen that static orifices located 3.2D from the base of the tip will read 0.5 per cent q too low.

(b) *Stem error.* From Fig. 3:5 it is seen that static orifices located 8.0D from the stem will read 1.13 per cent q too high.

(c) *Total error.* The static pressure therefore will be $1.13 - 0.5 = 0.63$ per cent q too high, and hence the indicated dynamic pressure will be too low. The data should be corrected as follows:

$$q_{true} = 1.0063 q_{indicated}$$

$$V_{true} = 1.0032 V_{indicated}$$

1. Accordingly the dynamic pressure will be 1.0063×12.05 in. of water, or 12.13 in. of water. From the appendix this is 12.13×5.198 or 63.20 lb per sq ft.

2. The indicated airspeed is

$$V_i = \sqrt{63.20/0.00256} = 157.8 \text{ mph}$$

3. The density is

$$\rho = 0.002378(518/572)$$

$$= 0.00215$$

The true airspeed is hence

$$V_t = \sqrt{0.002378/0.00215} \cdot 157.8$$

$$= 166.2 \text{ mph}$$

The accuracy of a standard pitot-static tube when inclined to an airstream is shown in Fig. 3:6.

The pitot-static tube can be used only in free air. When the tube is close to a lifting surface, the pressure gradient will totally nullify the worth of the reading as an indication of free stream velocity. It is possible to place the pitot-static tube in such a

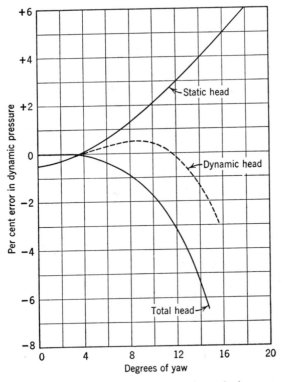

FIG. 3:6.   Performance of standard pitot tube in yaw.

place relative to an airplane wing that it makes the airspeed indicator read high at high speed and low at low speed, or vice versa.

3:4. Kiel Tubes. Kiel tubes (Fig. 3:7) are total-head tubes so arranged that their accuracy is unimpaired through wide

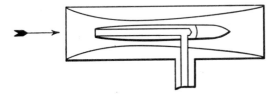

FIG. 3:7.   Kiel tube.

variations in yaw angles (Fig. 3:8). Inside cowlings and in
other places where the flow direction is uncertain, they are useful in measuring the total head (Ref. 3:14).

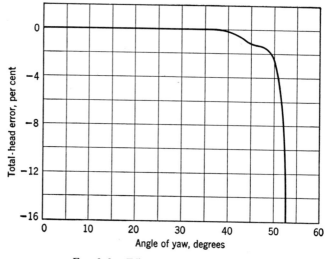

FIG. 3:8.   Effect of yaw on Kiel tube.

3:5. Stream Temperature. At low subsonic speeds the stream
temperature may be read to close enough limits by simply placing a thermometer in it at some place where the disturbance it
makes is of no consequence.

It is desirable to keep a record of the tunnel temperature on
each run since the Reynolds number varies widely with changes
in temperature (see Fig. 2:22).

3:6. Flow Direction. Flow-direction indicators of the weather-
vane type are in general not as satisfactory as the sphere type
(Figs. 3:9 and 3:10), which has two smooth orifices usually 90

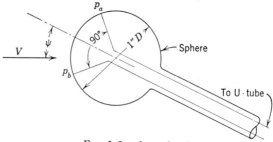

FIG. 3:9.   A yawhead.

degrees apart on the forward face of a sphere. Obviously, if they are exactly placed, they will read equal pressure when the flow is directed along the axis of the yawhead, or, alternately, they will read a fixed value of $\Delta p/q$ for each degree the flow is off center. The calibration may be made by rotating the yawhead at a single location in the airstream and then plotting $\Delta p/q$ against angle of yaw. A second and perhaps better method

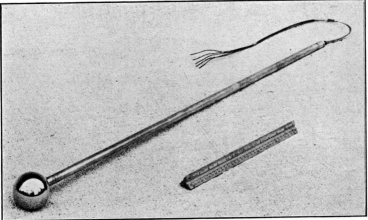

Courtesy Aerolab Development Corp.

FIG. 3:10. A typical yawhead, of the five-hole type. Such an installation is useful for measuring yaw in both vertical and horizontal planes.

is to plot $(p_a + p_b)/(p_a - p_b)$ against angle of yaw. The latter plot obviates the need for knowing the dynamic pressure q in order to compute the flow direction.

Theoretical and actual values of $\Delta p/q$ for a spherical yawhead are compared in Fig. 3:11. This calibration (for a 1-in.-diameter yawhead) is independent of Reynolds number from at least 40 mph to 120 mph, standard air.

From Fig. 3:11 it may be rightly inferred that a total-head orifice at the front of the yawhead sphere will read true for only small flow deflection angles. Indeed, at 5-degree yaw the total-head reading is down 1.2 per cent.

3:7. Rakes. A bank of total-head tubes is frequently employed to get many simultaneous total-head readings in, say, a wake, and less frequently a bank of static tubes is needed. The total-head rake is easy to make since it is hard to miss reading total head. Normally $\frac{1}{16}$-in. brass tubing is employed with a

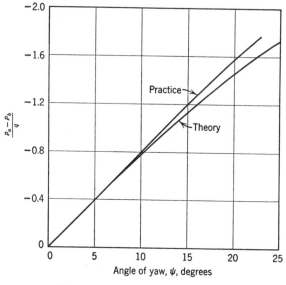

FIG. 3:11.   Calibration of yawhead.

lateral spacing of around ⅛ in.   It is particularly important that
the lateral spacing be exact, as when wake surveys (Sect. **4:16**)
are made a considerable error can arise from a small misplacement
of a tube.   The total-head tubes should be cut off square, and their
length is immaterial.   A typical rake is shown in Fig. **3:12**.

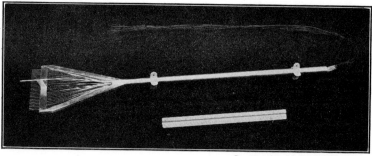

Courtesy Aerolab Development Corp.

FIG. 3:12.   A total head rake.   Note single static-pressure tube.

Wakes rapidly reach freestream static pressure, but frequently
one wants to make a few check points.   Hence it is customary to
find several static tubes supplied along with the total-head tubes.

These can be conveniently located out of the plane of the total-head tubes (by an inch or so), but they very surely must be calibrated before their readings can be accepted. Judicious filing on the hemispherical head with which they must be equipped can reduce their error to zero. Rarely, a total-head rake is provided with static-head tubes that slip over the total-head tubes and convert the rake into a static rake. Though this is convenient, the question of leaks is always an uncertainty that must be constantly checked.

Static-pressure rakes are seriously affected by the rake body and require a considerable amount of calibration and adjustment before they can be used. Usually the rake body makes the static readings high, and by shortening the tip-static-orifice distance the error can be eliminated. Krause in Ref. 3:18 discusses rake design parameters which yield the minimum static-pressure error.

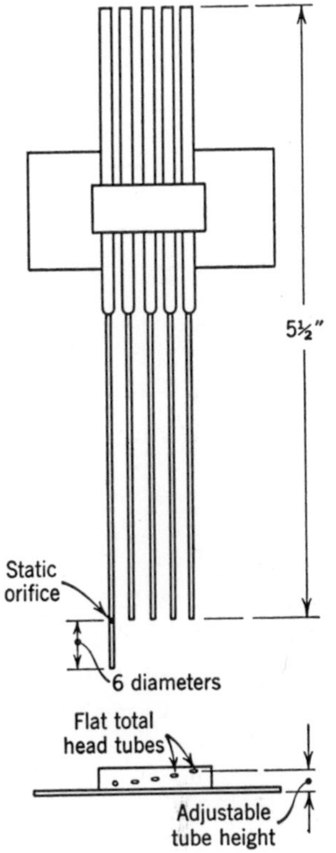

3:8. Boundary-Layer Mouse. The boundary-layer mouse (Fig. 3:13) is a bank of flat total-head tubes arranged to read the total head in several places very close to a surface (Ref. 3:13). It is used to locate the point of transition from laminar to turbulent boundary layer and to investigate boundary-layer thickness. The operation of the mouse is as follows:

FIG. 3:13.   A boundary-layer mouse.

The type of boundary-layer flow existing at some point on an airfoil may be determined from the velocity gradient in the boundary layer. Gradients for laminar and turbulent boundary layers appear in Fig. 3:14. The mouse is first attached to the wing (Scotch cellophane tape will do) near the leading edge with the total-head tubes adjusted to be in the boundary layer. Readings of the four total heads and one static head are taken, and, since the static pressure is essentially constant across the bound-

ary layer, the four velocities may be calculated. The mouse is
then moved to points farther back on the wing and the process
is repeated, yielding a plot similar to Fig. 3:15. A cross plot of
Fig. 3:15 yields Fig. 3:16, the velocity in the boundary layer at
a constant height above the surface. The interpretation of
Fig. 3:16 is that as the flow progresses along the wing the boundary layer thickens, and points at constant height become progressively deeper in the boundary layer and hence have slower

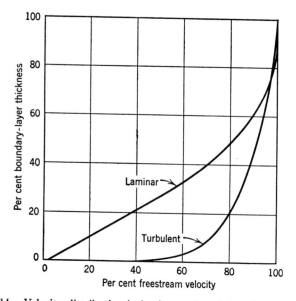

Fig. 3:14. Velocity distribution in laminar and turbulent boundary layers.

velocities. Finally the transition region is reached; the thick-
ened boundary layer is scrubbed off by the turbulent air; and the
point returns to a higher velocity. Figure 3:16 indicates that,
in the example graphed above, transition took place about the
18 per cent chord point. It will be noticed that the change from
laminar to turbulent flow occurs in a region rather than at a
point. The length of this region increases with Reynolds number.

Many methods are in use to determine the location of the
transition region. They include:

1. Plotting the velocity gradient in the boundary layer and
determining whether the flow is laminar or turbulent by the
slope of the gradient.

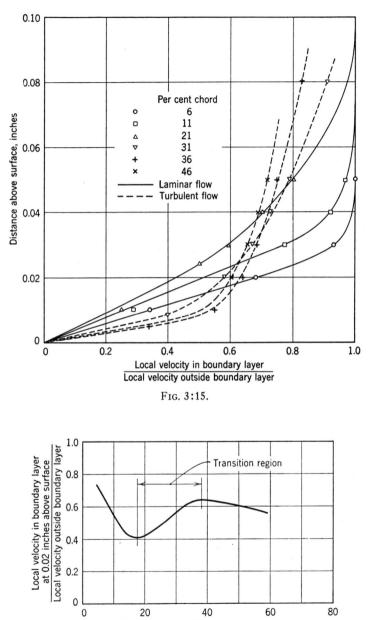

FIG. 3:15.

FIG. 3:16. The velocity in the boundary layer at a constant small height above the surface.

2. Crossplotting 1, determining the beginning of transition as the point where the velocity is lowest.

3. Reading the static pressure at a small height above the surface, determining the transition by a slight dip in the plot of static pressure vs. per cent chord.

4. Reading the dynamic pressure at a small height above the surface and noting the minimum value of q from a plot of q vs. per cent chord.

5. Reading either q, static pressure, or total head and noting the transition point by slight oscillations in the fluid column.

6. Reading the velocity at a small height above the surface with a hot-wire anemometer, and noting the transition as a region of unsteadiness in the meter.

7. Reading the velocity at a small height above the surface with a hot-wire anemometer, and noting start of transition as the point of minimum velocity.

8. Carefully emitting smoke from flush orifices, and noting transition by the dispersal of the smoke stream.

9. Painting the model with special chemicals that evaporate slowly. The evaporation will proceed most rapidly where the flow is turbulent.

10. Listening to the boundary layer with an ordinary doctor's stethoscope connected to a flat total-head tube which is moved progressively along the surface towards the trailing edge. As long as the flow is laminar one hears a soft *sh-sh-sh-sh*. When it is turbulent a distinct roar is heard. This same input fed into a transducer becomes quite graphic on an oscilloscope.

Of the above, 1 and 2 seem simplest and most direct. The "special chemicals" mentioned in 9 consist of an emulsion containing china clay and nitrobenzene. The procedure is to spray the wing with the emulsion, leaving a white finish. Just before a test the nitrobenzene is sprayed on. As its index of refraction is about the same as that of the china clay particles, the white completely disappears. When the wind stream is applied the nitrobenzene evaporates most quickly in the turbulent boundary layer, and in a few minutes the turbulent region has become white again, the laminar layer remaining unaffected. Photographs of this process are striking.

Still another method utilizing the more rapid evaporation in the turbulent boundary layer has been described by Gray in

Ref. 3:16. His method is to paint the model flat black and
spray it with a glycerin mixture just before a run in the t
After removal from the tunnel the model is dusted with talcum
powder, which sticks where the liquid is unevaporated, and a
photograph is made. Also see Sect. 11:14.

3:9. **Apparatus for Flow Visualization.** It would be difficult
to exaggerate the information that can be obtained from actually
seeing the flow pattern about complex models. Sometimes an
entirely new slant can be obtained, as well as a graphic verification of the spreading and contracting of the streamlines. Flow
patterns may be made visible by smoke or the Fales method;
separation can be identified with simple thread tufts.

Several chemicals, for example titanium tetrachloride and tin
tetrachloride, will produce smoke when brought into contact
with damp air. Both compounds are corrosive. Smoke "bombs"
and candles may be obtained from the Armed Forces, but they
are difficult to control. All in all, the smoke from rotted wood
seems to be as good as any.

Since most tunnels are of the return type in which returned
smoke might easily hide nearly everything, and since smoke
tests are at best messy except in specially designed smoke tunnels, it is suggested that the wind-tunnel operator utilize tufts
or streamers for visualization. These, usually ¾-oz. baby wool
or several strands of heavy cotton thread about 2 in. long may
be fastened to the surface (cleaned with carbon tetrachloride or
benzine) by Scotch cellophane tape. When the tape is removed,
any traces should be washed off with either of the above solvents.

Possibly the most rapid method of installing tufts is to attach
them about every 4 in. to the tape before application. Whole
strips can then be put on at once. For wing tests, streamers at
the 15, 30, 45, 60, and 75 per cent chord points are adequate,
and from them the whole stall pattern may be progressively
traced. A stall "picture" is illustrated in Fig. 3:17. This type
of set-up may not be photographed with the usual high shutter
speeds as the movement of the tufts due to unsteady flow would
not be apparent. However, at $\frac{1}{50}$ second the moving tufts show
up blurred, and the stall progress may be noted. Additional
visual observations are usually in order to establish the advent
of unsteady flow, intermittent stall, and full stall.

A more detailed stall study than that shown in Fig. 3:17, usually drawn for a single angle of attack, would show flow direction

by arrows, rough flow by wiggly arrows, intermittent stall by circled crosses, and full stall by crosses.

A streamer may also be of use mounted at the end of a fishpole so that vortices and roughness may be traced about the model without the proximity of the investigator disturbing the flow. If this necessitates the operator's entering the tunnel, goggles are needed. Although his appearance is a bit silly, a particle of dust in his eye at 60 to 100 mph is no laughing matter.

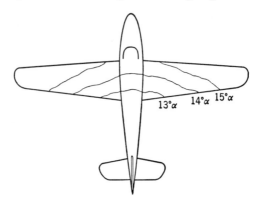

FIG. 3:17.   Typical stall pattern.   Note stall beginning at wing root so that ailerons remain effective.

Still another kind of tuft for flow visualization is the tufted wire grid developed by Bird at the NACA. Its construction is amply illustrated in Fig. 3:18. Much of its use has been concerned with checking the theories for the roll-up of the vortices of various wing platforms.

The Fales method consists of mounting a half model (split through the plane of symmetry) on a glass plate, and lightly coating both plate and model with a mixture of lampblack and kerosene. The air flow spreads the mixture along the streamlines so that after the tunnel has been stopped the flow pattern remains. Good pictures can then be made of the flow pattern, and if the lampblack is spread sufficiently thin only a minimum will be blown into the tunnel.

Having discussed the instruments needed for flow measurements, we now turn to the procedure followed when a new tunnel is put into use, both to determine the excellence of the flow and to correct the flow if it is not up to standard. Finally the tunnel engineer measures the energy ratio to compare with the assumptions made during the design for his own satisfaction and for correlation with future designs. First, however, we will look at the manner in which the speed is set in a low-velocity wind tunnel.

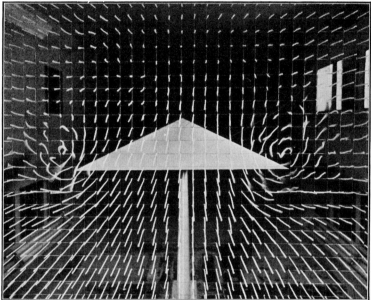

Official Photograph, National Advisory Committee for Aeronautics.

FIG. 3:18. Flow visualization by the grid-and-tuft method.

3:10. Speed Setting. It is not practical to insert a pitot-static tube (see Sect. 3:3) into the tunnel jet when there is a model in place because (1) it would interfere with the model, and (2) it would not read true owing to the effect of the model on it.

The solution comes from a consideration of Bernoulli's equation written between two points in the tunnel, preferably the large section, L, and a small section, S. The small section can be just ahead of the jet, far enough upstream to avoid any effects when the model is installed or moved (Fig. 3:19).

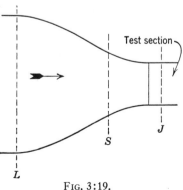

FIG. 3:19.

The total head at the two points will be nearly the same; the downstream head will be slightly smaller on account of the pressure drop between the two stations. Hence we have

$$p_L + q_L = p_S - q_S K_1 + q_S$$

where K_1 is the loss coefficient of the section between the static readings, and p and q are static and dynamic pressures. That is,

$$p_L - p_S = q_S - K_1 q_S - q_L$$

Now, if A is the section area,

$$A_S V_S = A_L V_L$$

Squaring, and multiplying through by $\rho/2$, we have

$$(\rho/2)A_S{}^2 V_S{}^2 = (\rho/2)A_L{}^2 V_L{}^2$$

Letting $q = (\rho/2)V^2$, and $K_2 = A_S{}^2/A_L{}^2$, we get $q_L = K_2 q_S$. This leads to

$$p_L - p_S = q_S - K_1 q_S - K_2 q_S = (1 - K_1 - K_2)q_S$$

Also, as

$$q_S = q_J(A_J{}^2/A_S{}^2) = K_3 q_J$$

where $K_3 = A_J{}^2/A_S{}^2$,

$$p_L - p_S = (1 - K_1 - K_2)K_3 q_J \qquad (3:1)$$

The tunnel can be run at various speeds, and $(p_L - p_S)$ can be read along with the jet dynamic pressure q_J. (The last is read by means of a pitot-static tube in the empty jet.) This evaluates $(1 - K_1 - K_2)K_3$, and future desired values of q_J can be set by running at the proper value of $(p_L - p_S)$. The effect of the presence of a model on the clear jet calibration may be found in Chapter 6.

Since the model loads vary only slightly with small changes of Reynolds number, but directly with q, it is much preferable to run at constant dynamic pressure rather than at constant velocity. This is accomplished by operating at constant values of $(p_L - p_S)$ (see eq. 3:1). The constant dynamic pressure used should be noted on the data sheet, or else the speed that would produce that dynamic pressure at sea level, i.e., the "equivalent airspeed," should be stated.

Each of the above-mentioned piezometer rings may conveniently have four orifices teed together, and the rings at the

front of the test section may be a double ring, each independent
of the other. One ring is needed as explained above for the speed
setting; the second can be used as a static reference for the manometers and a ready check on the first.

The calibration of a closed throat will not suffice if the walls
are removed to make an open throat since the airstream without
boundary will expand and develop a lower speed. Measurements
of this effect indicate that a free jet expands almost exactly at a
10-degree cone angle in the low-speed range. The expansion increases to about 15 degrees with jet exhausts.

3:11. Velocity Variation in the Jet. The variation of the
dynamic pressure, $q = (\rho/2)V^2$, may be measured across the
test section by means of a pitot-static tube. The local velocities
may then be obtained from

$$V = \sqrt{2q/\rho} \qquad (3:2)$$

The following paragraphs will discuss the methods of making
the survey and presenting the results. Suggestions are also
made for improving a poor velocity distribution.

For the velocity survey the pitot-static tube is moved around
the jet, and the dynamic pressure is measured at numerous stations. The velocities as calculated from the dynamic pressures
or the pressures themselves are then plotted, and the points are
connected by "contour" lines of equal values. The variation of
q in the working range of the jet should be less than 0.50 per cent
from the mean, which is a 0.25 per cent variation in velocity.

A plot of the dynamic-pressure distribution in a rectangular
test section is shown in Fig. 3:20. Of interest is the asymmetry
usually found, and the maximum variation well above satisfactory limits. The survey should have been carried to the walls.

The correction of an excessive velocity variation is not as serious a problem as the correction of excessive angular variation.
There are more methods of attack, for one thing, and less probability that the variation will change with tunnel speed, for
another.

It is not correct to think of the tunnel as having uniform flow.
The same particles of air do not reappear in a plane of the testing
section. Slowed by the wall friction, the particles closest to the
walls are constantly being overtaken and passed by the particles
of the central air. The greater loss near the walls would be expected to yield a lowered velocity near the perimeter of the test

section, and doubtless this would occur if the contraction cone did not tend to remove such irregularities.

If satisfactory velocity distribution is not obtained, there still remain several minor adjustments for improving the situation. The guide vanes may be adjusted * to move added air into the low-velocity regions. If the velocity variation is annular, a

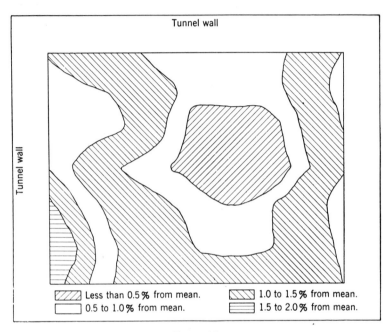

FIG. 3:20.

change of the propeller blade angle accompanied by a change in propeller hub fairing diameter may be tried. Screens may be added in the largest section of the tunnel, so located radially that they cover the sections that correspond to high-velocity regions in the jet. The improvement in velocity distribution by such screens is shown in Fig. 3:21. The loss in energy ratio due to them is quite small and far outweighed by the improvement in testing conditions.

Profound changes in flow near the walls can also be made by alteration of the entrance cone; an interesting example is shown in Figs. 3:22 and 3:23. For a special test a round jet was con-

* This method is very uncertain and unpredictable.

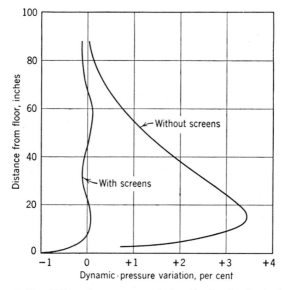

FIG. 3:21. Effect of screens on velocity distribution in the jet.

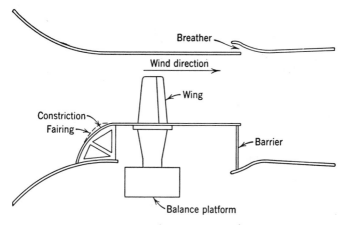

FIG. 3:22. Alteration to a contraction cone.

stricted into a semicircular one. Two opposite effects then occurred: (1) the constriction of the air in the lower part of the tunnel tended to make a high-velocity region over the lower part of the jet; (2) the abrupt expansion at the exit cone decreased the energy of the air in the lower part of the tunnel. Actually the abrupt expansion resulted in severe turbulence and complete mixing, instead of affecting only the lower half. The tunnel energy ratio dropped from 3.2 to 0.7. The velocity distribution showed a higher-speed region near the jet floor. A change in the shape of the entrance cone (shown dotted in Fig. 3:22) altered the velocity survey from the original (shown solid in Fig. 3:23) to the dotted curve. The latter proved to be satisfactory.

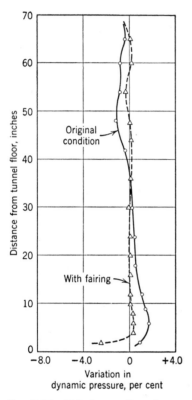

FIG. 3:23. Velocity gradient due to alteration.

3:12. Longitudinal Static-Pressure Gradient. The static-pressure gradient along the test section must be known in order to make the necessary buoyancy corrections. (See Sects. 6:3 and 6:9.) It may be obtained by reading the local static pressure with a pitot-static tube that is progressively moved from entrance cone to exit cone. Care must be taken that the pitot tube is headed directly into the wind and that no extraneous static pressure is created by the bracket holding the pitot tube.

3:13. Angular-Flow Variation in the Jet. The variation of flow angle in the jet of a wind tunnel may be measured by a yawhead (Fig. 3:9), either by holding the yawhead in a fixed plane and measuring the pressures in opposite holes separately or by connecting the two orifices across a manometer and rotating the yawhead until the pressure difference between the orifices is zero.

It is usually easiest to have the yawhead fixed in the tunnel and to determine the flow angularity by reading the pressure difference between the two orifices Δp and comparing with a previous calibration of the instrument.

Though many wind tunnels exhibit an angular variation of ± 0.75 degree or even ± 1.0 degree, it is not believed that accurate testing can be done with a variation greater than ± 0.50 degree. The larger angles of flow distort the span load distribution excessively. Unfortunately, the variation of the flow angle across the jet may change with the tunnel speed. If such a change is noted, a testing speed must be selected and the guide and anti-twist vanes adjusted to give smooth flow at that speed.

If it is not possible to correct the angularity to a satisfactorily small value, an average value for a given model may be found by measuring the flow angle at numerous stations and multiplying it by the model chord at the proper station. If the above product is plotted against the wing span and the area under the curve is divided by the total wing area the resultant will be a fair approximation of the average angle.

In conclusion, poor angularity shows up worse during pitching-moment tests of large swept reflection plane models since the area being subjected to twisted flow may be at a very great lever arm from the balance trunnion. Under such conditions it is easy to develop a $C_{m\frac{1}{4}}$ value of 0.05 at zero lift with only 0.5 degree angularity.

3:14. Turbulence. The disagreement between tests made in different wind tunnels at the same Reynolds number and between tests made in wind tunnels and in flight indicated that

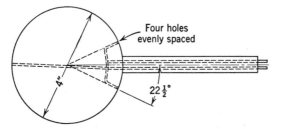

Fɪɢ. 3:24.   Turbulence sphere.

some correction was needed for the effect of the turbulence produced in the wind tunnel by the propeller, the guide vanes, and the vibration of the tunnel walls. It developed that this turbulence caused the flow pattern in the tunnel to be similar to the flow pattern in free air at a higher Reynolds number. Hence the tunnel test Reynolds number could be said to have a higher "effective Reynolds number." The increase ratio is called the "turbulence factor" and is defined by

$$RN_e = TF \times RN \tag{3:3}$$

The turbulence may be found with a "turbulence sphere" as follows:

The drag coefficient of a sphere is affected greatly by changes in velocity. Contrary to the layman's guess, C_D for a sphere *decreases* with increasing airspeed since the result of the earlier transition to turbulent flow is that the air sticks longer to the surface of the sphere. This action decreases the form or pressure drag, yielding a lower total drag coefficient. The decrease is so rapid in one range that both the drag coefficient and the drag go down. Obviously, the Reynolds number at which the transition occurs at a given point on the sphere is a function of the turbulence already present in the air, and hence the drag coefficient of a sphere can be used to measure turbulence. The method is to measure the drag, D, for a small sphere 5 or 6 in. in diameter, at many tunnel speeds. After subtracting the buoyancy (see Sect. 6:9) the drag coefficient may be computed from

$$C_D = \frac{D}{(\rho/2)\pi(d^2/4)V^2} \tag{3:4}$$

where d = sphere diameter.

The sphere drag coefficient is then plotted against the calculated Reynolds number, RN (Fig. 3:25), and the Reynolds number at which the drag coefficient equals 0.30 is noted and termed the "critical Reynolds number," RN_c. The above particular value of the drag coefficient occurs in free air at a $RN = 385,000$, so it follows that the turbulence factor

$$TF = 385,000/RN_c \tag{3:5}$$

The effective Reynolds number, RN_e, may then be found from eq. 3:3.

A second method of measuring the turbulence in a wind tunnel makes use of a "pressure sphere." No force tests are necessary, and the difficulties of finding the support drag are eliminated.

The pressure sphere (an ordinary duckpin ball will do) has an orifice at the front stagnation point and four more interconnected and equally spaced orifices at 22½ degrees from the theoretical rear stagnation point. A lead from the front orifice is connected across a manometer to the lead from the four rear orifices. After the pressure difference due to the static longitudinal pressure gradient is subtracted, the resultant pressure difference, Δp, for

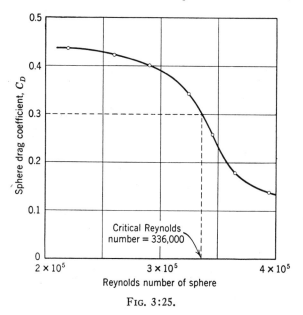

FIG. 3:25.

each Reynolds number is divided by the dynamic pressure for the appropriate RN, and the quotient is plotted against RN (Fig. 3:26). It has been found that the pressure difference $\Delta p/q = 1.22$ when the sphere drag coefficient $C_D = 0.30$, and hence this value of $\Delta p/q$ determines the critical RN. The turbulence factor may then be determined as before.

In all probability the turbulence factor will itself change slightly with tunnel speed. If information on this variation is needed, it may be obtained by finding the turbulence factor with spheres of several different diameters.

It is preferable to obtain the turbulence of a tunnel at the speed to be used for testing. This means that the sphere used must be the proper size so that the critical Reynolds number occurs at the right speed. If a rough estimate can be made of

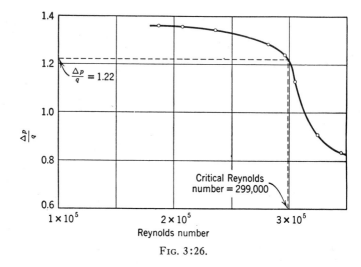

FIG. 3:26.

the expected turbulence, Fig. 3:27 will be of assistance in determining the proper size of the sphere. All turbulence spheres must be absolutely smooth to be successful.

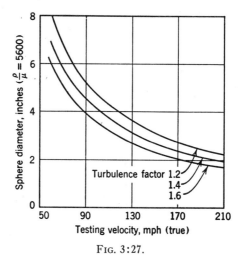

FIG. 3:27.

The turbulence will also vary slightly across the jet and probably diminish as the distance from the entrance cone is increased. Particularly high turbulence is usually noted at the center of the jet of double-return tunnels because this air has scraped over the walls in the return passage.

Turbulence factors vary from 1.0 to about 3.0. Values above 1.4 possibly indicate that the air has too much turbulence for good testing results. Although it appears from the above discussion on turbulence factors that high turbulence yields high effective Reynolds numbers, the truth is that the correction is not exact and that excessive turbulence makes the test data difficult of interpretation. Certainly very low turbulence is necessary for research on low-drag airfoils. The relation of the turbulence factor to the degree of turbulence present is shown in Fig. 3:28.

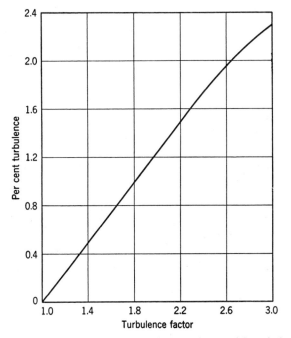

FIG. 3:28. The variation of the turbulence factor with turbulence.

Low turbulence may be designed into a tunnel by using the maximum number of fan blades and anti-swirl vanes with a very long, gradual nacelle, and by providing the maximum distance between propeller and test section.

A large contraction ratio does not (as previously believed) in itself reduce the turbulence. Usually it reduces the longitudinal component and increases the lateral components so that the net reduction, if any, is small. But a large contraction ratio inherently means a longer path from fan to test section, as well as from the last set of corner vanes, so that the large contraction ratio and low turbulence are associated through the greater time for turbulence to damp out. As will be seen, a large contraction ratio does provide a low-velocity location in which damping screens may be installed with the smallest loss.

If, after a tunnel has been built, the turbulence is still above a satisfactory level ($TF = 1.7$ for small student tunnels and 1.4

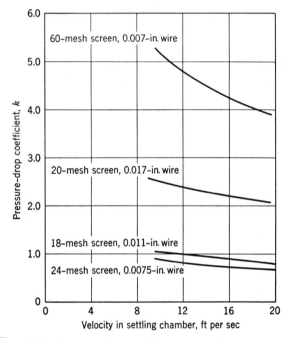

Fig. 3:29.   Pressure-drop coefficients for several screen sizes.

for 7 by 10 ft low-speed tunnels) damping screens will reduce the intensity of turbulence according to the relation

$$U_3'/U_1' = 1/(1 + k)^{n/2} \qquad (3:6)$$

where 1 and 3 refer to stations ahead of and behind the damping screens; U' is the root mean square of the velocity fluctuations u, v, and w; n is the number of screens; and k is the pressure drop through one screen in units of dynamic pressure (see Fig. 3:29). Equation 3:6 is from the work of Dryden and Schubauer as reported in Ref. 3:8. It should also be stated that station 3 is sufficiently far downstream (several feet) so that the turbulence caused by the screens themselves has time to damp out. The spacing between screens, incidentally, seems to make no difference as long as they do not touch.

The cost of screen drag is appreciable in almost all installations, running from 5 to 20 per cent of the total tunnel power, and their use should be avoided when cleaning up the tunnel will do the required job.

Example 3:3

A wind tunnel with a contraction ratio of 5.0 has a turbulence factor of 1.7. What turbulence would be expected if two house screens (18-mesh 0.011-in. wire) are installed in the settling chamber, and what will be the loss of power? Assume an atmospheric test section at 100 ft per sec.

1. From Fig. 3:28 a turbulence factor of 1.7 corresponds to 0.85 per cent turbulence. From Fig. 3:29, k for an 18-mesh screen at 20 ft per sec is 0.842.

2. From eq. 3:6

$$U_3'/U_1' = 1/(1 + 0.842)^{3/2} = 0.533$$

3. $U_3' = 0.0085 \times 0.533 = 0.00453$. From Fig. 3:14 the new turbulence factor will be 1.37.

4. The drag per square foot of screen will be $0.842q$, or 0.400 lb per sq ft for 20 ft per sec, and the power loss will be $0.400 \times 20 = 8$ ft-lb per sq ft for one screen, 16 ft-lb per sq ft for two. In a 7 by 10 ft tunnel with a contraction ratio of 5.0 this corresponds to $16 \times 350/550 = 10.4$ hp at the low speed of 100 ft per sec. This loss would increase with the cube of the speed.

Sometimes, particularly for measurements of maximum lift, it is desirable to increase the turbulence, and for this purpose hardware cloth is probably the most satisfactory. The amount of turbulence change in one tunnel is given in Table 3:2. Al-

TABLE 3:2.   Effect of Grids 8 Inches Ahead of Model on Turbulence

Tunnel Condition	Turbulence Factor
Clear jet	1.60
¼-in. hardware cloth	2.24
½-in. hardware cloth	2.46
¾-in. hardware cloth	3.00

though indicated turbulence factors above 5.0 may be obtained, the more general practice is to use artifices that raise the turbulence factors only to around 2.5. These arrangements are used solely for maximum lift measurements. (For the use of the turbulence factor and effective Reynolds number in extrapolating wind-tunnel results, see Chapter 7.)

The explanation of how the addition of screens may either increase or decrease the turbulence lies in the manner in which the screens act. Fine screens break the existing turbulence into smaller vortices. If a sufficient distance is provided, these small disturbances die out before they reach the model. Screens or grids to increase turbulence must both create turbulence and be close enough to the model so that the turbulence created does not have time to die out.

Below the degree of turbulence that corresponds to a turbulence factor of about 1.05 and above Mach numbers of 0.35, it is indicated that the turbulence sphere is not sufficiently accurate to get good results. Recourse is then had to more complicated devices. Though the design and operation of these devices are beyond the scope of this book, their principles are of interest. Further information is available in the references listed.

1. The hot-wire anemometer (Refs. 3:2, 3:3, 3:4). The hot-wire anemometer consists of a small-diameter platinum wire (about 0.015 mm) of short length (about 10 mm) which is placed in the airstream so that its length is perpendicular to the mean airflow direction. It is heated to a suitable temperature by an electric current. Fluctuations in the airstream produce fluctuations in the temperature of the wire and hence in its resistance. The ensuing voltage drops across the wire may be amplified by vacuum-tube amplifiers, and mean values of the current changes may be read by sensitive milliammeters. Sometimes the wave patterns are examined with cathode-ray oscillographs.

Fundamentally, the hot-wire anemometer is supposed to indicate the rapidity of the fluctuations by an identical frequency of current changes, and the amplitude of the fluctuations by the amount of current change. Actually, neither is directly accomplished, the fluctuating voltage of the anemometer being neither proportional to the amplitude nor in phase with the fluctuations in the airstream. Most of the difficulties are traceable to the heat-storing qualities of the wire which make it impossible for the temperature changes of the wire to follow the small high-frequency variations in the air. As would be expected, smaller wires exhibit less lag than large ones. Special compensating circuits further improve the accuracy of the anemometer. A rough idea of the size of the equipment needed to operate a hot-wire anemometer may be obtained from Fig. 3:30, and a typical installation is shown in Fig. 3:31.

2. The ultramicroscope (Ref. 3:5). A second device for determining the amount of variation of velocity in an airstream is called the ultramicroscope. Its principle of operation is as follows:

When viewed by an observer traveling at the speed of an airstream, particles of dust appear as specks of light. If the observer's speed is less or greater than that of the airstream, the

Courtesy Polymetron, Zurich.

FIG. 3:30.   The operating equipment for a hot-wire anemometer.

particles become invisible. The ultramicroscope possesses a rotating objective so designed that the speed of rotation may be varied in small increments both above and below the mean tunnel airspeed. The limiting speeds at which particles appear define the maximum and minimum speeds present.

3:15. Surging. One of the most vexatious problems a tunnel engineer may have to face is tunnel surging, a random low-frequency variation in velocity that may run as high as 5 per cent of q. A surprisingly large number of tunnels suffer from this defect at one time or another; some live with it; some find a cure.

Surging is ordinarily associated with separation and re-attachment in the diffuser, and usually it can be cured (with a considerable loss of power) by substantial tripper strips in the diffuser. One may, after a cure has been found, successively cut back on tripper numbers and size to save power. Better yet is some sort of boundary-layer control which corrects the difficulty rather than hides its effect. In one tunnel the author had to resort to 2 by 4's on edge in order to stop a serious surge. In another, a breather enlargement cured the trouble. Observa-

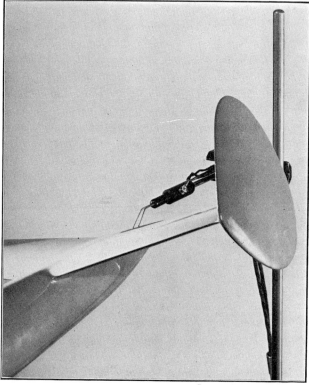

Courtesy Polymetron, Zurich.

FIG. 3:31. A hot-wire anemometer is shown measuring the boundary-layer flow on a tail surface.

tions made by means of tufts on tunnel walls and floor in both tunnels easily showed where the flow was periodically detaching.

Surging makes trouble for all measurements. It makes the balances run wildly trying to keep up, confuses the pressure reference for pressure measurements, raises doubts as to the validity of assigning a Reynolds number to the test, and usually makes dynamic testing impossible. Obviously, little surge is acceptable for high-grade work.

3:16. Energy Ratio. The ratio of the energy of the air at the jet to the input energy is a measure of the efficiency of a wind tunnel, though by no means a measure of the value of the tunnel for research. It is nearly always greater than unity, indicating that the amount of stored energy in the windstream is capable of doing work at a high rate before being brought to rest. The energy ratio, ER, is from 3 to 7 for most closed-throat tunnels.

It is unfortunate that an exact agreement on the definition of energy ratio has not been reached. Some engineers use the motor and propeller efficiency, η, in their calculations; some do not. This disagreement results in three definitions, as follows:

1. The tunnel energy ratio, based on the tunnel losses

$$ER_t = \frac{(qA\,V)_t}{550\eta\ \text{bhp}} \qquad (3:7)$$

where q = dynamic pressure in the jet, pounds per square foot; A = jet area, square feet; V = jet velocity, feet per second; η = fan efficiency; and the subscript t refers to the test section.

2. The input energy ratio (for d-c motors)

$$ER_I = \frac{(qA\,V)_t}{550EI/746} \qquad (3:8)$$

where E = input voltage, I = input amperage.

3. The fan energy ratio

$$ER_f = \frac{(qA\,V)_t}{550\ \text{bhp}} \qquad (3:9)$$

ER_t is always greater than ER_f which is always greater than ER_I. From a practical standpoint ER_I is by far the easiest to measure, since it only entails reading input meters. It sheds little light on the efficiency of the tunnel design, however. Although theoretically one could measure the pressure rise through the fan to obtain ER_t, in practice this operation is not easy. Complete motor-performance curves make possible the determination of ER_f.

Example 3:4

A wind tunnel with a test section 7 ft by 10 ft has an indicated airspeed of 100 mph at a pressure of 740 mm Hg and a temperature of 85° F. If input power is 25 amperes at 2300 volts, three-phase alternating **current** at an electrical power factor of 1.0, find (1) the true airspeed; (2) the Reynolds number of a 1-ft chord wing; (3) the input energy ratio (ER_I) of the tunnel, assuming the drag of the wing to be negligible.

Answer. 1. We first determine the air density ρ.

$$\rho = 0.002378 \frac{518}{(459 + 85)} \frac{740}{760}$$

$$= 0.002204 \text{ slug/cu ft}$$

(See p. 504 for standard conditions.) Hence

$$\sigma = \rho/\rho_0 = 0.927$$

and

$$V_{\text{true}} = Vi/\sqrt{\sigma} = 100/0.962 = 103.9 \text{ mph}$$

2. From p. 504 the viscosity of the air

$$\mu = [340.8 + 0.548(^\circ F)]10^{-9}$$

$$= [340.8 + 0.548(85)]10^{-9}$$

$$= 387.4 \times 10^{-9}$$

and hence

$$RN = \frac{\rho}{\mu} Vl = \frac{0.002204 \times 103.9 \times 1.467 \times 1.0}{387.4 \times 10^{-9}}$$

$$= 868,000$$

3.

$$ER_f = \frac{qAV}{550 \text{ hp}} = \frac{\frac{1}{2}\rho A V^3}{550 \dfrac{\sqrt{3} \, EI}{746}}$$

$$= \frac{\frac{1}{2}(0.002204)(7 \times 10)(1.467)^3(103.9)^3}{550 \times \dfrac{(1.732)(25)(2300)}{746}}$$

$$= 3.721$$

PROBLEMS

3:1. An alcohol-water mixture has a specific gravity of 0.802 at 23° C. Find (*a*) the water content and (*b*) the specific gravity at 26° C.

3:2. Sketch a pitot-static tube, locating the orifice to read (*a*) total head, (*b*) static head; (*c*) show the connections for reading dynamic pressure.

3:3. Assuming the critical Reynolds number of a sphere to be 235,000, find the turbulence factor of the tunnel.

3:4. A tunnel using 200 hp has a 10-ft-diameter round jet which is at standard atmospheric conditions. Find the energy ratio ER_f if a speed of 100 mph is attained.

3:5. Does a turbulence sphere measure turbulence or the effect of turbulence?

3:6. If the pressure head being measured during a test at 100 mph is too great for the manometer which is inclined at 30 degrees, suggest three cures.

3:7. A 6-in.-diameter turbulence sphere has a drag coefficient of 0.3 at 75 mph (true) in a wind tunnel with the jet at standard pressure and 100° F. Find the turbulence factor.

REFERENCES

3:1. E. R. Spaulding and Kenneth G. Merriam, Comparative Tests of Pitot-Static Tubes, *TN* 546, 1935.

3:2. H. L. Dryden and A. M. Kuethe, Effect of Turbulence in Wind Tunnel Measurements, *TR* 342, 1930.

3:3. Robert C. Platt, Turbulence Factors of NACA Wind Tunnels as Determined by Sphere Tests, *TR* 558, 1936.

3:4. F. L. Wattendorf and A. M. Kuethe, Investigations of Turbulent Flow by Means of the Hot-Wire Anemometer, *Physics*, January-June, 1934.

3:5. L. F. G. Simmons, A. Fage, and H. C. H. Towend, Comparative Measurements of Turbulence by Three Methods, *R&M* 1651, 1935.

3:6. H. L. Dryden and A. M. Kuethe, The Measurement of Fluctuations of Air Speed by the Hot-Wire Anemometer, *TR* 320, 1929.

3:7. W. C. Mock, Jr., and H. L. Dryden, Improved Apparatus for the Measurement of Fluctuations of Airspeed in Turbulent Flow, *TR* 448, 1932.

3:8. H. L. Dryden and G. B. Schubauer, The Use of Damping Screens for the Reduction of Wind Tunnel Turbulence, *JAS*, April, 1947.

3:9. J. E. Allen and K. V. Diprose, Calibration of the Royal Aircraft Establishment 24-Foot Wind Tunnel, *R&M* 2566, 1951.

3:10. G. B. Schubauer, W. C. Spangenburg, and P. S. Klebanoff, Aerodynamic Characteristics of Damping Screens, *TN* 2001, 1950.

3:11. Hugh L. Dryden and Ira H. Abbott, The Design of Low-Turbulence Wind Tunnels, *TR* 940, 1949.

3:12. William Gracey, Investigation of a Number of Total Pressure Tubes at High Angles of Attack, *TN* 2331, 1950.

3:13. Abe Silverstein, Determination of Boundary-Layer Transition on Three Symmetrical Airfoils in the NACA Full-Scale Wind Tunnel, *TR* 637, 1939.

3:14. G. Kiel, A Total-Head Meter with Small Sensitivity to Yaw, *TM* 775, 1935.

3:15. Sir Roy Fedden, German Laboratory Equipment for Aircraft and Power Plant Development, *Aeroplane*, Feb. 15, 1946, p. 195.

3:16. W. E. Gray, A Simple Method of Recording Boundary-Layer Transition, *Tech Note Aero* 1816, RAE, 1946.

3:17. J. H. Preston, Visualization of Boundary-Layer Flow, *R&M* 2267, 1946.

3:18. Lloyd N. Krause, Effects of Pressure Rake Design Parameters on Static Pressure Measurements for Rakes Used in Subsonic Free Jets, *TN* 2520, 1951.

Chapter 4

MODEL FORCE, MOMENT, AND PRESSURE MEASUREMENTS

The purpose of the load measurements of the model is to make available the forces, moments, and pressures so that they may be corrected for tunnel boundary, scale, and Mach number effects (Chapters 6, 7, and 11) and utilized in predicting the performance of the full-scale airplane.

The loads may be obtained by any of three methods: (1) measuring the actual forces and moments with a wind-tunnel balance; (2) measuring the effect that the model has on the airstream by wake surveys and tunnel-wall pressures; or (3) measuring the pressure distribution over the model by means of orifices connected to pressure gages.

These methods are considered in detail in the following sections.

4:1. Balances.* Besides lift, drag, and pitching moment, the airplane is subjected to rolling moment, yawing moment, and side force. This makes a total of six measurements in all: three forces, mutually perpendicular, and three moments about mutually perpendicular axes. The wind-tunnel balance must separate out these forces and moments and accurately present the small differences in large forces, all without appreciable model deflection. Further, the forces and moments vary widely in size. It is seen that the balance becomes a problem that should not be deprecated; in fact, it might truthfully be said that balance design is among the most trying problems in the field. The cost of a balance reflects these difficulties, ranging from $60,000 for a simple balance for a 7 by 10 ft 150 mph tunnel to $200,000 for a more complex apparatus for a larger tunnel.

In order to picture the situation most clearly, an impractical wire balance based on readings made with spring scales is shown

---

* In this chapter the term balance is defined to mean *external* balance, a type almost always found in low-speed work. *Internal* balances are discussed in Chapter 11. In the years to come they may well replace external balances.

in Fig. 4:1. The model, supposedly too heavy to be raised by the lift, is held by six wires, and six forces are read by the scales A, B, C, D, E, and F.

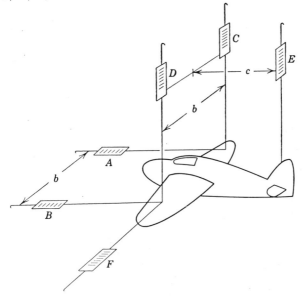

FIG. 4:1.   Diagrammatic wind-tunnel balance.

1. Since the horizontal wires A, B, and F cannot transmit bending, the vertical force (the lift) $-L = C + D + E$.

2. The drag $D = A + B$.

3. The side force $Y = F$.

4. If there is no rolling moment, scales C and D will have equal readings. A rolling moment will appear as $RM = (C - D) \times b/2$.

5. Similarly, the yawing moment $YM = (A - B) \times b/2$.

6. The pitching moment $M = E \times c$.

Exact perpendicularity between the components must be maintained. For instance, if the wire to scale F (Fig. 4:1) is not exactly perpendicular to wires A and B, a component of the drag will appear (improperly, of course) as side force. A similar situation exists in regard to lift and drag and lift and side force. Since the lift is the largest force by far in conventional wind-tunnel work, extreme care should be taken to assure its perpendicularity to the other components. (See Sect. 4:14.)

Before proceeding to more complicated balances, Fig. 4:1 should be studied until a clear picture is obtained of the forces and moments to be measured.

Four types of wind-tunnel balance are in general use, each possessing certain advantages over the others. These balances are named from their main load-carrying members—wire, platform, yoke, and pyramidal—and are discussed in the following paragraphs.

A different approach to the problem of measuring the forces on the model is the incorporation of electric strain gages (see Sect. 11:7) directly into the model at the mounting points.

4:2. Wire Balances. One approach to the problem of the wind-tunnel balance is to support the model by wires whose loads are in turn measured by as many scales * as necessary. The whole system is usually preloaded to assure adequate tension in all members. Such an arrangement is called a wire balance. An elementary one is outlined in Fig. 4:2.

With wire balances, models are tested inverted so that their "lift" adds to the weight. This precludes the chance of unloading the wires, which could lead to large shock loads. As shown, the forces are brought up to simple laboratory beam balances equipped with dashpots which must be brought into equilibrium by individual operators, using weights. The balancing arrangement described above is satisfactory for student instruction, but the manpower cost would be prohibitive for commercial work.

The wire balance shown in Fig. 4:2 is called a six-component balance because it measures the three forces (lift, drag, and side force) and the three moments (yaw, pitch, and roll). By locking off C, E, and F this would become a three-component balance measuring lift, drag, and pitching moment only.

The mounting bracket shown in Fig. 4:2 is by no means standard. Such arrangements are used only in the smallest tunnels where very small models preclude a satisfactory internal mount. Larger tunnels usually mount to locations about halfway out the wing span. The 45-degree wire is used by some to get the drag force vertically into a beam balance.

Wire balances are probably the simplest and easiest to build, but they have several serious disadvantages. They have large

---

* Spring scales are not satisfactory, as any deflection in the system may change the model's angle of attack or the location of the moment center of the balance.

tare drags that cannot be accurately determined. The wires usually have a tendency towards crystallization and corrosion, and probably every wire balance in existence has at one time or another broken a wire. Breakage of a wire can lead to loss of the model and other disastrous results.

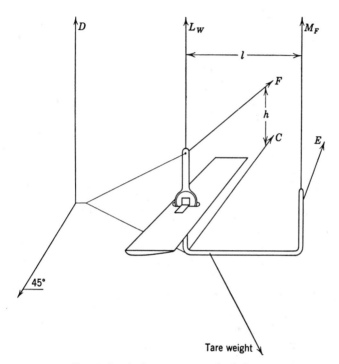

FIG. 4:2.   A six-component wire balance.

This particular balance shown in Fig. 4:2 mounts the models at the quarter chord. The results are read as follows:

$$\text{Lift} = L_W + M_F$$

$$\text{Drag} = D$$

$$\text{Side force} = C + E + F$$

$$\text{Pitching moment} = -M_F \times l$$

$$\text{Rolling moment} = (C - F)(h/2)$$

$$\text{Yawing moment} = -E \times l$$

4:3. Strut-Type Balances.   The simple balances discussed
above are rarely used in the larger tunnels because of the objections already mentioned.   Instead they are replaced by many-
ton strut-type balances which support the model, provide for
changing its angle of attack and angle of yaw, and transmit the
model loads down into a system of linkages which separate them
into their proper components.   Such an apparatus is shown dia-

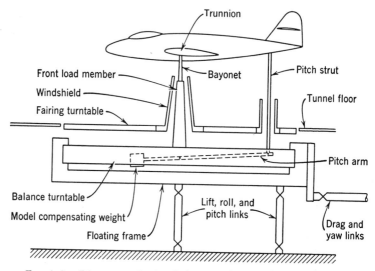

Fig. 4:3.   Diagrammatic sketch (greatly simplified) of some balance
components.

grammatically in Fig. 4:3, and a linkage system is shown in
Fig. 4:4.   The general massiveness of a balance structure may
be seen in Fig. 4:5.

Tracing the pathway followed by the loads from model to
measuring unit (Fig. 4:3) we see first that the model is supported
on two front load members or "struts," and a tail strut.*   The
struts in turn connect to the inner part of a floating ring frame
which is free to turn (model yaw), and a mechanism is provided
to raise or lower the tail strut to produce model pitch.   The outer
part of the floating frame is held in place by a system of struts,
specially designed to be strong in tension and compression but
very weak in bending.   These struts separate the components of

* This is the most frequently used arrangement.   Others are discussed in
later pages.

the load by means of a linkage system and feed them into the measuring units. Above the floating frame is a fairing turntable on which the windshields for the load members are mounted. The load turntable operates the fairing turntable by closing microswitches, and, as the fairing turntable rotates, the wind-

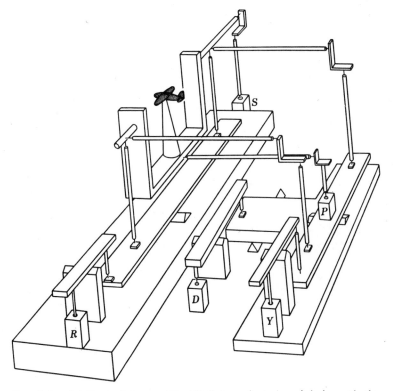

Fig. 4:4. A balance linkage. The lift linkage (not shown) is beneath the roll table.

shields are gear-driven to remain parallel to the airstream. In some balances the tail-strut fairing is moved up and down in order to keep the exposed length of tail strut always constant. The windshields are in addition insulated, and upon contact with the load members they activate fouling lights so that the trouble may be noted and corrected.

Thus a balance has three main identification features: the manner (number of struts) by which the model is fastened to the floating frame; the type of linkage system that separates the components; and the type of measuring unit. Normally the accuracy of a balance is a function of the deflections permitted and the number of measuring units needed to read one component. Thus, if three lift readings must be added to get lift, the error from measuring units alone may be three times that which will

FIG. 4:5.   The massiveness of a wind-tunnel balance is well illustrated by this photograph of a balance designed for a 150-mph wind tunnel with a 9-ft-diameter test section.   During this early set-up in the factory the load members have been dropped in place without going through their respective windshield support bases.   As shown, the balance has approximately 45 degrees of negative yaw.

occur if the three readings are added in the linkage system and fed into one measuring unit.   Linkages have no relative motion and are hence virtually frictionless.

The linkage systems by which the forces and moments are separated have gradually worked into three * different fundamental types, each possessing some advantages over the others. These are named *platform, yoke,* and *pyramidal,* according to the manner in which the main system is assembled.   They will be

* There are many others.

discussed further in the following paragraphs. In addition to
the above types of balances, there is also an internal type which
fits into the model and is widely used in high-speed applications.
(See Chapter 11.)

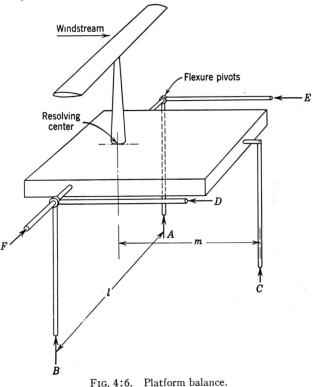

FIG. 4:6.   Platform balance.

4:4. Platform Balance. The platform balance (Fig. 4:6)
utilizes either three or four legs to support the main frame. For
the three-legged type, the forces and moments are:

$$\text{Lift} = -(A + B + C)$$

$$\text{Drag} = D + E$$

$$\text{Side force} = -F$$

$$\text{Rolling moment} = (A - B)(l/2)$$

$$\text{Yawing moment} = (E - D(l/2)$$

$$\text{Pitching moment} = C \times m$$

Platform balances are widely used. Rugged and orthogonal, they may be constructed and aligned with the minimum of difficulty. But they also have disadvantages: (1) the moments appear as small differences in large forces, an inherently poor arrangement; and (2) the balance resolving center is not at the model, and the pitching moments must be transferred.

4:5. Yoke Balance. The yoke balance (Fig. 4:7) offers an advantage over the platform balance in that moments are read

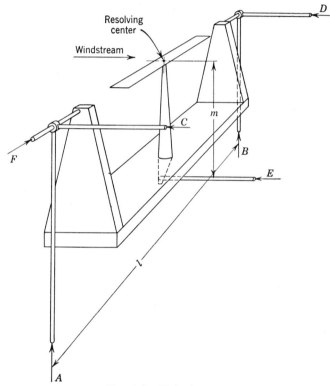

Fig. 4:7. Yoke balance.

about the model. However, the inherent design of the yoke leads to bigger deflections than the platform balance, particularly in pitch and side force. Because the balance frame must span the test section in order to get the two upper drag arms in their proper positions, the yaw lever arm is exceptionally long. The high supporting pillars are subject to large deflections. Once again the final forces must be summed up: the drag is the addition of three forces, and the lift is the sum of two. The yoke balance brings out the pitching moment in the drag system instead of in the lift.

$$\text{Lift} = -(A + B)$$

$$\text{Drag} = C + D + E$$

$$\text{Side force} = -F$$

$$\text{Rolling moment} = (B - A)(l/2)$$

$$\text{Pitching moment} = -E \times m$$

$$\text{Yawing moment} = (D - C)(l/2)$$

4:6. Pyramidal Balance. The complaints usually heard against the platform and yoke balances are largely overcome by the ingenious engineering of the pyramidal type. However, as usually happens, additional difficulties are added.

These are the advantages: the pyramidal balance reads the moments about the resolving center, and the six components are inherently separated out and read directly by six measuring units. No components need be added, subtracted, or multiplied. The difficulties involved in reading the small differences in large forces are eliminated, and direct reading of the forces and moments simplifies the calculating equipment.

Several criticisms of the pyramidal balance are warranted. The alignment of the inclined struts is so critical that both the construction and calibration of the balance are greatly complicated. Further (and this appears quite serious), deflections of the inclined struts may so change their alignment that the moments are not accurate. This effect must be thoroughly investigated during the calibration of the balance.

The manner in which the pyramidal balance separates out the moments is not simple, and it behooves the student to approach the set-up using an elementary truss system. Consider a truss in which two legs are jointed (Fig. 4:8). The force D, acting through the pin joint O, produces only tension in OE and compression in OF. No force is registered at A. However, the force G, not acting through O, produces bending in OE, and OE would collapse unless the force $A = aG/b$ were present. If G and b are known, the size of the force A determines the point of action of G. In this manner, if G were a known drag force, its pitching

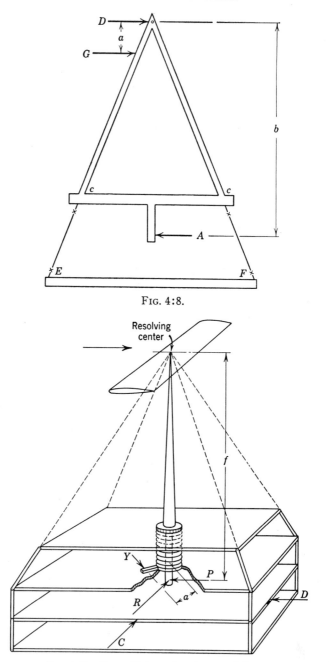

Fig. 4:8.

Fig. 4:9. Pyramidal or virtual center balance.

moments about the resolving center O would be determined by the force A.

Though the above example illustrates the principle of the pyramidal balance, in actual practice a considerable revision is required. In order to prevent the legs of the pyramid from being in the airstream, they are cut off at what would be C in Fig. 4:8. The truncated legs are then carefully aligned so that their extensions pass through a common point. The complete set-up is illustrated in Fig. 4:9.

$$\text{Lift} = \text{total weight on lowest table}$$

$$\text{Drag} = D$$

$$\text{Side force} = -C$$

$$\text{Pitching moment} = -P \times f$$

$$\text{Rolling moment} = \dot{R} \times f$$

$$\text{Yawing moment} = Y \times a$$

4:7. Balance Design. We cannot begin a discussion of wind-tunnel-balance design without a note of warning to those who might undertake the job with little experience. A wind-tunnel balance is an immensely complicated piece of apparatus, and its design and construction are much better left to balance engineers rather than to tunnel engineers. Scarcely a wind tunnel exists that has not been held back from use by exorbitant delays due to balance calibration, and sad indeed have been many many tunnel engineers who found that they were saddled with research on balances rather than on airplanes. Buy the balance, then, if it is at all possible, and insist that it be set up and calibrated at the factory. If delays occur there, the tunnel is free for additional calibration, pressure tests, tuft studies, and a host of other problems particularly besetting a new tunnel.

Balance design starts with a determination of the maximum loads the balance must measure, and the accuracy which is needed for the minimum loads. These are not simple to determine. The loads and accuracies must make allowance for every type of model ever to be tested in the tunnel, and overestimation of maximum loads leads to less accuracy for minimum ones.

Table 4:1 lists the maximum coefficients values that probably will be reached. If the values given in this table are used with wings or complete models having a span of 0.8 tunnel diameter,

TABLE 4:1.   PROBABLE MAXIMUM COEFFICIENTS DEVELOPED BY COMPLETE OR PARTIAL MODELS *

C_L	+3.0,	−1.4	C_n	±0.02
C_D	+1.0,	−0.1	C_l	±0.05
C_{mcg}	−1.0,	+0.4	C_y	±0.3

* Based on lifting area.

or panels having 0.7 tunnel height, and with the maximum dynamic pressure likely ever to be available in the tunnel, a group of design loads will result for the measuring (or "metrical") system. However, it should be noted that the loads as determined

Courtesy Taller and Cooper Co.

FIG. 4:10.   Typical control table for automatic printing balance. Dials usually read dynamic pressure q, angle of attack α, angle of yaw ψ, lift, drag, side force, and rolling, pitching, and yawing moments.

from Table 4:1 are for forces and moments about the balance trunnion or resolving center. One must also consider the activating load in respect to the whole balance system. Thus if a panel has a 1000-lb sideload, which produces a 2000-ft-lb rolling moment about the balance resolving center, the total applied moment tending to overturn the balance could be (depending on the balance design) 1000 lb times the distance to the floor.

The results of the maximum load and permissible accuracy are then combined into a loading table as shown in Table 4:2.

TABLE 4:2. BALANCE DESIGN LOADS AND ACCURACIES FOR A 150-MPH 9-FT-DIAMETER TEST SECTION WIND TUNNEL

For high loads an accuracy of 0.1 per cent will be requested. (The high side load is a provision for panel testing, not a complete-model load.)

Component	+Load	−Load	Total Range	Accuracy (Low Loads), lb or ft-lb
Lift, lb	1600	1600	3200	±0.10
Drag, lb	400	100	500	±0.05
Pitching moment, ft-lb	500	500	1000	±0.20
Rolling moment, ft-lb	1200	1200	2400	±0.125
Yawing moment, ft-lb	1200	1200	2400	±0.125
Side force, lb	800	800	1600	±0.10

In addition to the loading table, ranges for the pitch and yaw angle must be given. Pitch angle range will vary with the rearward distance of pitch strut from front struts but should in any event provide for ±40 degrees. Usually yaw from −40 degrees to +190 degrees is allowed for. Two degrees per second is a good rate of change for both pitch and yaw.

Having the design loads, the balance engineer next selects a strut system, a linkage system, and a type of measuring unit, and proceeds with the balance design. The very subject would justify a book by itself: the size of drive motors, types of microswitches, optimum flexures—all these and dozens more questions must be answered.

Answered also must be the question what system of axes are to be the primary references. There are three choices: wind, body, or "stability." Wind axes in wind-tunnel parlance mean that the forces and moments are measured about axes parallel and perpendicular to the wind-tunnel centerline, and almost all external balances use wind axes. Body axes move with the airplane, and all internal balances (see Chapter 11) have body-axes references. A few external balances yaw the roll-reading linkage with the model to yield stability-axes data. (For this system the yaw axis is not pitched with the model.) For transferring data from one set of axes to another, see Sects. 5:11 and 11:7.

The desired accuracies are similarly attacked by first preparing a permissible error list from the aerodynamicist's viewpoint (Table 4:3).

TABLE 4:3. PERMISSIBLE MEASURING ERRORS IN THE VARIOUS AERODYNAMIC COEFFICIENTS

The larger of the two values given is in each case the acceptable one, but for balance design requirements the actual loads should be figured using the smallest model expected to be tested and the lowest dynamic pressure. In some cases the tolerances can be relaxed somewhat.

	Low Angle of Attack	High Angle of Attack
Lift	$C_L = \pm 0.001$, or 0.1%	$C_L = \pm 0.002$, or 0.25%
Drag	$C_D = \pm 0.0005$, or 0.1%	$C_D = \pm 0.0020$, or 0.25%
Pitching moment	$C_m = \pm 0.001$, or 0.1%	$C_m = \pm 0.002$, or 0.25%
Yawing moment	$C_n = \pm 0.0001$, or 0.1%	$C_n = \pm 0.0010$, or 0.25%
Rolling moment	$C_l = \pm 0.001$, or 0.1%	$C_l = \pm 0.002$, or 0.25%
Side force	$C_Y = \pm 0.001$, or 0.1%	$C_Y = \pm 0.002$, or 0.25%

A critical maximum error condition may arise during power testing of complete models, as the dynamic pressure of the tunnel may then be unusually low.

Depending on the amount of money available, a number of accessories may be incorporated that can materially reduce both the operating time and the work-up. A number of balances, for instance, read six *loads* directly that must be worked into the desired three forces and three moments. Obviously, a linkage system that presents final loads is far preferable, and usually more accurate. Many balances incorporate printers so that all data are simultaneously printed when the tunnel operator presses a button. This too is a great time-saver, although, since the printer might catch varying loads at the end of their swing instead of reading a mean, it is sometimes necessary to take several prints of each point.

A remotely controlled weight that can be adjusted to make the model center of gravity coincide with the balance trunnion is also convenient, relieving the need for numerous gravity runs and the resultant extra work-up. The cost of the model compensating weight may frequently be made up in *one program* through elimination of this extra work. In order to realize the size of the gravity pitching moment for a typical uncompensated model, (7 by 10 foot tunnel size) it may be mentioned that an increase

of 10 to 20 ft-lb may develop as the model is pitched from
−8 to +20 degrees.

4:8. Balance Installation. The balance installation is started
by assuming a test-section centerline and constructing a lateral
axis perpendicular to it. Punch marks or a wire mounting in
floor or ceiling plus a recorded distance to the centerline will
suffice for the first, and the second, which later becomes a horizontal line through the eyes of the balance bayonets, will require
wire guide holes. Two more references are needed, since, when
the loading device (called a *tee*) is installed, it will block wires
along the basic references. These additional references are a
lateral axis 6 or 8 in. *ahead* of the balance lateral axis, and another lateral axis 1 ft *above* the balance lateral axis. All these
axes may be located with a transit in the exit cone, and they
should be so marked and located that a single swing of the transit
will pick them all up. Their locations must be accurate to $\frac{1}{64}$ in.

The balance is then brought in and installed, its orientation
being such that a taut wire along the lateral balance axis goes
exactly through the center of the eyes of the load members, and
the $\psi = 0$ axis is directly under the test-section centerline. Once
this orientation is obtained, a permanent setting is employed.

4:9. Calibrating the Balance. Let us start by making clear
the immensity of a wind-tunnel-balance calibration: with a
competent crew the first calibration of a new balance will take
3 months *at least*. This figure supposes that adequate shop
facilities for all sorts of changes are available.

Calibration embraces loading the elements of the balance to
see whether they read what they should; ascertaining the deflections of the set-up; loading the balance in combined cases which
simulate the conglomeration of loads the model will put on it;
loading with the balance yawed; measuring the natural frequency
of the balance so that resonance will not be encountered; and
applying fluctuating loads so that it can be determined that balance reads the mean.

All the above requires considerable added equipment, and it is
a good idea to make as much of it permanent as possible, since
calibration checks will be needed many times during the life of
the balance. First in this list comes a loading tee (Fig. 4:11).

This tee * provides knife-edge hooks such that cables may be
attached to load yaw, drag, and side force, and weights may be

---

* Some "tees" are crosses, the extra leg being for loading negative pitch.

hung to simulate lift, roll, and pitch. The balance calibration can be no better than the disposition of these hooks, a reasonable tolerance for their location being 0.005 in.

The cables mentioned above must have accurately located pulleys (usually about 16 in. in diameter) over which the load may be applied. The pulleys must be virtually free from deflection for the maximum loads. They should be set on pads so that they can be adjusted a small amount in all directions. The distance from the tee to the pulleys should be enough to give good

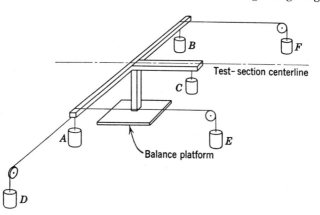

Fig. 4:11.   Balance loading tee.   Weights added at *A*, *B*, or *C* should produce no drag or crosswind force, and a weight moved from *E* to *F* should produce no indicated change in drag.

angular adjustment to the tunnel centerline, but not far enough to give appreciable dip to the loading cables: 8 to 12 ft is reasonable. It is of course desirable to load all six components in both their plus and minus directions, but the difficulties of a scaffolding in the entrance cone for applying negative drag and pulleys in the ceiling for positive lift are such that they are sometimes neglected, the assumptions being that the missing loads have the same characteristics as their missing counterparts.

A set of calibrated weights will be needed; if it is decided not to buy a full set, they may usually be borrowed from the local state highway department. A half dozen dial gages for measuring deflections will also be needed.

The first step in the actual running of the balance is to check out the measuring units and see whether they are operating properly. Next, the dead weight of the balance has to be balanced out. Usually the beams have lead containers built in, and the balancing takes only a few hours of lead pouring. The pitch arm and floating frame should also have weights added until their centers of gravity are at the center of the balance. When this occurs, no pitch reading arises when the arm is moved up or down, and no rolling or pitching moment reading is created by yawing the balance.

After the check-out of the measuring units and the completion of the dead-weight balancing, each component of the balance should be loaded to its maximum in fairly large increments to make certain that deflections are not excessive. Reasonable deflections in drag or side force for maximum load are 0.05 in. for a 7 by 10 ft tunnel installation. If excessive deflections are present they should be carefully located with the dial gages and reduced to satisfactory limits. During this preliminary loading, sensitivity loads of 0.1 lb may be added from time to time to make sure the balance is not becoming sluggish with load. (Usually this is not a problem.)

Then comes single loading of each component and adjusting of the balance "slopes." This operation is simple, consisting of loadings of each component separately, checking linearity of reading, sensitivity, and failure to return to zero ("drift"). A chart with a 0.1 per cent error line may be prepared to present the single load errors. (See Fig. 4:12.)

We next come to the extremely arduous task of determining and eliminating (at least as much as possible) the extraneous reading due to misalignment. By this we mean adjusting the balance linkages until the application of any one particular load produces negligible readings in the other five components.*

It is during this stage that the tunnel engineer usually learns that he knows about one-tenth as much about taking moments as he thought he knew. At first, 1000 lb of, say, lift, will produce a few pounds of drag, some yaw, and perhaps some negative roll. Gradually, as the weeks roll by a "feel" for the linkage, coupled with actual calculations as to how far specific linkages should be moved on their adjustable pads, will arise, as will a final feeling that the limit of accuracy of the balance is being approached. During this procedure the tunnel engineer will be

---

* There *should* be a pitch reading under pure drag load since the deflection of the mounting struts allows the tee to produce a gravity moment about the trunnion. Similarly side force will produce a roll reading.

everlastingly grateful if the balance design engineer has equipped each link with pads that are *separately* adjustable in each direction without disturbing the other adjustments. Towards the end of the battle, adjustments of 0.003 or 0.004 in. are considered *large*.*

Possibly a good procedure in determining when to give up trying to improve the alignment is to continue until the various extraneous readings change sign as the primary load is increased.

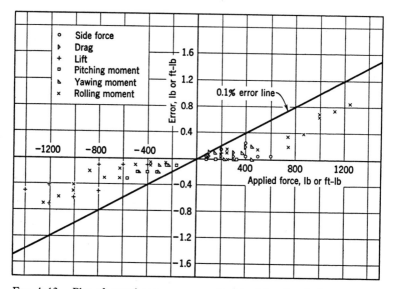

Fig. 4:12. Plot of actual error versus applied load for the six force systems when each component is loaded separately. The straight line indicates the maximum permissible error of 0.1 per cent of the applied load.

This action indicates deflections which, if they cannot be reduced, finally determine the limit of accuracy of the balance.

Complete freedom from interaction is probably not possible, especially since it is desirable to have interactions very small not only when the balance is subjected to one load but also when it has all the loads applied simultaneously. Thus a certain amount

* It is a good idea to store the loading weights in a basket hung from the model loading crane. This serves the double purpose of reducing the distance weights must be moved during the loading process and of keeping the rather large total load off the balance platform where it could cause extraneous deflections.

of combined loading is necessary.* Here, to avoid an infinity of permutations, we may calculate reasonable loads for a number of model types and flight conditions and see whether under each of these interactions are still small. Usually around six conditions are enough to examine for satisfactory assurance of security.

When the alignment procedure is finally stopped, all linkages should be pinned in place and a careful record made of the degree of misalignment remaining. Sooner or later a special test will come along when the accuracies thought sufficient earlier prove to be inadequate, and the remaining extraneous components must be taken out in the work-up.

A good way to record the interactions is in the form of table (as Table 4:4) so that a rapid check may be made at any time

TABLE 4:4. TABULATIONS OF INTERACTIONS FOR A THREE-COMPONENT BALANCE

Lift contains	$1.001L$	$0.000D$	$0.000PM$
Drag contains	$0.0001L$	$0.9990D$	$0.00026PM$
Pitching moment contains	$-0.0018L$	$0.000D$	$1.016PM$

to see whether special work-up is required. With most balances interaction attention is very rarely needed. Estimated values of L, D, and PM may be substituted and summed to get the total error due to interactions.

The tee may now be removed, and possibly the removal of its great weight will change the stability characteristics of the balance so that the response and damping may need changes.

4:10. Mounting the Model. Any strut or wire connecting the model to the balance will add three quantities to the forces read. The first is the obvious drag of the exposed strut or wire; the second is the effect of the strut's presence on the free air flow about the model; and the third is the effect of the model on the free air flow about the strut. The last two items are usually lumped together under the term "interference," and their exist-

* Loading with the balance yawed may be considered part of the interaction procedure, since it determines whether yawing the balance puts extraneous loads into the system. The point about which the balance takes moments is the *balance resolving center;* the point about which the model is yawed and pitched is called the *trunnion.* Obviously these two points should be one and the same, but unfortunately sometimes they are not. When they do differ, the amount of error introduced should be carefully studied and if of consequence must be incorporated in the work-up of the data or otherwise removed.

ence should make clear the impossibility of evaluating the total tare by the simple expedient of measuring the drag on the struts with the model out.

The earliest attachments were by means of wires or stream-line struts. The ruling criterion was to add the smallest possible drag and then either estimate it or neglect it. With the advent

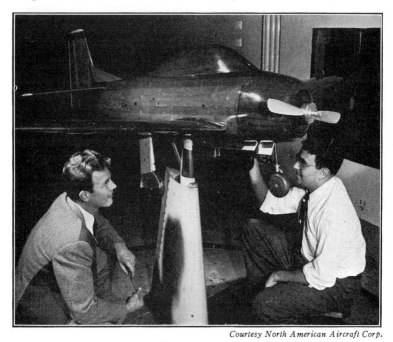

Courtesy North American Aircraft Corp.

FIG. 4:13.   T-28 trainer model on single-support mounting.

of the image system of evaluating the tare and interference (Sect. 4:15), wires became obsolescent; they were rarely adaptable for image tests and had the added hazard of occasionally failing as the result of crystallization.

The mounting struts employed at first still tended towards the minimum drag criterion and were of airfoil shape. Later, however, many mounting struts were made of polygonal cross section (see Fig. 4:13). The idea behind this trend was that the Reynolds number of the mounting struts would always be very low and they might therefore have not only a large drag but also a drag that varied widely under minute changes (see Fig. 4:14). Roughening the leading edges of all struts is an excellent idea.

. Only a minimum of strut is exposed to the airstream, the remainder being shielded by fairings not attached to the balance. In this way the tare drag of the mounting is decreased, sometimes being only 50 per cent of the minimum drag of an average wing. It is not advisable to try to decrease the tare drag of the "bayonets" by continuing the windshields up close to the model because a fairing close to the model can increase the interference effects more than it decreases the tare. The proper balance between amount of exposed strut and proximity of the windshield

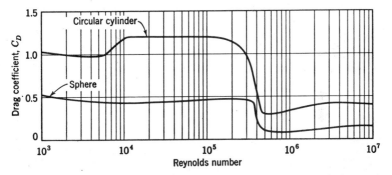

Fig. 4:14. The variation of the drag coefficient of circular cylinders and spheres with Reynolds number.

to the model may be found by having adjustable sleeves at the windshield top. The sleeve location at which $C_{d0\ min.}$ for model plus tare and interference is a minimum is the best, as this indicates that the tare plus interference is a minimum too.

Some balances yaw the model support struts oppositely to the model, so that the struts always remain parallel to the airstream and hence contribute the smallest possible effect when the model is yawed. Another useful arrangement is to have several sets of supports of varying size from which the smallest can be selected according to the load range.

One feature sometimes considered necessary for the ordinary support system is a rubber diaphragm seal that prevents flow from around the balance up between the supports and shields into the tunnel. There are two types of pressures that may cause this flow. The first is due to the basic tunnel design, which not infrequently results in a jet static pressure below the atmospheric pressure, and hence a pressure differential, sometimes quite large, between the balance chamber and the jet. The cure for this trouble is to seal off the balance room and allow sufficient time after the tunnel has reached speed for the excess air to drain into the tunnel.

The second pressure is that due to the attitude of the model. This is much smaller than the first and can be taken care of simply by a light diaphragm seal. Closing off the balance room in no way changes the necessity for the support column seal.

The attachment fittings usually come into the wing about the 30 to 50 per cent chord point. In complete airplanes, the most rearward center of gravity location is used to give maximum room for the fittings. If a model of a multiengined airplane is to be tested, the mounting strut interference will be smallest if the struts do not attach at a nacelle point.

The various arrangements of mounting are enumerated herewith:

1. Single-strut mounting. This arrangement is by far the simplest. Only a single windshield is needed, and it need not move as the model is rotated in yaw. The single strut is satisfactory for small models and nacelles (see Fig. 4:13) and may be used in conjunction with wingtip supports to evaluate tare and interference. Unfortunately, the usual model size is such that one strut is not rigid enough, particularly in torsion. In a typical installation the deflection of a single strut in yaw is about 0.003 degree per foot-pound of torque.

2. Single strut with fork. An increase in resistance to roll deflections may be gained by splitting the single strut into a fork at the top (Fig. 4:15). However, this method does not appreciably increase the torsional rigidity of the mounting. The fork has increased interference as compared with the straight strut and does not lend itself to inverted mounting for image tests.

3. Two-strut mounting. The two-strut mounting surpasses the single strut for rigidity but adds the complication that the windshields must be moved and rotated as the model is yawed (Fig. 4:16).

4. Three-point mounting. The conditions of rigidity, tare, and interference evaluation and the ease of varying the angle of attack are all met satisfactorily by the three-point supporting system. It is also the most complex and requires that two and sometimes three windshields be arranged to yaw with the model (Fig. 4:17). The rear strut introduces side forces that complicate the yawing moment measurements of a yawed model.

Courtesy McDonnell Aircraft Corp.

Fig. 4:15. Banshee model on fork-type mounting strut. Note simple flap
attachment brackets.

Courtesy North American Aircraft Corp.

Fig. 4:16. Navy bomber model on two-strut support system.

Courtesy Boeing Airplane Co.

FIG. 4:17. Stratocruiser model on three-point support. Note extensible rear strut windshield to keep the rear strut tare constant.

Courtesy McDonnell Aircraft Corp.

FIG. 4:18. Floor-mounted split model of jet fighter.

5. Wingtip mounting. When it becomes necessary to determine the pressure distribution of regions close to the mounting struts, the models are frequently mounted from the wingtips, leaving the fuselage and nacelles in air unobstructed by support fittings. Models of larger scale may be tested with wingtip mounting, and valid comparisons can be obtained of the effect of component parts. See Fig. 2:21.

6. Split models. The very largest-scale models may be tested by having them split down the plane of symmetry, only one-half of the model being present. Asymmetric flow is prevented by a large plate at the plane of symmetry, or by mounting the model on the tunnel floor. See Fig. 4:18. Such an arrangement, though obviously being unsuited for yaw tests, yields accurate pitch, lift, and downwash data at the maximum Reynolds number, but care should be taken that the horizontal tail does not approach the tunnel wall too closely or stability at the stall will appear much too optimistic.

It should be noted that any device that increases the model size also increases the size of the tunnel-wall corrections, sometimes extending them into a range where their accuracy is most doubtful.

7. Mounting from the tunnel roof. A few balances mounted above the tunnel support the model in an inverted position for "normal" running. As far as can be gathered, this arrangement is a holdover from early wire balances that supported the model similarly so that the lift forces would put tension in the wires. No particular advantage seems to accrue from inverted testing. On the contrary, such a balance position hinders the use of a crane to install models, and the terminology of testing "normal" and "inverted" becomes obscure.

8. Mounting from a tail sting. Engineers using small supersonic tunnels initiated a system of mounting the models on cantilever tail stings that obviate the need for any wing struts. Certainly tail stings tend to make the model drag appear low through stabilizing the wake. Other mounts for high-speed testing have sweepback to lessen interference. See Chapters 11 and 12.

The use of large-scale panel models for investigation of control surfaces is discussed in Sects. 5:7–5:10. These panels require mounting arrangements different from those for wings and complete models. Several mountings are discussed below.

1. Mounting on a turntable (see Fig. 5:15). When the model is mounted on a turntable flush with the tunnel wall, the forces

and moments on the turntable are included in the data and are difficult to separate out. Fortunately, for the type of tests usually sought with this arrangement, the absolute value of the drag is not needed, and the effect of the endplate on lift is negligible.

2. Mounting on a short strut. Mounting the panel model on a short strut (see Fig. 4:19) has the advantage of decreasing the tare drag of the set-up, but it is hard to evaluate the effect of the slot. Theoretical considerations indicate that a slot of 0.001

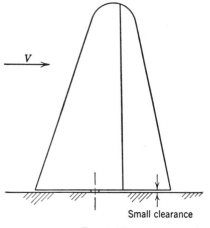

Fig. 4:19.

span * will decrease the effective aspect ratio enough to increase the induced drag by 31 per cent; a slot of 0.01 span will cause an increase of 47 per cent. The effect of viscosity (not included in the above figures) will tend to decrease the error listed above, but the degree of viscous effect has not been clearly established. If the slot can be held to less than 0.005 span its effect will probably be negligible; few engineers believe that 0.02 span is acceptable.

3. Mounting as a wing with an endplate. Mounting the panel as a wing with a small endplate to assist in keeping the spanwise lift distribution as it should be is shown in Fig. 4:20. No endplate of reasonable size will prevent tip flow; hence the spanwise load distribution with this mounting will be greatly in error.

* This "span" is of course the complete wing span, not the panel span.

The last paragraphs draw attention to the advantage of having a yoke-type balance frame, whether the balance is a yoke balance or not. The presence of lateral brace members to which bracing wires may be attached is a great convenience. Such members are obviously necessary for wingtip mounting.

Some balances have a ring that completely encircles the tunnel jet. Though the ring offers a number of brace points, the part of

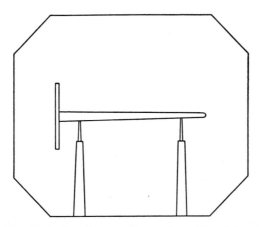

FIG. 4:20. Panel mounted as a wing with endplate.

the ring above the test section interferes with the installation of the image system.

4:11. Deflections. One of the most troublesome problems of wind-tunnel balances is rigidity. Deflections in the balance may move the model from the resolving center and invalidate the moment data or nullify the balance alignment so that part of the lift appears as drag or side force.

The answer to the problem is obvious: either the deflections must be kept down to where they are negligible, or they must be evaluated and accounted for in the work-up. Of course, keeping them down is preferable.

The largest source of deflection is the mounting system. This must be long to reach out of the test section and thin to avoid excessive interference. Both these requirements are in direct antithesis to the criterion of minimum deflection. The only attack that the wind-tunnel engineer can make is utilizing materials of high modulus of elasticity for the strut. The desire for the shortest mounting strut possible is a strong argument for the selection of a rectangular or elliptic jet shape. Deflections in the balance frame may be diminished by having a deep and rigid framework. None of the common measuring units have deflections large enough to be serious, and so they rarely cause this type of trouble.

The effects of deflections are evaluated during the process of calibrating the balance, and the corrections if necessary are either incorporated into the calculating machinery or given to the computing staff for inclusion in the work-up.

4:12. Balance Measuring Units and Linkages. So far, except for stating the impossibility of directly using deflecting scales for the measuring units of the wind-tunnel balance, no mention has been made of the types of units that are employed. These are usually either mechanical beam balances, hydraulic cel's, springless scales, or electric devices. First let us consider how the forces are brought to the measuring units.

Most measuring units operate best with loads that are brought to them vertically. Hence horizontal forces must be led through linkages that rotate them 90 degrees, and usually the vertical forces must also be brought out to a more convenient location. Each link in the system and particularly each joint represents a potential source of friction and deflection. Obviously the number of joints must be kept to a minimum, and those absolutely unavoidable must be designed with the utmost care. Friction also must be kept to a minimum. Surprisingly, ball bearings are almost never used. Their type of construction is better suited to apparatus having large motion between the parts. Instead, the joints of a wind-tunnel balance are either knife-edges or flexure plates.

Knife-edges are poorly named, for they are not sharp. They are actually wedges whose working edges have a small radius. They are of hardened steel, and their seats are hardened, too. Trouble with knife-edges is more likely to result from too sharp a "knife" than too dull a one.

The flexure plates are steel plates that have been milled down very thin at one section, so that they have very small resistance to bending in one direction while good rigidity is maintained in the other. Flexure plates (or pivots) have the added advantage that they can take tension as well as compression and are not subject to the troubles of corrosion and dirt like the knife-edges.

Besides the ability to measure small variations in large forces, the measuring unit should have two added qualities: it should maintain an invariable slope of the curve of applied load vs. indicated load, and it should return to zero when the load is removed very gradually. Of the two, occasional failure to return to zero is the lesser evil. Such action is instantly spotted by an alert tunnel crew, and runs are repeated or corrected as the evidence demands. A change of the balance constant is far more difficult to catch. Almost the only simple methods are to repeat a basic run occasionally or to calibrate the balance. It goes without saying that no measuring system is supposed to "slip calibration," but probably every wind-tunnel engineer has had that very thing occur at one time or another.

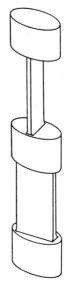

Fig. 4:21. Typical flexure. Hard steel milled to a working stress of 10,000 psi is customary practice.

It is a fundamental of measuring that a device can be made to read more accurately if it is subject only to loads up to 100 lb than if it must accommodate loads up to 1000 lb. In order to maintain the greatest accuracy, most measuring units have small capacities, and large loads are measured by balancing out the preponderance of the load with "unit" weights. Thus a load of 457 lb might be read by adding unit weights of 400 lb and reading 57 lb with the measuring unit. Depending on the balance design, the unit weights may be added either manually or automatically.

A short discussion of the four most popular types of measuring units follows.

1. The automatic beam balance. The automatic beam balance is shown in Fig. 4:22. It consists of a weighing beam that has an electrically driven rider. When the beam drops down, a contact is made that causes the driving motor to move the rider in the direction that will balance the beam. A counter on the motor shaft locates the rider and may be calibrated to read the force weighed. The pendulum H (see Fig. 4:22) can be adjusted to balance out the destabilizing component due to the weight of the beam.

2. Hydraulic capsules. The hydraulic capsule is a device that measures forces through the pressures they exert on pistons of

known area. They are not exactly null, but the amount of deflection of the piston is so small as to be negligible.

The operating principle of the hydraulic capsule is as follows (see Fig. 4:23).

Oil from a pressure source enters the cylinder part of the capsule through an inlet tube and leaks out through a gate directly

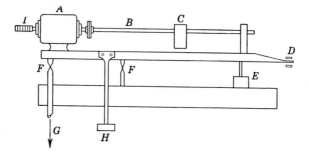

Fig. 4:22. Beam balance. *A*. Driving motor. *B*. Threaded rod. *C*. Rider. *D*. Reversing contacts. *E*. Dashpot. *F*. Flexure pivot. *G*. Applied load. *H*. Pendulum weight. *I*. Counter.

behind the piston. A load on the piston deflects the diaphragm so that the exit area is decreased, allowing the pressure in the cylinder to build up until the piston location and pressure balance out. The resulting pressure is a function of the size of the load and is measured through accurate pressure gages.

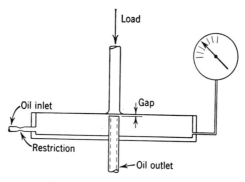

Fig. 4:23. Hydraulic capsule.

3. Electric measuring devices. Electric strain gages of the wire gage type (see Sects. 4:13 and 11:7) have been tried as measuring devices in several external balances with a satisfactory

degree of success. The electromagnetic arrangement that measures the forces by the amount of current needed to maintain zero deflection in the unit has also been successful. These systems often have a unit weight addition set-up in order to extend their range with maximum accuracy.

4. Springless scales. Although it has been mentioned previously that spring scales or the familiar weight-and-lever systems known as "springless" scales are unsatisfactory because of their large deflections under load, it is important to note that some wind-tunnel balances are being redesigned to utilize such devices as measuring units. Their deflection is taken out of the system by having automatically extending links (called "compensators") in the balance so that the model does not move.

Any measuring system must be checked under vibratory load to obtain the damping and balance that yield the greatest accuracy.

4:13. Electric Measuring Devices. There are several methods for measuring forces or pressures electrically, most of them depending on amplifying the effect that tiny deflections have on the capacitance, inductance, or resistance of the unit. For example, the resistance of a carbon pack varies as the pressure on it, and the current it passes for a fixed voltage may be used as an index of the load. The amount of current needed to keep the core of a solenoid in a fixed location is an index of the load on it. The change in capacitance of a plate condenser with small deflections of the plates may again indicate a load. The resistance of a wire changes with the tension of the wire, and the current passed for a fixed voltage may indicate the tension. And so ad infinitum. A hundred different set-ups may be possible. It should be borne in mind that through amplification the most minute changes may be noted and that remarkable accuracy is possible.

By far the most widely used of the electric measuring devices is the electric wire strain gage, of which an elementary unit is shown in Fig. 4:24. Basically, the wire strain gage consists of a resistance made of very fine wire cemented to a flexure. The load F, by deflecting the beam by a minute amount, stretches the wires glued to the beam and changes their resistance and the amount of current that will flow through them for a fixed applied voltage. The current, being proportional to the load F, thus becomes the indicator of the size of F.

The above circuit, elementary as it is, serves to illustrate the principle of the gage itself, but many refinements are needed before a useful electric strain gage can be realized. For instance, for the above circuit, a change in temperature would cause the

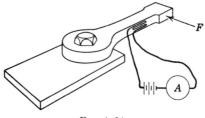

FIG. 4:24.

flexure to expand, stretching the gage and indicating an extraneous "load." Temperature compensation is accomplished by gluing a second gage on the opposite side from the one shown in Fig. 4:24, and connecting it to a Wheatstone bridge circuit as shown in Fig. 4:25. It will be seen that, as long as both resistances (marked 1 and 2 in Fig. 4:25) are equally increased or

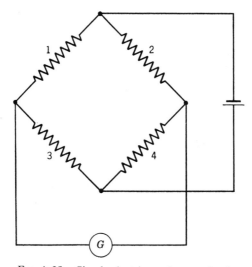

FIG. 4:25. Simple electric-strain-gage circuit.

decreased, there will be no change in the potential measured by the potentiometer. Thus the flexure-gage combination is insensitive to heat.

Manual winding of gages has been almost entirely superseded by commercially available gages and is used only for very special installation when unusual gage characteristics are required. The gages are glued to the flexures with a Bakelite bond, and normally require 4 to 12 volts applied voltage. Current practice is to design the beams for a working stress of 6000 to 12,000 psi, although very much higher values, up to as much as 65,000 psi, have been used with good success. Some engineers prefer to taper the flexure to get a uniform stress over the gage; others find this unnecessary. A discussion of the strain-gage balances, which are largely used for transonic (and supersonic) testing, will be found in Chapter 11.

Brief experience with strain gages has indicated that before they are put into service their amplifiers should be left on all night to obtain maximum stability. Minimum gage voltage should always be employed, with scale range coming from the amplification rather than beam deflection. Excessive amplification may, however, result in too much drift. Gage output is proportional to applied voltage, and so a variable source of 2.5 to 10 volts will supply a 4-to-1 scale expansion for the usual readout.

It will be necessary to bring out strain-gage leads from rotating machinery on some occasions, and change of the resistance due to poor contact on slip rings can make much trouble. One of the most satisfactory solutions is to use a copper-silver ring ("coin" silver) and a silver graphite brush with about 30 psi brush pressure. Results with ring tangential speeds up to 100 ft per sec have been good with this arrangement.

4:14. Balance Alignment. In order to have the drag scales read pure drag without including any component of lift, the wind-tunnel balance must be properly aligned with the airstream: lift perpendicular to it and drag parallel with it.

The difficulties come under four heads:

1. The air flow will have some variation of angularity, and hence an average perpendicular must be assumed. It will be the true average for one wing planform only.

2. The variation of q will cause the change in angularity to have more effect at some places than others. Again, an average must be assumed; and again it can be the average for one planform only.

3. The mean air flow will in all probability not be horizontal or parallel to the tunnel centerline, and alignment to these criteria is not sufficient.

4. Variation in q and angle may change with airspeed, and hence the alignment will too.

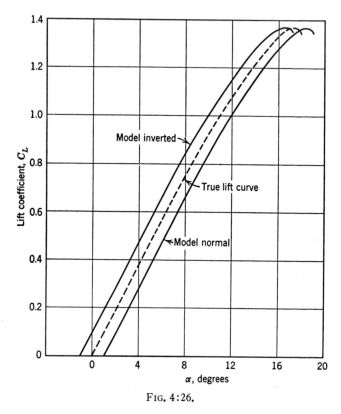

Fig. 4:26.

One item simplifies the alignment: the lift for most tests is from 5 to 25 times larger than the drag, and it is usually sufficient to align so that no lift appears in the drag-reading apparatus without checking to see whether any drag appears in the lift-reading mechanism beyond ascertaining that the drag system is perpendicular to the lift.

The balance alignment is generally accomplished by running a wing both normal and inverted from zero lift to stall. To assure equal support strut interference for both normal and inverted runs, dummy supports, identical to the conventional ones, are installed downward from the tunnel roof. They are then as shown in Fig. 4:31. The data from both normal and downward lift are plotted as lift curves (C_L vs. α), polars (C_L vs. C_D), and moment curves (C_L vs. C_m). The negative lifts and moments are plotted as though they were positive. (See Fig. 4:26.) The

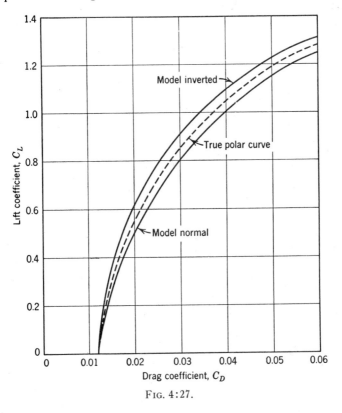

Fig. 4:27.

angular variation between the lift curves is twice the error in setting the angle of attack and as shown indicates that the α is set too high. That is, when the balance angle indicator reads +1 degree, the model is really at 0 degrees to the average wind. The polar shows that the lift is not perpendicular to the relative wind, part of it appearing as drag. Here the balance is tipped forward in reference to the relative wind, for a component of the lift is increasing the drag when the lift is positive and decreasing it when the lift is negative (Figs. 4:27 and 4:28).

The same procedure outlined above for a wing must be followed for each complete model: runs with the image system in; model both normal and inverted. These runs yield the true angle of zero lift and alignment correction. The additional runs needed for tare and interference are discussed in the next section.

If angular and velocity variations in the airstream are large, the above alignment would apply only to wings whose span and

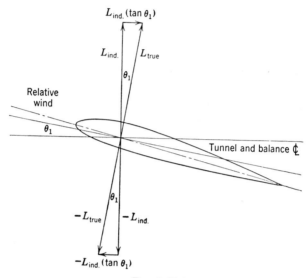

Fig. 4:28.

chord approximate the test wing. In the section on angularity (Sect. 3:13), a compromise method is outlined.

It is impracticable to align the balance for each model, and hence the misalignment correction is applied in the data work-up as follows:

Suppose that the polars of the normal and inverted runs appear as in Fig. 4:27. With the wing in the normal position the balance reads

$$C_{D \text{ indicated}} = C_{D \text{ true}} + C_{L \text{ indicated}} (\tan \theta_1) \qquad (4:1)$$

where θ_1 = angle of misalignment (Fig. 4:28). Hence

$$C_{D \text{ ind.}} - C_{D \text{ true}} = C_{L \text{ ind.}} \tan \theta_1 \qquad (4:2)$$

The correct $C_D (C_{D \text{ true}})$ lies halfway between the $C_{D \text{ normal}}$ and

$C_{D \text{ inverted}}$ curves. Let the difference between the curves at some C_L be ΔC_D. Then

$$C_{D \text{ ind.}} - C_{D \text{ true}} = \Delta C_D / 2 \qquad (4:3)$$

and, if the difference between the curves is read at $C_L = 1.0$, the angle of misalignment, θ_1, may be found from

$$\tan \theta_1 = (\Delta C_D / 2)_{C_L = 1.0} \qquad (4:4)$$

When working up the data, the correct drag may then be found from

$$C_{D \text{ true}} = C_{D \text{ ind.}} - (C_{L \text{ ind.}}) \tan \theta_1 \qquad (4:5)$$

A second and simple method is to plot $\Delta C_D / 2$ against C_L and pick off the proper values during the data work-up. True C_L is close enough to $C_{L \text{ indicated}}$ so that usually no correction to C_L is needed.

Two further important points in regard to the evaluation of the alignment correction remain. First, it should be realized that, in order to have the tare and interference effects identical for both the model normal and inverted runs, the image system must be installed and the dummy struts arranged as per Fig. 4:31. Second, the misalignment corrections found necessary for a certain model will not suffice if the same model is to be tested at a later date, for expansion of the tunnel due to weather conditions may cause variations of the mean flow angle in the jet.

The error in setting the angle of attack, $\Delta \alpha'$, is found from the normal and inverted lift curves as per Fig. 4:26, the corrected angle in this case being

$$\alpha = \alpha_N - \Delta \alpha' \qquad (4:6)$$

where α_N = angles of attack read with model in normal position; $\Delta \alpha'$ = half the angular difference between lift curves for normal and inverted positions. The angular correction for misalignment is usually incorporated into the work-up of the data.

In order to correct for misalignment of the side-force balance, two runs must be made, with both the tare and interference dummies in. The model in normal position should be yawed in one direction and then inverted and yawed in the same direction relative to the tunnel. The correct side-force curve will be halfway between the curves made by model normal and model inverted. The inversion is necessary to nullify effects of the model's irregularities.

Side-force corrections as outlined are rarely made as they entail a set of dummy supports that can be yawed; moreover, extreme accuracy in side force is not usually required. The principles of the correction, however, are important.

It should be recalled that changes in the shape of a polar curve may be due to scale effects and that comparisons of various tests of similar airfoils must be made from readings at the same effective Reynolds number. (It has been shrewdly noted that, if the section selected is one of the more "popular" types that have been frequently tested, it is nearly always possible to find some results that will "agree" with yours.)

4:15. Tare and Interference Measurements. Any conventional wind-tunnel set-up requires that the model be supported in some manner, and, in turn, the supports will both affect the free air flow about the model and have some drag themselves. The effect on the free air flow is called "interference"; the drag of the supports, "tare." Although tare drags could be eliminated entirely by shielding the supports all the way into the model (with adequate clearances, of course), the added size thus necessitated would probably increase the interference so that no net gain would be achieved.

The evaluation of the tare and interference is a complex job, requiring thought as well as time for proper completion. The student invariably suggests removing the model to measure the forces on the model supports. This procedure would expose parts of the model support not ordinarily in the airstream (although the extra length could be made removable) and would fail to record either the effect of the model on the supports or the effect of the supports on the model.

First let us consider a method rarely used that evaluates the interference and tare drag separately. Actually the value of the sum of the two will nearly always suffice without determining the contribution of each, but, besides being fundamental, this long method may offer suggestions for determining interference for certain radical set-ups. The procedure is as follows:

The model is first tested in the normal manner, the data as taken including both the tare and interference. In symbolic form we have:

$$D_{\text{measured}} = D_N + I_{LB/M} + I_{M/LB} + I_{LSW} + T_L \quad (4:7)$$

where D_N = drag of model in normal position; $I_{LB/M}$ = interference of lower surface bayonets on model; $I_{M/LB}$ = interference of model on lower surface bayonets; I_{LSW} = interference of lower support windshield; T_L = free air "tare" drag of lower bayonet.

FIG. 4:29.   Two of tare and interference runs in the DC-6.

Next the model is supported from the tunnel roof by the "image" or "mirror" system. The normal supports extend into the model, but a small clearance is provided (Fig. 4:30a). The balance then reads the drag of the exposed portions of the supports in the presence of the model.   That is:

$$D_{\text{measured}} = T_L + I_{M/LB} \qquad (4:8)$$

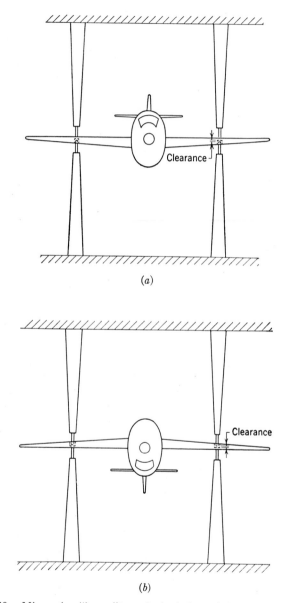

(a)

(b)

Fig. 4:30.   Mirror (or "image") method of determining the effect of the
supports on the model.

For the interference run the model is inverted and run with the mirror supports just clearing their attachment points (Fig. 4:30b). We then get

$$D_{\text{measured}} = D_{\text{inv.}} + T_U + I_{UB/M} + I_{USW} + I_{M/UB} + I_{LB/M} + I_{LSW} \quad (4:9)$$

where $D_{\text{inv.}}$ = drag of model inverted (should equal the drag of the model normal, except for misalignment) (see Sect. 4:14) and the symbol U refers to the upper surface.

Then the mirror system is removed and a second inverted run is made. This yields

$$D_{\text{measured}} = D_{\text{inv.}} + T_U + I_{UB/M} + I_{M/UB} + I_{USW} \quad (4:10)$$

The difference between the two inverted runs is the interference of supports on the lower surface. That is, eq. 4:9 minus eq. 4:10 yields

$$I_{LB/M} + I_{LSW} \quad (4:11)$$

By subtracting eqs. 4:8 and 4:11 from the first run (eq. 4:7), the actual model drag is determined if the balance is aligned. As explained more fully in Sect 4:14, the difference between runs made in the normal and inverted position with the mirror system in can be used to find the proper corrections for alignment.

The support tare and interference effects can be found in three runs instead of four by using a slightly different procedure. In this case the normal run is made, yielding

$$D_{\text{measured}} = D_N + T_L + I_L \quad (4:12)$$

where $I_L = I_{M/LB} + I_{LB/M} + I_{LSW}$. Next the model is inverted and we get

$$D_{\text{measured}} = D_{\text{inv.}} + T_U + I_U \quad (4:13)$$

Then the dummy supports are installed. Instead of the clearance being between the dummy supports and the model, the exposed length of the support strut is attached to the model, and the clearance is in the dummy supports (Fig. 4:31). This configuration yields

$$D_{\text{measured}} = D_{\text{inv.}} + T_L + I_L + T_U + I_U \quad (4:14)$$

The difference between eq. 4:13 and eq. 4:14 yields the sum of the tare and interference $T_L + I_L$.

The second procedure has the advantage that the dummy supports do not have to be heavy enough to hold the model, nor do they require any mechanism for changing the angle of attack.

A third method of evaluating the tare and interference, sometimes employed where an image system is impracticable, consists of adding extra dummy supports on the lower surface and assuming their effect to be identical with the actual supports.

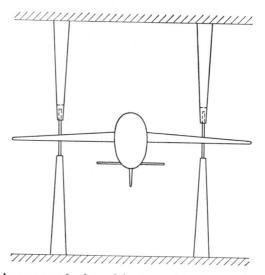

Fig. 4:31. Arrangement for determining tare and interference simultaneously.

Sometimes there is danger of mutual interference between the dummies and the real supports.

Doubtless the increase of runs necessary to determine the small tare and interference effects and the concern expressed about the difference between those effects on the upper and lower surfaces seem picayune. Yet their combined effect represents from 10 to 50 per cent of the minimum drag of the whole airplane—clearly not a negligible error.

It should be noted that the tare and interference forces vary with angle of attack and with model changes. They must be repeatedly checked and evaluated, particularly for major changes of wing flaps, cowling flaps, and nacelle alterations close to the support attachment. With many models every configuration must have its own support interference evaluated, a long and tiresome test procedure.

The image-system method of tare and interference evaluation assumes that there is no mutual interference between the real and image supports. Also, unless added struts are placed on the lower surface to evaluate the lower strut effect, it must be assumed that $C_{L\,max.}$ is unaffected by the lower surface mounting struts.

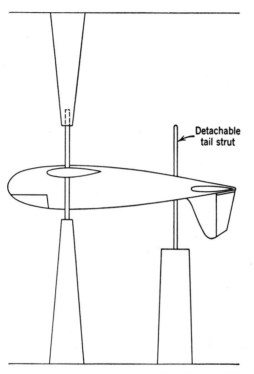

Detachable tail strut

FIG. 4:32. Set-up for determining the tare and interference of the tail support.

As the model angle of attack is changed, its center of gravity will probably change, producing a pitching moment. This moment must be evaluated by pitching the model with the tunnel wind off and by subtracting the pitching-moment tare from the wind-on runs. Or it must be balanced out by weights hung on the pitch-measuring system to bring the total ship-plus-weights center of gravity on the balance resolving center.

The tare and interference evaluations for the tail support have been omitted from the above discussion because they are generally treated in a slightly different manner. The reason for this new treatment is that the length of the tail support varies as the

angle of attack is changed. This factor so complicates the
dummy arrangements that a system is usually employed that
does not require a complete dummy tail support.

The procedure is as follows: Consider the second method of
evaluating the tare and interference. When the image system
is brought down to the inverted model, a short support is added
to the then upper surface of the model where the tail support
would attach in a normal run. The piece attached corresponds
in length to the minimum exposed portion of the tail support
and increases the drag of the model by the interference and tare
drag of a tail support on the model's lower surface. For angles
of attack other than that corresponding to minimum length of
exposed tail support, the drag of the extra exposed tail support
length must be evaluated and subtracted.

A rear support windshield that moves with the rear support
to keep a constant amount of strut in the airstream could be
employed as long as the added interference of the moving shield
is evaluated by a moving shield dummy set-up.

The evaluation of the tare, interference, and alignment of a
wing-alone test follows the procedure outlined above, except
that further complication is introduced by the presence of a
"sting" that must be added to the wing to connect it to the rear
strut of the support system. The tare and interference caused
by the sting may be found by adding a second sting during the
image tests. As may be noted in Fig. 4:33, the attachment of
the sting to the rear support includes a portion of the strut above
the connection, and the dummy sting has a section of support
strut added both above and below its connection point. This
complication is needed to account for the interference of the strut
on the sting, as follows.

When the wing is held at a high angle of attack, there will be
an obtuse angle below the sting. When the wing is inverted and
held at a high angle relative to the wind, there will be an acute
angle below the sting, for the rear strut will then be extended to
its full length. To eliminate this difference between the normal
and inverted tests the support strut is extended above the sting
attachment point, so that the sum of the angles between the
sting and the support is always 180 degrees. Similarly, the
image sting has the same arrangement. It is noted that, although
the angles between the sting and the rear support vary with the
angle of attack, the image sting is always at right angles to its

short "rear support strut." Further, the image rear support strut does not remain vertical but changes its angle with the wing. The error incurred by failing to have the sting image system simulate the exact interference and rear strut angle is believed to be negligible.

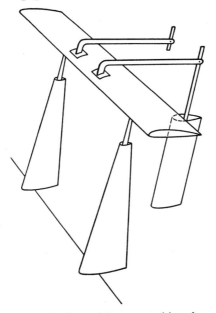

FIG. 4:33.   Set-up for determining tare and interference of sting.

Figure 4:34 shows the results of a wing-alone test for a NACA 0015 wing of $AR = 6.0$. The wing in this particular test was small, and the corrections for tare, interference, and alignment are correspondingly large, but the variation of the corrections is typical. The following points are of interest.

1. The correction for tare and interference decreases as C_L (and α) increases.

2. The incidence strut drag decreases with increasing α. (The amount of strut exposed decreases with α.)

3. The alignment correction increases with C_L.

A large amount of interference may arise from air bleeding through the windshields that surround the support struts to protect them from the windstream. These struts frequently attach at points of low pressure on the model, and, if the shield is brought close to the model, a considerable flow may be in-

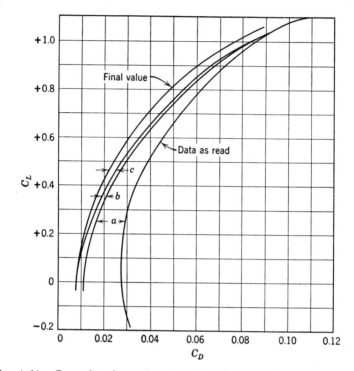

Fig. 4:34. Corrections for a wing-alone test. *a.* Sting and support tare and interference. *b.* Drag of exposed incidence strut. *c.* Alignment.

duced that will run along the model. This flow may stall the entire underside of the model and produce results not only wrong but also unsteady and difficult to evaluate. It is, therefore, fre-

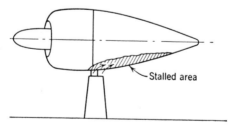

Fig. 4:35. Effect of "bleeding."

quently advantageous to terminate the windshields well below the model and let the test be subjected to added but well-defined tare drag. (See Fig. 4:35.)

4:16. Profile Drag by the Momentum Method. It should be noted that a balance is not always required in a wind tunnel. The drag may be obtained by comparing the momentum in the air ahead of the model with momentum behind the model, and the lift may be found by integration of the pressures on the tunnel walls. These artifices are most generally employed in airfoil section research in a two-dimensional tunnel. Spanwise integration is unnecessary then, and section coefficients may be directly obtained.

The basic theory of the wake survey measurement is as follows. Consider the flow past an airfoil (Fig. 4:36). It may be

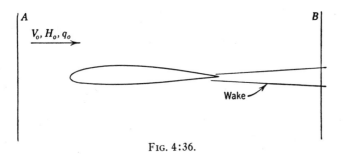

Fig. 4:36.

seen that the part of the air that passes over the model suffers a loss of momentum, and this loss is evidenced by and equal to the profile drag of the airfoil, or

$$D = \frac{\text{Mass}}{\text{Sec}} \times \text{Change in velocity}$$

$$D = \iint \rho V \, da (V_0 - V)$$

where D = drag; V_0 = initial airspeed (at A); V = final airspeed in the wake (at B); da = small area of the wake perpendicular to airstream. Hence

$$D = \iint (\rho V V_0 \, da - \rho V^2 \, da)$$

and

$$c_{d0} = 2 \iint \left(\frac{V}{V_0} \frac{da}{S} - \frac{V^2}{V_0^2} \frac{da}{S} \right)$$

Also

$$V_0 = \sqrt{2q_0/\rho}$$

and

$$V = \sqrt{2q/\rho}$$

Therefore

$$c_{d0} = 2 \iint \left(\sqrt{\frac{q}{q_0}} - \frac{q}{q_0} \right) \frac{da}{S} \tag{4:15}$$

For a unit section of the airfoil, $S = c \times 1$, and the area $da = dy \times 1$, where y is measured perpendicular to the plane of the wing. Finally,

$$c_{d0} = 2 \int \left(\sqrt{\frac{q}{q_0}} - \frac{q}{q_0} \right) \frac{dy}{c} \tag{4:16}$$

From Bernoulli's equation

$$H_0 - p_0 = \tfrac{1}{2}\rho V_0{}^2 = q_0$$

and

$$H - p = \tfrac{1}{2}\rho V^2 = q$$

where H and H_0 = total head in wake and free stream respectively; p and p_0 = static head in wake and free stream respectively. Hence we have

$$c_{d0} = 2 \int \left(\sqrt{\frac{H - p}{H_0 - p_0}} - \frac{H - p}{H_0 - p_0} \right) \frac{dy}{c} \tag{4:17}$$

The ordinary pitot-static tube reads $(H - p)$ directly, but practical difficulties usually prevent the construction of a bank of them. The customary method of obtaining values for eq. 4:16 is to use a wake survey rake (Fig. 3:12). This is simply a bank of total head tubes spaced about a tube diameter apart with the total head orifice about one chord ahead of the rake body. The tubes are individually connected in order to the tubes of a multiple manometer; and, since only the ratio q/q_0 is needed, the readings are independent of the specific gravity of the fluid in the manometer and its angle.

The manometer will appear as in Fig. 4:37. In actual practice many more readings will be available through shimming up the rake in small increments. A small amount of "splash" outside the wake proper may also appear, caused probably by the lateral static-pressure gradient present in the tunnel. The engineer must fair the curve according to his experience.

The constant readings of the outside tubes indicate that they are out of the wake and hence may be used to determine q_0. It should be noted that q_0 should be used from the manometer reading, not from the tunnel q at the model location, as the longitudinal velocity gradient in the tunnel invalidates q calibrations made upstream. The other tubes read the values of q corresponding to their position on the rake.

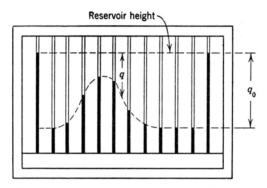

FIG. 4:37. The wake as it appears on the multiple manometer.

It will be seen that the proper values of q can be obtained only if the rake is situated far enough behind the wing so that the wake has returned to tunnel static pressure since a difference in static pressure across the wake will void the values for q. A solution to this problem is to locate the rake at least 0.7 chord behind the trailing edge of the wing, by which time the wake will be approximately at tunnel static pressure. A second solution is to equip the rake with static orifices, the usual practice being to employ three, one at each end and one in the middle, which are averaged. Since the measurement of freestream static pressure close to a body is a difficult thing at best, extreme caution must be exercised in locating the static holes. A satisfactory procedure is to locate them out of the plane of the rake body as in Fig. 3:12, and calibrate them with a standard pitot-static tube, adjusting the tip length of each static tube until true static is read. If the tunnel is not at atmospheric static pressure normally, reference tubes on the multiple manometer should be connected to tunnel static pressure.

It is a tedious job to measure the pressure in each tube, divide it by q_0, take the square root, and perform the other measures necessary for the calculation of eq. 4:16. Since the ratio q/q_0 is close to 1.0 if the rake is fairly well downstream, the assumption that $\sqrt{q/q_0} = 0.5 + q/(2q_0)$ is valid. Substituted into eq. 4:16 it yields

$$c_{d0} = \frac{Y_w}{c} - \frac{1}{q_0 c} \int q \, dy \qquad (4:18)$$

where Y_w = wake width.

Equation 4:18 makes possible the direct integration of the wake survey data as received, greatly reducing the time necessary for calculation.

The wake survey rake cannot be used to measure the drag of stalled airfoils or of airfoils with flaps down. Under these conditions a large part of the drag is caused by rotational losses and does not appear as a drop in linear momentum.

If practical reasons prohibit the location of the rake far enough downstream so that the wake has not yet reached tunnel static pressure, additional corrections are necessary (Ref. 4:1), and if tests are made at large Mach numbers still further changes are required.

It has been found that a round total head tube will not read the true pressure at its centerline if it is located in a region where the pressure is varying from one side of the tube to the other. An allowance may be made for this (Ref. 4:1), or the total head tubes may each be flattened at the tip. The latter procedure is recommended, although the usual correction for the lateral pressure variation is quite small.

4:17. Integrating Wake Survey Rake. An ingenious integrating rake that can be calibrated to read the drag coefficient directly on a single pressure tube has been proposed by Silverstein (Ref. 4:3). It consists of a simple bank of total head tubes connected to a reservoir (Fig. 4:38). The drag is a function of the average pressure in the reservoir, assuming that the wake curve is similar

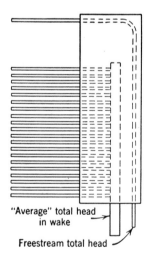

"Average" total head in wake

Freestream total head

FIG. 4:38. Wake rake with integrating head.

to a (cosine)^2 curve. Though the integrating wake survey rake is a wonderful time-saver when many tests of similar airfoils are to be made, it is sometimes difficult to get accurate results without calibrating the integrating rake to each new set-up. Unless the rake is attached to the wing being tested, the usual non-integrating rake must be present so that the integrating rake can be centered.

Several types of integrating or averaging manometers have been used in an effort to eliminate the laborious calculations of eq. 4:17. With any of them, extreme caution is needed in interpreting the results.

4:18. Lift and Drag by Pressure Distributions. Still a third method exists whereby the lift and drag may be measured: the integration of the static pressures over the wing. For these tests the airfoil is equipped with many flush orifices, each individually connected to a tube of a multiple manometer. For lift determinations the pressures are plotted perpendicular to the chord, yielding the normal force coefficient C_N. When plotted parallel to the chord, they give the chord force coefficient, C_C. The approximate C_L may be found from

$$C_L = C_N \cos \alpha \qquad (4:19)$$

The actual static-pressure distribution over a wing is shown in Fig. 4:39A. The same pressure distribution plotted normal to the chord for the determination of normal force is shown in Fig. 4:39B, and parallel to the chord for chord force determination in Fig. 4:39C. Several of the pressure readings are labeled so that their relative positions may be followed in the various plots.

The growth of the pressure distribution with angle of attack is shown for a typical airfoil in Fig. 4:40; in this figure may also be found a partial answer to the oft-repeated question "Which lifts more, the upper or the lower surface?" At zero lift, both surfaces have both positive and negative lift. With increasing angle of attack the upper surface increases its proportion until it finally is lifting about 70 per cent of the total.

Many interesting observations may be made from pressure distributions. These include:

1. The location of the minimum pressure point and its strength.
2. The load that the skin is to withstand and its distribution.

3. The location of the point of maximum velocity and its value. This follows from item 1.

4. The location of the maximum pressure point and its strength.

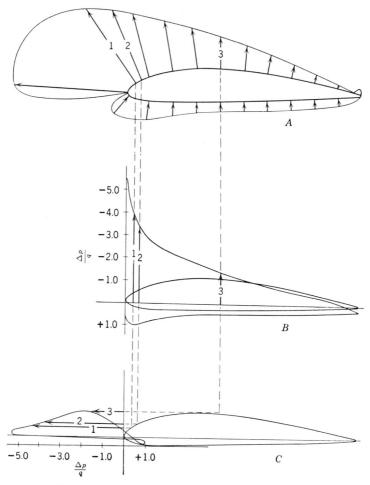

Fig. 4:39.   The actual pressure distribution and its presentation.

5. The probable type of boundary-layer flow and its extent.

6. The center of pressure location.

7. The critical Mach number. This follows from item 3.

8. The airfoil ideal angle. This occurs when the flow enters the leading edge smoothly, i.e., when there is no measurable

pressure differential between upper and lower surfaces at the
leading edge. The ideal angle is more familiar to practical aerodynamicists as the middle of the drag bucket.

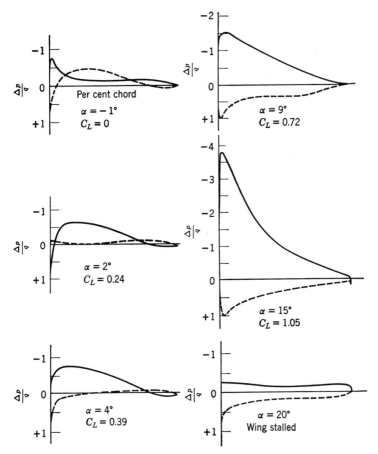

FIG. 4:40. Growth of static-pressure distribution with angle of attack.

It may be worth while to note that a stagnation point on the
trailing edge of an airfoil occurs, even theoretically, only when
the airfoil does not have a cusp trailing edge.

Pressure distributions are usually plotted as follows:

Pressures are read with a multiple manometer that may or
may not be inclined. The true head in any one tube, p, equals
($p' \sin \theta$) × (sp. gr. of liquid), where p' is the measured head as

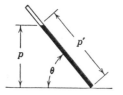

FIG. 4:41.

defined in Fig. 4:41. The normal force

$$N = \int \Delta p \, dS$$

where $\Delta p = p_u - p_l$; p_u = pressure on upper surface; p_l = pressure on lower surface; S = wing area.

For a unit depth of span,

$$N = \int \Delta p \, dc$$

where c = wing chord.

By definition,

$$N = (\rho/2)SV^2 C_N$$

and hence

$$C_N = \frac{N}{qc} = \frac{1}{c} \int \frac{\Delta p}{q} \, dc \qquad (4:20)$$

It follows that the pressures may be plotted in units of dynamic pressure against their respective locations on the chord. Further, the area under such a curve divided by the chord is the normal force coefficient, and the moment of area about the leading edge divided by the area is the center of pressure.

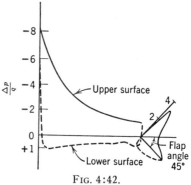

FIG. 4:42.

When a trailing edge flap is lowered, it is customary to show the flap pressures normal to the flap chord in its down position. (See Fig. 4:42.) For finding the total C_N due to the main wing and flap we have

$$C_N = C_{N \text{ wing}} + C_{N \text{ flap}} \cos \delta_F \qquad (4:21)$$

where δ_F = flap angle.

It should be noted that, though good agreement between C_N and C_L can be obtained, the drag measured by the pressure distribution, $C_{D\text{ press.}} = C_C \cos \alpha + C_N \sin \alpha$, does not include skin friction or induced drag.

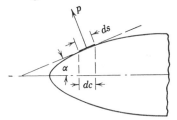

FIG. 4:43.

The point is sometimes raised that a fallacy is involved in plotting the pressures that act normal to the curved surface of the wing as though they were normal to the chord. Actually there is no error. A simple analogy is observable in the pressure which is acting radially in a pipe but whose force trying to split the pipe is the pressure times the section area made by a plane that contains a diameter.

The mathematical explanation is as follows. Consider a small element of surface ds, which is subjected to a static pressure p acting normal to it. The total force on the element is $p\,ds$, directed along p, and the component of this force normal to the chord line is $p\,ds \cos \alpha$.

But $ds \cos \alpha = dc$, where dc is a short length of the chord, so that the total force normal to the wing chord line is $N = \int \Delta p\,dc$.

It will be noted in Fig. 4:40 that a maximum stagnation pressure of $\Delta p/q = +1.0$ is usually developed near the leading edge of a wing. This may be accepted as the rule for section tests, but swept-back panels will show less than $\Delta p/q = +1.0$ at all stations except at the plane of symmetry.

PROBLEMS

4:1. Define balance alignment.

4:2. Explain how to attain alignment.

4:3. Explain the situation and suggest the necessary corrections if the drag is less when the wing lifts normally than when it is inverted.

4:4. Discuss the difference between the effect of the model on the supports and the effect of the supports on the model.

4:5. State several difficulties inherent in a wire balance.

4:6. Sketch an airplane, and show the forces and moments on it.

4:7. Under what conditions does a wake survey fail to read the drag?

4:8. How would you find the effect of a sting employed for a wing-alone test?

4:9. Draw and explain a set-up that could be used to determine the effect of the model on the supports.

4:10. Is a fork-type support used to decrease model yaw deflection?

4:11. Give the runs and procedure to get the tare and interference of a three-finned bomb on a single support.

REFERENCES

4:1. B. Melvill Jones, Measurement of Profile Drag by the Pitot-Traverse Method, *R&M* 1688, 1936.

4:2. Joseph Bicknell, Determination of the Profile Drag of an Airplane Wing in Flight at High Reynolds Numbers, *TR* 667, 1939.

4:3. A. Silverstein, A Simple Method for Determining Wing Profile Drag in Flight, *JAS*, May, 1940.

Chapter 5

TESTING PROCEDURE

There is very little sense to testing an aircraft component or complete model unless the data are going to be used. Accordingly, we could say that the discussion of each testing procedure should be followed by a few words on the degree to which the

Courtesy Aerolab Development Corp.

FIG. 5:1. Assembly of model of turbo-prop powered fighter.

data may be trusted. This plan has been decided against, however, and the use of wind-tunnel data in general has been treated in a single chapter (Chapter 7). This permits a more direct approach when extrapolation to full scale is under consideration.

Before we go into testing procedure, however, it seems in order to discuss the building of the models for testing; planning the tests; and obtaining a tunnel. Additional comments on helicopter models and those models especially designed for high-speed testing will be found in Chapters 10, 11, and 12.

5:1. Model Design and Construction. The type and the construction of the wind-tunnel model are dictated by the tunnel in which it is to be tested and the type of test to be made. After the obvious and paramount necessity of extreme accuracy, accessibility and maintenance are next in importance. Working conditions in a wind tunnel are at best very trying. The temperature

Courtesy Aerolab Development Corp.

FIG. 5:2. Fitting laminated wood profile to steel spar of model. Pressure leads attached to metal sections may be seen running down both leading and trailing edges of the spar.

may vary from 30° F in winter to 140° F in summer. The model is usually so placed that accessibility is at a premium, and repair facilities may or may not be available. All these factors demand that changes be as simple as possible, and that the model with all its parts and additions be thoroughly tested outside the tunnel before tests are commenced.

In general, models made of laminated mahogany will be adequately strong without steel beams for tests up to 100 mph.

Above that, and to about 300 mph, wood models with steel load members are satisfactory (see Fig. 5:2); for the higher speeds metal is in order. These speed criteria are, of course, very rough and general. A very thin model might easily require solid steel construction although testing is to be at only 100 mph. The criterion for model strength is deflection rather than yield load limits, as great rigidity is desirable.* In the high-speed range margins of safety of the order of 4.0 are usually required. It is advisable to provide metal beams for any control surfaces in order to maintain the best accuracy of the hinge alignment.

The only serious design changes between model and full scale include (1) provision of variable horizontal and vertical tail incidence whether the real airplane will have them or not, and (2) omission of miniature parts such as pitot tubes, etc., whose Reynolds number would be too low at model scale.

A wing fitting of the type shown in Fig. 5:3 is in general use. It will be seen that it provides an attachment for a dummy bayonet. Two sealing blocks are needed for both upper and lower surfaces, one with a slot to allow a strut to pass, and one solid to be used when the dummy system is not employed. (It will be recalled that during the process of testing the model must be mounted both normal and inverted, with and without the image system.) The second set of blocks may be omitted and the slot sealed with tape if so desired.

The most satisfactory material for wind-tunnel models to be used up to about 300 mph is well-seasoned Honduras mahogany. This wood is easy to work, glues well, takes all types of finish, and is little subject to warping. A second choice is walnut, also a nice wood to work but likely to have curly grain and hence being more difficult to work to close tolerances. Holly has high tearing resistance and is excellent for trailing edges. Some of the softer woods, plastic, plaster, and metals can be used; each has its characteristic advantages and disadvantages for construction and maintenance.

The mahogany form block should be composed of laminations from $\frac{3}{8}$ to $\frac{3}{4}$ in. wide. They should be cut from larger pieces and have alternate strips turned end for end so that any warping tendency will be resisted. The block should be glued according to standard practices; i.e., glue should be fresh, pressure ade-

* Unless, of course, the deflection is intentional and controlled (See Sect. 5:16).

quate, and drying time sufficient (1 to 5 days). When practical, 2 or 3 week's seasoning is desirable.

Necessary pressure tubes and steel beams may either be in-corporated in the block or added later, depending on the design.

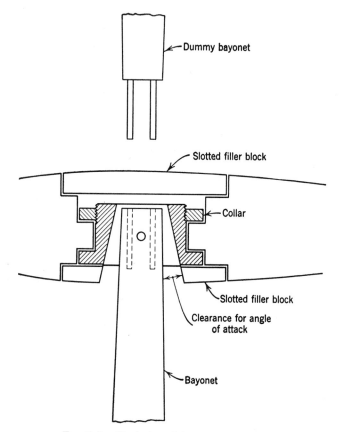

Fig. 5:3.   Typical model attachment fitting.

Usually models have many component parts, each to be made separately. This works out well with the construction procedure because it is advisable to make each part from $\frac{1}{16}$ to $\frac{1}{8}$ in. over-size and allow some additional seasoning over and above that needed for the block, to allow any strains in the block a chance to be relieved by warping.

The last fraction of an inch is then worked down to female templates by files, scrapers, and sandpaper. The day should be so planned that time remains to spray at least one coat of clear lacquer after the piece is done to seal it and prevent warping due to changes in its moisture content.

Hinged surfaces present a problem for the model designer largely because the smallest hinge possible to construct is far too large scalewise. In view of the hopelessness of accurate reproduction the designer just does the best he can.

Several basic types of hinges are in general use. The first is simply a set of brackets for each angle setting. This is a slow method as far as model changes go, and it makes for lengthy model construction as well. A serious factor is that, if test results indicate during the program that additional angles are required, the new brackets usually require shop work above the level of tunnel engineers and tie up the tunnel during fitting as well.

A second method is to furnish the surfaces with hinges and to use an exterior sector with drilled holes for each angle setting. This is a good positive method that at least yields the same setting for repeat points, and it is only the work of a moment if additional settings become necessary. It has to be assumed, of course, that such a sector in the "breeze" will not cause appreciable trouble.

A third method is to furnish hinges and an interior setting lock. The author has had too many of these slip, and has broken too many, to be enthusiastic about this type except when it is designed by some one with much experience. The engineer using this type of hinge should check the setting at the end of each run.

Model makers differ in their opinions of suitable finishes. The choice is usually between three types, all quick drying: shellac, clear lacquer, or pigmented lacquer. Shellac and the clear lacquers seem to yield a slightly thinner coat (0.002 to 0.005 in.) than the pigmented lacquer (0.003 to 0.008 in.). On the other hand many model makers believe that the smoothest finish is obtained only with the pigmented lacquer. Regardless of the choice, an adjustment in the templates should be made to allow room for the finish. Finishes put on and sanded back to zero thickness are not believed to offer sufficient protection and moisture seal.

The usual procedure to follow in applying a finish is to apply and sand four to six coats, using progressively finer waterproof sandpaper. When inspection indicates the surface to be filled, a rubbing compound may be used to obtain a high gloss. The model should be waxed before shipping and again after it is mounted in the tunnel.

A model for a 7 by 10 tunnel should have the wing contour accurate to 0.005 in. to the true contour, and fuselage to within 0.01 in. No perceptible ridges or joints should be permitted.

Air passages, radiator openings, and cooling entrances may be simulated by an indenture of the entry without any completed

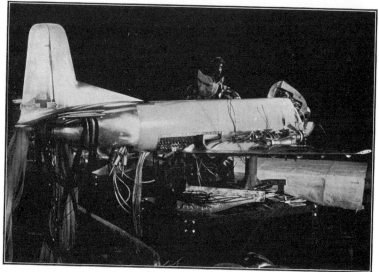

Courtesy Douglas Aircraft Co.

Fig. 5:4.   The extraordinary complexity of a pressure model is well illustrated by this YC-124B model being readied for wind-tunnel test.

flow passages. Such passages if completed could have Reynolds numbers too low for satisfactory testing. A parallel situation exists for all small excrescences: aerials, bomb racks, pitot-static tubes, and the like. They too would show such scale effect that their true effect could not be measured, and hence they are left off.

Pressure models for tests of the type described in Sect. 4:18 (see Fig. 5:4) require additional care in design and construction. Usually the pressure taps on the wing are located at 0, 1.25, 2.5, 5.0, 10.0, 15.0, 20.0, 30.0, 40, 50, 60, 70, 80, 90, 95, and 100 per cent of the chord on both upper and lower surface at several spanwise stations. This obviously necessitates a large number of tubes, which should be brought out from the model under circumstances least influencing the flow. First, however, let us consider the design of the pressure orifices themselves.

If static-pressure orifices are kept small (say about $\frac{1}{32}$ in. in diameter), negligible difference is found between drilling them perpendicular to the surface or pendicular to the chord. But it is certain that they must be absolutely flush. A copper or brass tube has a tendency to form a slight ridge as the softer wood is filed down about it. Some designers use metal strips at the section where the orifices are to be, thus avoiding the difficulties of filing dissimilar materials. An artifice practiced by the Canadian National Research Council seems a satisfactory arrangement. This embraces a solid transparent plastic plug leading down to the buried brass tubes. After the airfoil is shaped, holes are drilled down to the tubes through the plastic. As the plastic offers filing characteristics similar to those of wood, remarkable smoothness is attained. If the wings of the model are exceedingly thin, it is sometimes advantageous to put the upper-surface orifices on one wing and those for the lower surface on the other. In metal models, pressure tubes may be laid in grooves which are then peened over and filled with zinc metal spray and finally drilled at the proper station.

Though many satisfactory pressure models have been built using copper tubing, a savings in manometer fill time can usually be attained by going to annealed stainless steel tubing since, for a given (and usually critical) outside diameter, its inside diameter is a maximum. The stainless tubing is less likely to kink than copper, but it is harder to solder without an acid treatment.

Manometer fill times, which run as much as 2 minutes under some circumstances, may be estimated with good accuracy from the data in Refs. 5:12 and 5:13.

The leads from the model are most easily made of plastic tubing, which has little tendency to kink or leak and has good bending qualities. A sort of multiple tube is available that furnishes 10 leads about $\frac{1}{32}$ in. in diameter in a thin flat strip $\frac{1}{16}$ in. thick by 1 in. wide. It is hard to envision a more compact arrangement.

The connection of the model tubes to the multiple manometers is most easily made through commerically available cluster plugs. These connect 50 tubes in a leakproof trouble-free manner and save a great deal of tunnel time. It is suggested that multiple manometers be designed with 52 tubes to allow a static tube at each end and yet make full use of the standard cluster connectors.

When speed rather than accuracy is the major factor, pressure models can be made from the solid type by belting the model parallel to the airstream with strips of the multiple plastic tubing mentioned above. Holes drilled in the tubing at the selected stations enable pressures to be read at one chordwise station per tube. Actually, of course, the presence of the flat tubing alters the true contours and hence also alters the pressure distribution about the model. The error so introduced is often surprisingly small.

Though perhaps not a wind-tunnel-design criterion per se, the fact remains that wind-tunnel models have to be moved about, and, depending on their size, this may become a ticklish problem. Most tunnels have a lifting crane for moving the model into the test section, and in turn whenever possible model designers should provide an attachment near the center of gravity of the model. Some tunnels provide canvas sandbags for supporting the model when it is resting on the floor or a table.

Some sort of modeling-clay-type material is frequently needed for filling cracks, covering screw holes, and making minor contour changes. Children's modeling clay or, better, sculptors' Plastalina No. 4, will suffice for low-speed work. When extra strength or high temperatures must be considered, a stiff wax made according to the formula given below will be found excellent. The acetone and pyroxylin putties are also very good although they require a few minutes' drying time.

Tunnel Wax Formula

Beeswax	About 80% by weight
Venice turpentine	About 20% by weight
Powdered rosin	About $\frac{1}{2}$% by weight

Bring turpentine to a boil; add the rosin, and stir. Add the beeswax in small chunks and allow to melt. Stir thoroughly.

Remove from heat and pour into trays for cooling.

5:2. Planning the Test. A wind-tunnel test should be run only if (a) some new knowledge is desired and (b) the test as planned has a reasonable chance of obtaining the knowledge sought with the necessary accuracy. In view of the cost of models and tunnel time, it should be determined that the "new knowledge" does not already exist. In many cases—too many cases—a good library search could have saved both time and money.

It is hard to write specific rules for setting up a test and taking data since there are many types of tests. However, the following procedures do stand as being accepted and good. If some seem obvious to the experienced engineer, the author hastens to add that at one time or another he has seen all the rules stated below completely disregarded.

1. Check all calibration curves of new equipment before, during, and after a test. Always calibrate for the full-load range, and always use a number of loads—not a single load and the assumption that the calibration is linear.

2. Take enough points so that the loss of any one point will not hurt the fairing of the curve.

3. Always repeat the wind off zero and the wind on first point at the end of the run. Have acceptable balance "drift" limits set up before the program starts (0.1 or 0.2 per cent of maximum reading is a reasonable drift allowance).

4. Take points on base runs at every degree plus 0.5-degree readings at the stall or other points of interest. Take routine runs with 2-degree readings and 1-degree increments at the stall.

5. Check all models against their templates and check the templates. Do not hesitate to cancel a program and pay the cancellation fee if the model is not within acceptable limits. If you do, the *new* shop foreman will have future models right.

6. Be very careful when you shorten a program by omitting "irrelevant" components. For instance, changes that primarily affect the pitching moment only might lead one to read only the pitching balance. This omission would make it impossible to plot the data completely since the angle-of-attack correction is affected by the lift, which must also be known, and, indeed, if later a change to a new center of gravity seems desirable the drag values must be obtained.

Similarly reading less than six components in the interest of saving time on yaw runs can also lead to serious work-up troubles of the same nature.

7. Plan model variations of wide enough scope to bracket needed data so that interpolation rather than extrapolation is in order.

8. Whenever possible find out how others do the type of test you contemplate and profit from their experience.

9. Be clear in all instruction and data presentation. Never use the word "pressure" when "static pressure" or "total pressure" might be confused. Always use a subscript for pitching and yawing moments to indicate the axis about which they are measured.

5:3. Tunnel Occupancy Procedure. Each tunnel has a somewhat different procedure for its use, and no exact rules can be written to cover them all. Nevertheless, it may prove useful to go through a typical tunnel procurement in order to have a general familiarity with the system.

Most of the large wind tunnels are scheduled about 6 months in advance, and hence an inventor seeking to prove some new idea may be very disappointed in the delay he may be subjected to. Aircraft companies get around this trouble by regularly scheduling tests of 12 to 100 hours' duration every few weeks. Then, as their time approaches, they select from needed tests the one upon which the greatest urgency rests. As a testing time approaches, the following procedure becomes in order.

1. About 2 months before a test, the tunnel is informed of the tunnel configuration to be desired: external balance, swept strut, two-dimensional test section, etc. If the desired set-up does not meld with the other programs scheduled about that time, a shift of a week or so may be necessary to avoid excessive tunnel changes.

2. Three weeks before the test complete model drawings, stress analysis, desired tunnel operating conditions, and a preliminary run list are sent to the tunnel manager.

3. Two weeks before the test a meeting is arranged between the engineers who will supervise the test for both the tunnel and the airplane company. At this meeting any points not apparent in the pretest information may be ironed out. If corrected Mach numbers are to be run a drag curve of the model is presented to the crew chief for work-up into his operating chart.

Agreement on the special equipment to be needed is reached: shadowgraph, schlieren, manometers (number of tubes and expected pressure ranges), cameras both still and moving. If a punch-in system is used the items to be punched in and the number of significant figures involved are discussed. The realistic definition of desired accuracy should include forces and moments, angle settings, pressures, and model location, and by accepting reduced accuracy where it actually is not needed considerable savings in time and money are quite possible.

A list of plots needed and the form of the tables of data are presented. Agreement is reached on a date for the presentation of preliminary data and for the final report.

4. One week before the test the company representatives arrive with the model and commence as much of the set-up and gravity tares as is feasible outside the tunnel. There may still remain some questions about the program which must be settled before running. The representatives must do a certain amount of legwork to ascertain that all the items previously agreed upon have actually been accomplished.

5. During the last day before the test, company representatives remain on an hour alert, ready to move into the tunnel and start their test.

5:4. General Testing Procedure. Depending on the innovations incorporated and terms of the development contract or program, a new model airplane may require from one to six models (or more) and up to six different wind tunnels. A typical program is as follows:

After the preliminary layout of the proposed new airplane has been made, a "complete" model is designed and constructed. This first * model, usually of 6 to 16 per cent scale, is a breakdown model; that is, the different configurations of the airplane may be built up progressively through additions to the wing alone, enabling the relative effect of each component to be evaluated. Testing this model requires measurement of all six forces and moments: lift, drag, side force, and rolling, yawing, and pitching moments. The important criteria of maximum lift (stalling speed), minimum drag (high speed), and static stability are evaluated. The breakdown model aids in determining the exterior configuration of the airplane so that the specialized models can be designed. (See Fig. 5:5.)

The second model (after the first breakdown model there is no specific order for the additional ones) may be a small-scale spin model for determining the spin-recovery characteristics in a spin tunnel. Here the model is put into a tailspin in the vertical airstream of the tunnel, and a remotely operated mechanism moves the control surfaces as desired to bring the plane out of

---

* High-speed tests for transonic airplanes may precede the low-speed tests.

Fig. 5:5.   Breakdown of Globemaster YB-124B wind-tunnel model.   Across the top of the picture are the smooth nacelles for the power-off tests, and just ahead of the nose is the nose wheel.   Below the power-off nacelles are the power-on nacelles, each with an electric drive motor.   The main landing gear doors are between the pairs of power-on nacelles, and at the same level but farther out are the propellers.   Just above the wing leading edge are the main wheel assemblies.   The wing leading edge section has cut-outs for the nacelles and motor mounts, and at its tips are the wing-tip heaters.   The wing trailing edge section has the slot-lip ailerons removed and placed just aft of the trailing edge.   At the base of the fuselage are the elevator and rudder actuators, and just outside of them are the wing-fuselage fillets.   The tail on the left is complete with both horizontal and vertical surfaces; to its left is an alternate dorsal.   The smooth tail cone at the bottom right is for the tail-off runs.   The span of this model is approximately 8 ft.

the spin.   Moving pictures of the recovery can be examined to see whether the procedure is satisfactory.

A third model, also light and fragile, may be flown in a free-flight tunnel where moving pictures record its stability and maneuverability.

A fourth model, so constructed that its rigidity is related to the full-scale airplane, may be tested for critical flutter speed (Ref. 2:1).

If the design appears satisfactory or can be made so after these preliminary tests, larger models of component parts are tested. Aileron panels and tail surfaces to perhaps 40 per cent scale may be tested, and nacelles to a similar scale may be investigated for cooling and drag. Compressibility effects are investigated with high-speed models in high-speed tunnels. Sometimes additional section tests of the airfoils to be used are made in a two-dimensional tunnel, and if the design is entirely untested pressure distributions over the flap, flap vanes, etc., may be taken to determine design loads for the structural design.

Finally, when the first actual airplane is finished it can be tested in a full-scale tunnel for aerodynamic "clean-up" changes. Here also the manufacturing irregularities can be examined and improvements suggested. Military airplanes can be subjected to simulated battle damage so that studies can be made of possible catastrophic effects.

The cost of such a program is not small, of course. Yet, compared to the cost of building the actual airplane, testing it, and changing it, the model-testing cost becomes minor indeed. Rarely would a single concern have the entire facilities required by a complete testing program. The customary solution is for the complete model and the control surface panels to be tested in the company's own wind tunnel, leaving the spin, stability, flutter, and high Mach number work to tunnels specially designed for them.

The basic parameters of the tunnel that need direct attention before the wind is turned on include considerations of the average angle of flow, average q, and the balance loads.

The average angle of flow need not be considered before the full test of a three-dimensional wing. As shown in Sect. 4:14 it is accurately determined by the model normal and inverted tests of the alignment determination. A two-dimensional model should also be run normal and inverted. However, when inversion is not to be employed for any of a number of reasons, or when it is actually impossible as for a panel model, the procedure outlined in Sect. 3:6 may be followed for finding the average angle for a given model. A rough check may be made from the first run by comparing the expected and obtained angles of zero lift. Indeed, particularly for the panels, so much advantage accrues in the analysis of later data by assuming the models to be absolutely accurate and hence making expected and obtained angles of zero lift identical that this is the usual procedure.

As most tunnels expand somewhat with warmer weather, the mean flow angle in the tunnel may vary and should be checked at least several times a year.

The engineer who upon finding a change in the data for a second series test of a certain model proclaimed that $\alpha_{Z.L.}$ was "not where he left it" was not entirely without scientific backing.

The average dynamic pressure must be calculated for each model of different planform by a method like that for obtaining the average angle. That is, the product of local q (from the dynamic-pressure survey of the test section) and the model chord at the same station is plotted against the model span. If the area under the qc vs. span curve is then divided by the total wing area the resulting quotient is the average dynamic pressure. This average dynamic pressure is *not* used to find the various coefficients until it is increased by the blocking factor obtained from Chapter 6.

Last, but not least, a check of expected loads should be made in order to ascertain that ample provision is secured to run the entire program at one speed. Changing the tunnel speed during a program adds one more effect to the data.

1. After the first run has been made, it should be checked thoroughly against expected results. If possible, the set-up should be arranged so that the first run is simple enough for comparison with previous tests. Items to be checked include $\alpha_{Z.L.}$, $dC_L/d\alpha$, $C_{L\ max.}$, $C_{D0\ min.}$, and C_{m0}.

2. Determine the testing accuracy by:

(a) Running a test twice without any change in it at all. This tests the reproducible accuracy of the balance and the speed control.

(b) Resetting and repeating a run made previously after there have been several intervening runs. This determines the reproducible accuracy of setting the flaps, tabs, etc., as well as the accuracy of the balance and speed control.

3. Keep a running plot of all data as they come out. Any uncertain points can be substantiated immediately by taking readings at small increments above and below the uncertain ones.

4. Occasionally repeat a basic run. This will indicate any gradual model warpage or other alterations occurring with time.

5. Repeat the first reading at the end of each run. This will

indicate any control surface slippage, etc. Inspect the model frequently, checking all control settings, and wherever possible make angular measurements of controls, etc., with the inevitable slack taken out in the loaded direction.

6. Make every data sheet self-contained. Avoid using expressions such as "Same as Run 6," as this necessitates looking up Run 6. Every data sheet must contain the model designation, configuration, test speed, date, and tunnel temperature and pressure. Further data, such as effective Reynolds number and model dimensions, are valuable.

7. Keep an accurate log of everything that happens. When analyzing the data the exact point at which changes were made may be of paramount importance.

8. Always keep a run list in chronological order; never assign a number like "Run 3b" just because the later run is a check of Run 3.

The size and design of the tunnel determine the size of the model that can be accommodated and, sometimes, other important criteria such as model weight or power arrangements. Occasionally a gasoline engine can be operated in the tunnel (Ref. 5:1). The tunnel itself also determines the complexity of the model and hence its cost. The cost ranges from about $25 for the simplest small wing of 15-in. span to $165,000 for a complete four-engined bomber model using remotely operated ailerons, elevators, rudders, cowl flaps, landing gear, bomb-bay doors, and electrically driven propellers. The amount of remotely operated equipment is a function of the number of tests to be made and the type of tunnel.

5:5. Testing Three-Dimensional Wings. The first wind-tunnel tests ever made were concerned with the behavior of wings, and probably more tests are made today on this item than on any other. Much progress has been made on airfoil design, but wing design is still in its infancy. The variables of sweepback, twist, section, taper, and tips are too much for any short research program.

The foremost difficulties encountered in making wing-alone tests include the necessity of obtaining a moderately high Reynolds number (at least 2,500,000) if extrapolation to higher Reynolds numbers is to be attempted. Further, this Reynolds number should be obtained by a high-speed or large model, not by the introduction of turbulence into the airstream.

A second and serious difficulty is that the tare and inter-ference of the mounting system will be at least as large as the wing minimum drag, and extreme care must be taken if good data are to result.

Tare and interference drag can be reduced by careful engineer-ing of the supports and attachment points. (See Sect. 4:10.)

Wings that are part of a systematic airfoil research program should be made as simply as possible, preferably without taper

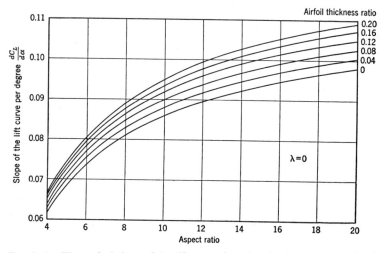

FIG. 5:6.   Theoretical slope of the lift curve for wings having a taper ratio of zero (pointed tips).

and with simple tips. Their span should be held to less than 0.8 tunnel span to avoid excessive wall effects. For most wing tests all wall corrections should be investigated.

In general the aerodynamicist will be most interested in $dC_L/d\alpha$, $C_{L\,max.}$, $\alpha_{Z.L.}$, $C_{D0\,min.}$, e, the aerodynamic center, C_{mac}, and the center of pressure. The following comments will give the tunnel engineer some feel for the problem.

(a) $dC_L/d\alpha$. The theoretical relation for the slope of the lift curve of a finite span wing has been given as eq. 10:44 of Ref. 6:39. This equation allows for the effect of the downwash at the wing (but not streamline curvature), the variation of down-wash across the span, and the Jones edge effect. For modern wings with thin boundary layers, the theoretical relations usually are slightly high (about 0.003 per degree), possibly owing to the neglect of the streamline curvature effect. For general comparison with experimental results the theoretical values are presented for a wide range of tapers and aspect ratios in Figs. 5:6–5:9. Figures covering other taper ratios and elliptic planforms may be found in Chapter 10 of Ref. 6:39.

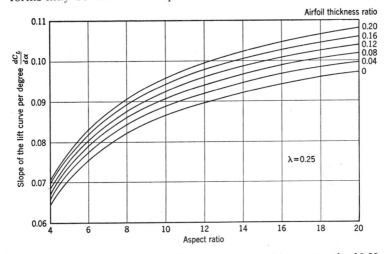

FIG. 5:7. Theoretical slope of the lift curve for wings with a taper ratio of 0.25.

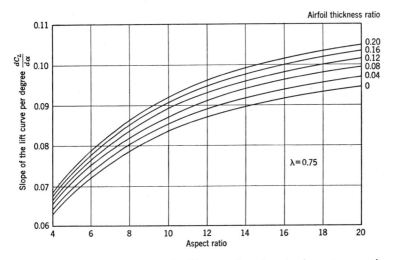

FIG. 5:8. Theoretical slope of the lift curve for wings having a taper ratio of 0.75.

A far shorter but much less accurate relation that is useful for rough approximations * is

$$\frac{dC_L}{d\alpha} = 0.1 \frac{R}{R + 2} \qquad (5:1)$$

where R = aspect ratio.

The lift curve slope decreases with sweep roughly by the cosine of the sweep angle of the quarter chord. For lift curve slopes of

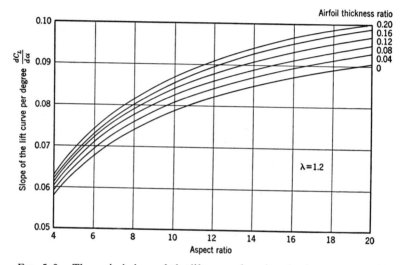

Fig. 5:9. Theoretical slope of the lift curve for wings having a taper ratio of 1.2.

swept and delta wings the latest NACA reports should be consulted.

(b) $C_{L\text{ max}}$. The maximum lift coefficient for airfoils varies from 0.6 for very thin profiles to about 1.7 for highly cambered thick profiles. In general it increases with Reynolds number. (See Chapter 7.) The wing maximum lift coefficient usually runs from 85 to 90 per cent of the airfoil values, never more than the airfoil values. Swept wings show a loss considerably more than the above values. It is a little-known but well-substantiated fact that $C_{L\text{ max}}$ is affected by Mach number even in the low-speed range around $M = 0.2$. Accordingly, comparison tests for maxi-

---

* The familiar value of 2π per radian is the theoretical slope for *thin* airfoils and is frequently exceeded in practice.

mum lift should be run at the same values of both Reynolds and Mach numbers.

(c) $\alpha_{Z.L.}$. The angle of zero lift in degrees is roughly equal to the amount of camber in per cent for airfoils and untwisted wings of constant section. It requires a considerable amount of calculation to determine $\alpha_{Z.L.}$ for a twisted wing.

(d) $C_{D0\ min.}$. The minimum coefficient of drag decreases with increasing Reynolds number (see Chapter 7) and usually has a value between 0.0050 and 0.0085 in the tunnel after the tare and interference have been subtracted.

(e) e. The customary definition of the drag coefficient

$$C_D = C_{D0\ min.} + \frac{C_L^2}{e^2 \pi R} \qquad (5:2)$$

makes the determination of the span efficiency factor e of importance. This value may be determined most easily by making a plot of C_D vs. C_L^2 (Fig. 5:10). It will appear as a straight line

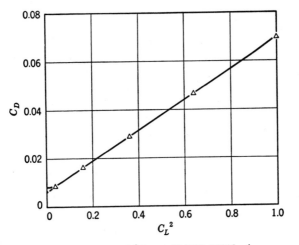

FIG. 5:10. C_D vs. C_L^2 for an NACA 23012 wing.

along the major part of the plot, with a slight bending at both the lower and higher C_L's.* The significance of the divergence from the straight line at the low lift coefficients is that $C_{D0\ min.}$

* Some of the newer airfoils may have to be broken down into two or three straight lines. When this occurs different values of e and $C_{D0\ min.}$ must be used for the appropriate range of C_L.

does not occur at $C_L = 0$ for a cambered airfoil. The divergence at the higher C_L's is due to flow separation. At any rate, the equation of the straight line (which is extended until it intersects the abscissa) is

$$C_D = C_{D0\ \text{min.}} + KC_L{}^2 \qquad (5:3)$$

and hence

$$K = \frac{1}{e^2 \pi R} \qquad (5:4)$$

and *

$$e = \sqrt{\frac{1}{K\pi R}} \qquad (5:5)$$

It has been suggested that, as the low drag coefficient indicated by the intersection of the straight line and the C_D axis does not exist in a practical sense, it should be indicated not as $C_{D0\ \text{min.}}$ but as an effective parasite drag coefficient C_{DPe}. Hence we have

$$C_D = C_{DPe} + \frac{C_L{}^2}{e^2 \pi R} \qquad (5:6)$$

The value of e as defined above will run around 0.85 to 0.95 for straight wings, and an approximate value may be found from the empirical relation

$$e = 1.00 - 0.009R \qquad (5:7)$$

where R = aspect ratio.

For swept wings of fairly low aspect ratio, rough empirical values for e may be found from

$$e = 1.00 - 0.00008\Lambda^2 \qquad (5:8)$$

where Λ = sweep angle in degrees.

It should be noted that concentrating on getting a high value for e is misplaced emphasis, since the induced drag is much more closely related to aspect ratio than to e. Carrying this philosophy a little further, the untwisted elliptic wing has the minimum induced drag (greatest e) for a given span. Yet it should never † be used because for a given wing root bending moment (wing weight) a little increase of span yields a greater aspect ratio and less drag, even though e (the so-called efficiency) is less.

---

* Many engineers use e where the author has used e^2. Watch for this.

† One exception: when maximum span has been fixed.

The above discussion has treated e as though it mostly accounted for the "loss" in not using an elliptic wing. Actually it also includes the change of profile drag with angle of attack and other miscellaneous items, but inclusion of these items does not change the conclusions given above.

Example 5:1

Values of C_L and C_D are as given in Table 5:1. Find the span efficiency factor e if $AR = 6.0$.

TABLE 5:1

α	C_L	C_D
−1.2	0.0	0.0079
0.2	0.1	0.0079
1.6	0.2	0.0090
4.3	0.4	0.0167
7.0	0.6	0.0298
9.7	0.8	0.0467
12.3	1.0	0.0673
15.1	1.2	0.0928
17.9	1.4	0.1260

From a plot of C_D vs. C_L^2, the slope, K, is found to be 0.0611. Hence

$$e = \sqrt{\frac{1}{K\pi R}} = \sqrt{\frac{1}{0.0611\pi \cdot 6}}$$

$$e = 0.932$$

It is also noted that $C_{DPe} = 0.0064$.

(f) Location of the aerodynamic center may be computed as follows.* Consider a wing mounted so that the axis of rotation is at some point behind and below the probable location of the aerodynamic center (Fig. 5:11). (The aerodynamic center is

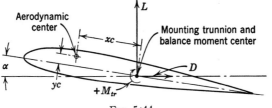

FIG. 5:11.

* A second method of calculating the location of the aerodynamic center is given in the appendix of NACA *TR* 627.

defined as the point about which the moment coefficient is constant. Let the distance along the chord from the trunnion to the aerodynamic center be x_1, and let the distance above the trunnion be y_1. Both x_1 and y_1 are measured in fractions of the MAC. *

It will be seen that

$$M_{ac} = M_{tr} - x_1 c(L \cos \alpha + D \sin \alpha$$
$$- y_1 c(D \cos \alpha - L \sin \alpha) \quad (5:9)$$

where M_{tr} = the moment measured about the mounting trunnion. Hence

$$C_{mac} = C_{mtr} - x_1(C_L \cos \alpha + C_D \sin \alpha)$$
$$- y_1(C_D \cos \alpha - C_L \sin \alpha) \quad (5:10)$$

Applying the condition that C_{mac} does not vary with C_L we get

$$\frac{dC_{mac}}{dC_L} = 0 = \frac{dC_{mtr}}{dC_L} -$$

$$\left[\left(1 + C_D \frac{d\alpha}{dC_L}\right) \cos \alpha + \left(\frac{dC_D}{dC_L} - C_L \frac{d\alpha}{dC_L}\right) \sin \alpha \right] x_1 -$$

$$\left[\left(\frac{dC_D}{dC_L} - C_L \frac{d\alpha}{dC_L}\right) \cos \alpha - \left(1 + C_D \frac{d\alpha}{dC_L}\right) \sin \alpha \right] y_1 \quad (5:11)$$

The data may easily be used to find C_L, C_D, α, and also the slopes dC_{mtr}/dC_L and $d\alpha/dC_L$ since they are straight lines. The determination of dC_D/dC_L is difficult, for it is a curve.

If the wing efficiency factor has been determined, dC_D/dC_L may be found directly from

$$C_D = C_{D0\ min.} + \frac{C_L^2}{e^2 \pi R}$$

$$\frac{dC_D}{dC_L} = \frac{2C_L}{e^2 \pi R} \quad (5:12)$$

If information for the above equation is not available, the slope of the drag curve at the proper point may be obtained by

* The mean aerodynamic chord may be found from

$$MAC = \frac{2}{3}\left(C_T + C_R - \frac{C_T C_R}{C_T + C_R}\right)$$

where C_T = wing tip chord; C_R = wing root chord.

the familiar mirror method. In this method a small hand mirror is set directly on the plotted curve and adjusted until the reflected curve appears as a smooth continuation of the original. Under these conditions the plane of the mirror will be perpendicular to the drag curve at the selected C_L, and the drag-curve slope may then be computed.

Equation 5:11, having two unknowns, requires the substitution of two points and then the simultaneous solution of the resulting equations. The approximation of measuring dC_D/dC_L may be eliminated for one of these points by selecting for the point the angle at which C_D is a minimum. At this point, obviously, $dC_D/dC_L = 0$.

Example 5:2

Find the aerodynamic center of an airfoil whose tests yield the data in Table 5:2. The mounting trunnion is at the 49 per cent chord point and 5.0 per cent below the chord line.

TABLE 5:2

α	C_L	C_D	C_{mtr}
−2	−0.086	0.0120	−0.023
0	0.111	0.0095	0.024
2	0.326	0.0087	0.079
4	0.531	0.0096	0.131
6	0.737	0.0138	0.183
8	0.943	0.0195	0.231
10	1.118	0.0267	0.281
12	1.260	0.0369	0.317

Plots of the data yield $dC_{mtr}/dC_L = 0.254$.

$$dC_L/d\alpha = 0.1025 \text{ per degree}$$

$$= 5.87 \text{ per radian}$$

At $\alpha = 2.3°$, $C_L = 0.34$, $C_{D0 \text{ min.}} = 0.0084$, and $dC_D/dC_L = 0$.

At $\alpha = 8.8°$, $C_L = 1.00$, $C_D = 0.0210$, and by the mirror method $dC_D/dC_L = 0.048$.

Substituting into eq. 5:11, we have:

$$\left[\left(1 + C_D \frac{d\alpha}{dC_L}\right) \cos\alpha + \left(\frac{dC_D}{dC_L} - C_L \frac{d\alpha}{dC_L}\right) \sin\alpha \right] x_1$$

$$+ \left[\left(\frac{dC_D}{dC_L} + C_L \frac{d\alpha}{dC_L}\right) \cos\alpha - \left(1 + C_D \frac{d\alpha}{dC_L}\right) \sin\alpha \right] y_1 = \frac{dC_{mtr}}{dC_L}$$

$$\left[\left(1 + \frac{0.0084}{5.87}\right)(0.999) + \left(0 - \frac{0.34}{5.87}\right)(0.0401)\right] x_1$$

$$+ \left[0 - \frac{0.34}{5.87}(0.999) - \left(1 + \frac{0.0084}{5.87}(0.0401)\right)\right] y_1 = 0.254$$

and

$$\left[\left(1 + \frac{0.0210}{5.87}\right)(0.988) + \left(0.048 - \frac{1.0}{5.87}\right)(0.153)\right] x_1$$

$$+ \left[\left(0.048 - \frac{1.0}{5.87}\right)(0.988) - \left(1 + \frac{0.0210}{5.87}\right)(0.153)\right] y_1 = 0.254$$

These equations simplify to

$$0.99811x_1 + 0.0178y_1 = 0.254$$

$$0.9728x_1 + 0.0645y_1 = 0.254$$

and hence

$$x_1 = 0.252$$

$$y_1 = 0.136$$

The aerodynamic center is $25 - (49.0 - 25.2) = 1.2$ per cent ahead of the quarter chord point, and $(5.0 - 13.6) = 8.6$ per cent above the chord.

In order to save time in locating the aerodynamic center, the assumption is sometimes made that the moment is due entirely to the lift and that the aerodynamic center is on the chord line. Since the lift and drag act through the aerodynamic center, the moment about the trunnion is

$$M_{tr} = M_{ac} + L(tr - ac)c \qquad (5{:}13)$$

where M_{ac} = moment about the aerodynamic center, and tr = chordwise location of the balance trunnion.

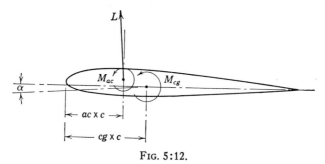

Fig. 5:12.

Rewriting eq. 5:13 in coefficient form, we have

$$C_{mtr} = C_{mac} + C_L(tr - ac) \qquad (5{:}14)$$

and differentiating and transposing $(dC_{mac}/dC_L = 0)$

$$ac = tr - dC_{mtr}/dC_L \qquad (5{:}15)$$

The aerodynamic center is theoretically a small amount behind the quarter chord. In practice, it is found ahead of the quarter chord for the older profiles and behind for the newer profiles.

Example 5:2a

Calculate the location of the aerodynamic center for the data of example 5:2, using eq. 5:14.

1. From a plot of C_{mtr} vs. C_L,

$$dC_{mtr}/dC_L = 0.254$$

2. Substituting the trunnion location and dC_{mtr}/dC_L in eq. 5:15 we have $ac = 0.49 - 0.254 = 0.236$. This compares with 0.241 by the method of eq. 5:11.

Equation 5:14 indicates that, when $C_L = 0$, $C_{mac} = C_{mtr}$. In other words, the value of the moment coefficient at the point where the curve strikes the C_L axis is approximately the value of C_{mac}. Rather than call it that, the usual practice is to label the above intersection C_{m0}.

(g) After the location of the aerodynamic center has been obtained the moment coefficient about it may be found from

$$C_{mac} = C_{mtr} - x_1(C_L \cos \alpha + C_D \sin \alpha)$$
$$- y_1(C_D \cos \alpha - C_L \sin \alpha) \quad (5{:}16)$$

C_{mac} varies with the amount and shape of the camber line. It is about zero for symmetrical wings; -0.007 for a 23012; and -0.07 for a Clark Y. Flap-down values may exceed -1.0.

Example 5:3

Calculate the C_{mac} for example 5:2.

Substituting each point into eq. 5:10 we have the data shown in Table 5:3.

TABLE 5:3

α	C_{mac}	α	C_{mac}
−2	−0.001	6	0.000
0	−0.003	8	−0.001
2	−0.002	10	0.000
4	−0.002	12	0.000

It is not unusual to find some small spread in the values of C_{mac}, although strictly speaking the definition states that it must be constant.

It is a surprising fact that the location of the aerodynamic center is practically unchanged by flaps. The explanation lies in the manner in which the moment is generated:

$$C_{m\ total} = C_{m\ due\ to\ changing\ \alpha} + C_{m\ due\ to\ camber}$$

As indicated by theory, the C_m due to changing α is constant about the quarter chord. The C_m due to camber is a constant about the half chord. Hence adding camber in the form of flaps merely increases the value of C_{mac} without changing the location of the aerodynamic center as determined by changing α.

(h) The center of pressure is defined as "that point on the chord of an airfoil through which the resultant force acts." Though its usefulness has declined with the introduction of the concept of the aerodynamic center, it must occasionally be determined from force tests. (See Sect. 4:18 for determining the center of pressure by the pressure-distribution method.) The procedure is as follows:

The forces measured appear as a lift force L, a drag force D, and a moment about the mounting trunnion M_{tr} (Fig. 5:13). At

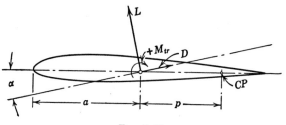

FIG. 5:13.

the point through which the resultant force acts, the moment vanishes. Hence

$$M_{CP} = 0 = M_{tr} + L(p \cos \alpha) + D(p \sin \alpha)$$

where p is the distance from the trunnion to the center of pressure, positive to the rear of the trunnion.

We then have

$$-C_{mtr} = C_L(p/c) \cos \alpha + C_D(p/c) \sin \alpha = 0$$

and

$$\frac{p}{c} = \frac{-C_{mtr}}{C_L \cos \alpha + C_D \sin \alpha}$$

The location of the center of pressure from the wing leading edge is then

$$CP = (p/c) + (a/c) \qquad (5{:}17)$$

Example 5:4

A wing is mounted with the trunnion at the 23.5 per cent chord point. At $\alpha = 7.3$, $C_L = 0.6$, $C_D = 0.0320$, $C_{mtr} = -0.011$. Find the center of pressure.

$$\frac{p}{c} = \frac{-C_{mtr}}{C_L \cos \alpha + C_D \sin \alpha} = \frac{0.011}{(0.6)(0.9919) + (0.0320)(0.127)}$$

$$= 0.0184$$

$$CP = 0.0184 + 0.235 = 0.253 = 25.3\%$$

5:6. Testing Two-Dimensional Wings. Alterations to airfoil sections are frequently investigated in two-dimensional tunnels wherein a short constant chord section of a wing completely spans the jet width (Fig. 5:14), simulating infinite aspect ratio. The jet is usually $2\frac{1}{2}$ to 4 times higher than it is wide. In most tunnels of this type the drag is read by the momentum survey method, and the lift by the pressure on the tunnel walls (Sect. 4:16). The pitching moment may also be read from the pressure on the tunnel walls, but in many cases the wing is mounted on trunnions and the moment is read with a simple beam balance. The proportionately large drag of two endplates prohibits accurate drag measurements by the usual force tests and complicates the endplate seal.

As the models customarily used in two-dimensional tunnels are larger in proportion to jet size than others, corrections for constriction, buoyancy, and camber must be considered (Chapter 6). Excessive errors due to wall effect will arise in $c_{l\,max.}$ if the model chord exceeds $0.4h$ and in $c_{d0\,min.}$ if it exceeds $0.7h$, where h is the tunnel height.

The information obtained from two-dimensional tests will be reducible to section coefficients c_l, c_{d0}, and $c_{m\frac{1}{4}}$. These coefficients (unlike wing coefficients C_L, C_D, and $C_{m\frac{1}{4}}$, which are an average of conditions including varying Reynolds number and effective angles of attack across the span) consider only a section under constant load and hence constant effective angle of attack. It is customary to consider the minimum profile drag coefficient C_{D0} as equivalent to c_{d0} when both are at the same Reynolds number. Likewise, it is assumed that $C_{mac} = c_{mac}$. The lift coefficients c_l and C_L may also be considered equal except at their maximum, where the spanwise lift distribution usually results in a diminution in lift of at least 5 to 10 per cent for straight wings. Expressed symbolically,

$$C_{L\ max.} = 0.90c_{l\ max.} \quad \text{(approximately)} \quad (5:18)$$

It has been found difficult to apply data made with a two-dimensional set-up to three-dimensional wings because spanwise

Official Photograph, National Advisory Committee for Aeronautics.

Fig. 5:14.   Model in a two-dimensional jet.

pressure gradients frequently induce spanwise flow and invalidate the purely chordwise information.   Yet the two-dimensional tunnel, by simplifying model construction and increasing the speed of testing and work-up of data, has an important place in the field of aeronautical research.   Reduction of lift, drag, and moment data is covered in Chapter 6.

The location of the aerodynamic center and the center of pressure may be calculated as discussed in Sect. 5:5 (*f*) and (*h*).

The slope of the lift curve of a two-dimensional wing will suffer from four effects when extrapolated to the finite case.

1. Losses associated with downwash at the wing due to the trailing vortex system, both average flow direction and a stream-line curvature effect.

2. Losses associated with variation of angle of attack across the span if the wing is not elliptic and untwisted.

3. Losses associated with the fact that some air now goes around the wing and not over it (Jones edge effect).

4. Losses associated with varying Reynolds number due to taper.

5:7. Testing Component Parts of an Airplane. The testing of large-scale models of part of an airplane offers many advantages provided that the data can be properly applied to the airplane. Nacelles, tail surfaces, dive brakes, and ailerons are items belonging in this group.

To take a concrete example, models of 8-ft span are about the maximum usually tested in a 10-ft tunnel. If the original ship has a wing span of 80 ft the largest model that can be tested will be $\frac{1}{10}$ scale. This reduction in size makes it nearly impossible to reproduce small items accurately; their Reynolds number will be very small; and it will be exceedingly difficult to measure the hinge moments of control surfaces. A 30 per cent model of the vertical tail could be tested as well as a 30 per cent aileron model, but, if such large-scale panel models are to be employed, they must of course be tested under flow conditions that simulate those on the complete airplane. Mounting the panel like a complete wing (Fig. 4:20) permits an endflow about the inboard tip not actually existent on the real airplane. Such flow may easily invalidate the test results, and unfortunately even the addition of an endplate will not provide sufficient sealing to produce complete ship flow conditions.

Two alternative arrangements are satisfactory: mounting the panel on a turntable (Fig. 5:15), or with a small gap (less than 0.005 span) between its inboard end and the tunnel floor (Fig. 4:19). Either of these set-ups will seal the inboard end of the panel and subject it to nearly the same flow conditions as would occur on the actual ship. Usually the effective aspect ratio then developed will be about $0.95(2b)^2/(2S_p)$, where b is the panel span and S_p the panel area.

An important and sometimes insoluble problem may arise for aileron panels from sweptback wings. Here the flow over the aileron is affected very strongly by the remainder of the wing and

cannot be simulated by any simple reflection plane. It is therefore suggested that a thorough study of spanwise loadings be
made and adequate correlation assured before attempting panel
tests of such ailerons. A full half-span model is satisfactory.

Courtesy the Glenn L. Martin Aircraft Co.

FIG. 5:15.   Aileron panel in wind tunnel.

A minor point in panel testing of the type shown in Figs. 4:19
and 5:15 is that, though the hinge moments should be reduced
to coefficient form by using the tunnel dynamic pressure, the
force coefficients should be based on tunnel dynamic pressure corrected to allow for the diminished velocity in the boundary layer.
This corrected q is usually about 99 per cent of the centerline q.

Minimum confusion in applying the test data will result if the panel is selected so that positive tunnel directions are positive airplane directions. Thus a left panel should be mounted on a right wall,* and a right panel on a left wall. Floor-mounted models should be left airplane panels.

In selecting the panel span the inboard juncture of aileron or flaps should not occur at the floor but a few inches above it.

Owing to asymmetry much of the panel data will require that the loads from the panel with flap or aileron zero be subtracted from those with surface deflected in order to determine the contribution of the control. Obviously, since the surface zero data are to be repeatedly used only very good data should be used for the base run, but good data are not always obtainable. For instance, the deflection of the surface will cause a change of lift and hence a change in wall correction angle. The proper basic coefficient should be obtained from curves of surface zero data plotted against corrected angle of attack. The problem is further confused by the fact that the surface deflected may allow greater angles of attack than the surface zero run and no basic data can exist for the entire range.

Details of the calculations necessary for referring panel tests of ailerons, rudders, and elevators to the complete ship are given in the following sections.

5:8. Testing Controls: Aileron Panels. The airplane designer is interested in three items concerning proposed ailerons. One, rolling moment, he is seeking. The other two, yawing moment and hinge moment, are the price that must be paid. The tunnel engineer in addition is concerned with referring the data to the complete airplane. The problem first apparent is that the panel model will not have the same lift curve slope as the complete wing. Actually, however, this is of small import as long as the roll due to a given aileron deflection is at a known wing lift coefficient. This, it will be shown, requires that the complete wing be previously tested and its lift curve known and available. The procedure for then referring the aileron panel angles of attack to the complete wing is as follows:

1. From the estimated performance of the airplane, note the speeds that correspond to various important flight conditions such as top and cruising speeds at various altitudes. Calculate the complete wing lift coefficients that correspond to these speeds.

* Not upside-down on a left wall.

2. Plot the span loading curve. (See below.) The total area under this curve, A_T, divided by the total wing area S_T is a measure of the wing lift coefficient. Likewise, the area of that part of span loading curve above the panel span A_p when divided by the area of the wing panel S_p is a measure of the panel lift coefficient. The ratio of these two ratios, then, is the ratio of the complete wing lift coefficient C_{Lw} to the panel lift coefficient C_{Lp}. That is,

$$\frac{C_{Lw}}{C_{Lp}} = \frac{A_T/S_T}{A_p/S_p} \tag{5:19}$$

Equation 5:19 may be used to find the panel lift coefficients that correspond to the selected wing lift coefficients.

3. Test the panel with aileron zero and obtain a plot of C_{Lp} vs. α_u, where α_u is the angle of attack uncorrected for tunnel-wall effect.

4. From item 3, read the uncorrected angles that should be set to read the desired panel lift coefficients. The tunnel operator may then set these uncorrected angles with arbitrary aileron deflections and maintain proper panel model to complete model correlation.

The span loading as required above may be simply found by a method proposed by Schrenk (Ref. 5:8), or by one proposed by Pearson (Ref. 5:9). Schrenk's method for untwisted wings without flaps is as follows:

1. Plot the wing chord against the span.

2. On the same graph, plot a quarter ellipse whose area is equal to half the wing area, and whose span equals the wing span.

3. The span loading will be represented by a line midway between 1 and 2. (See Fig. 5:16.)

The data for an aileron test require some special consideration, for three reasons: the structural loss due to cable stretch and wing twist; the carry-over arising from the wall reflection simulating a symmetrical case (see Sect. 6:26); and the doubled force increments arising from the same source. Cable stretch and wing twist are problems that must be evaluated by the structural engineers for a particular airplane. Assuming that the carry-over is small, one is fully justified in using the measured force data (corrected for wall effects and blocking) for computing the rolling and yawing moments about the ship centerline. But, if one is interested in the complete wing lift, drag, and pitching moment, the measured data, including as they do the full reflection, are too large. In other words a 50-lb lift increment ($\Delta C_L = 0.1$, say) for one aileron down is not a 100-lb increment ($\Delta C_L = 0.1$) when the whole wing is considered since the image aileron should not

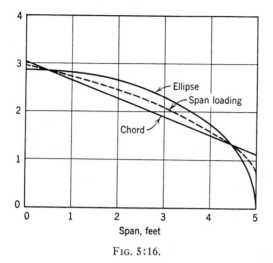

Fig. 5:16.

be down. Thus, letting a subscript p mean aileron down, and o mean control neutral, wing data for an unsymmetrical model may be found from

$$C_L = \frac{C_{Lo} + C_{Lp}}{2} \tag{5:20}$$

$$C_D = \frac{C_{Do} + C_{Dp}}{2} \tag{5:21}$$

$$C_m = \frac{C_{mo} + C_{mp}}{2} \tag{5:22}$$

The roll and yaw data may be treated as outlined below.

In testing one panel of a wing, it is seen that a yawing and rolling moment about the imaginary ship centerline is produced that in actuality would be canceled by the panel on the other side. Thus it is necessary to subtract the moments due to the panel with aileron zero from the moments with the aileron deflected. The subtraction also acts to remove the tare effects of the turntable, the net result being the yawing and rolling moments due to the deflection of the aileron only. The only proviso is that the test conditions must simulate the proper spanwise loading over the aileron.

In working up the data, the coefficients must be corrected to complete wing areas and spans so that the results will be usable. The definitions are as follows (the subscript p indicates "panel"):

$$C_{Lp} = \frac{L_p}{qS_p} \quad \text{panel lift coefficient}$$

$$C_{D'p} = \frac{D'}{qS_p} \quad \text{panel drag coefficient including mounting plate drag}$$

$$C_{np} = \frac{YM_p}{qS_w b_w} \quad \text{panel yawing moment coefficient}$$

$$C_{lp} = \frac{RM_p}{qS_w b_w} \quad \text{panel rolling moment coefficient about balance rolling axis, based on wing area and span.}$$

To get the rolling moment at the ship centerline we have (Fig. 5:17)

$$RM_{\text{ship}} = RM_p + La'$$

and

$$C_{l'\text{ship}} = C_{lp} + C_{Lp} \frac{S_p}{S_w} \frac{a'}{b_w} \qquad (5:23)$$

where a' is the distance from balance rolling moment axis to airplane centerline.

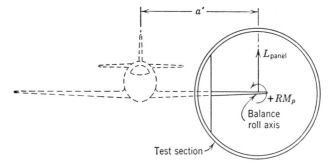

Fig. 5:17.   Panel rolling moment and its relation to the rest of the airplane.
(Front view.)

However, this represents the moment of one panel plus the aileron about the ship centerline; to find the part due to the aileron only, we subtract the rolling moment coefficient of the

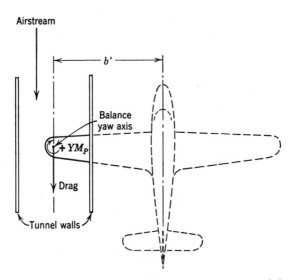

FIG. 5:18. Panel yawing moment and its relation to the rest of the airplane. (Plan view.)

panel with aileron zero, C_{l0}. Hence the rolling moment coefficient of one aileron about the airplane centerline is

$$C_l = C_{lp} + C_{Lp}\frac{S_p}{S_w}\frac{a'}{b_w} - C_{l0} \qquad (5:24)$$

By a similar process, the yawing moment coefficient due to one aileron is

$$C_n = C_{np} - C_{D'p}\frac{S_p}{S_w}\frac{b'}{b_w} - C_{n0} \qquad (5:25)$$

where $C_{np} = YM_p/qS_wb_w$; b' = distance of balance yaw axis to ship; C_{n0} = yawing moment coefficient of one panel about ship centerline, aileron zero.

For structural purposes, or a check of the spanwise load calculations, the lateral center of pressure may be found by dividing the semi-span rolling moment about the airplane axis of symmetry by the lift.

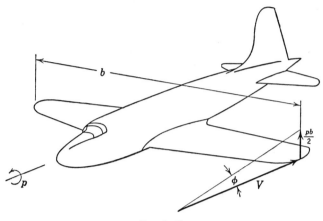

FIG. 5:19.

Although not directly apparent, the rolling moment coefficient also determines the helix angle (see Fig. 5:19) as follows:

At a given rate of steady roll the rolling moment is opposed by an equal and opposite damping moment. In the usual symbols, the rolling moment

$$RM = (\rho/2)SV^2C_l b = DM$$

where DM = damping moment. Dividing through by the helix angle, $pb/2V$ (p = rolling velocity, radians per second),

$$DM = \frac{pb}{2V}\frac{\rho}{2}SV^2 b \frac{C_l}{pb/2V} = \frac{\rho}{2}SVp \frac{b^2}{2}\frac{dC_l}{d(pb/2V)}$$

The term $\dfrac{d(C_l)}{d(pb/2V)}$ is called the damping moment coefficient (frequently written C_{lp}) and is a function of wing taper and aspect ratio, both of which are constant for a given airplane. Values of C_{lp} may be found in Fig. 5:20. The helix angle is then *

$$\frac{pb}{2V} = \frac{C_l}{C_{lp}} \qquad\qquad (5:26)$$

and the rolling velocity is

$$p = \frac{2V}{b}\frac{C_l}{C_{lp}} \qquad\qquad (5:27)$$

* Equation 5:26 applies only to roll without yaw or sideslip and can be misleading at high angles of attack where adverse yaw in flight may be appreciable.

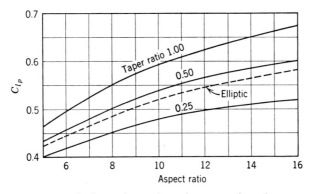

FIG. 5:20. C_{lp} for various values of aspect ratio and taper.

The maximum rolling velocity is usually limited by stick force considerations rather than by the airplane's actual ability to roll. Power-driven controls as well as aerodynamic balances to decrease the hinge moments are used to increase the rolling velocity.

Example 5:5

Data from a test run at $q = 25.6$ lb/ft^2 on a wing panel of 12 ft^2 yields $C_L = 0.789$, $C_D = 0.0599$ at $\alpha = 5.44°$, left aileron down 15°. (Data have been corrected for tunnel-wall effect.) $C_{lp} = -0.0102$, $C_{np} = -0.0010$. Find the rolling and yawing moments about the ship centerline if the distance from the balance roll axis to the ship centerline is 8 ft.   The rolling moment for aileron zero is $C_{l0} = 0.0191$, and yawing moment, $C_{n0} = -0.0028$. $S_w = 70$ ft^2, $b_w = 25$ ft.

$$C_l = C_{lp} + C_{Lp}\frac{S_p}{S_w}\frac{a'}{b_w} - C_{lp0}$$

$$= -0.0102 + 0.789\frac{12}{70}\frac{8}{25} - 0.0191$$

$$= -0.0102 + 0.0433 - 0.0191 = 0.0140$$

$$C_n = C_{np} + C_{D'p}\frac{S_p}{S_w}\frac{b'}{b_w} - C_{np0}$$

$$= -0.0010 - 0.0599\frac{12}{70}\frac{8}{25} + 0.0028$$

$$= -0.0015$$

Example 5:6

Assume that sufficient control force exists to develop the above C_l at 150 mph. Calculate the helix angle and rate of roll. The wing taper ratio is 2:1 ($\lambda = 0.50$), and the model is 40 per cent scale.

1. $AR = \dfrac{b^2}{S} = \dfrac{25^2}{70} = 8.93$. From Fig. 5:10 at $AR = 8.93$ and $\lambda = 0.50$,

$$C_{lp} = 0.520$$

$$\frac{pb}{2V} = \frac{C_l}{C_{lp}} = \frac{0.014}{0.520} = 0.0269 \text{ radian}$$

2. $p = \dfrac{pb}{2V} \dfrac{2V}{b} 57.3$

$\qquad = 0.0269 \dfrac{(2)(150)(1.47)}{25/0.40} 57.3$

$\qquad = 10.9°/\text{sec.}$

Typical data that might be expected from tests of a modern aileron are shown in Figs. 5:21, 5:22, and 5:23. The roll vs. yaw plot is particularly useful when figuring ratios for differential ailerons.

Perhaps at this point it would be fitting to discuss the lateral axis more fully in order to explain the reaction obtained before and during a roll. Consider the case when the ailerons are deflected, but no roll has yet had time to develop, or perhaps an asymmetrical span loading is being resisted. The down aileron creates more lift and induced drag and usually more profile drag, whereas the opposite effect is noticed for the up aileron. The net result is a yawing moment opposite in sign to the rolling moment: left yaw for right aileron. This condition is undesirable, of course; in many planes the pilot merely adds a slight extra rudder deflection and never notices the aileron effect. In others, particularly where powered ailerons are employed to obtain the maximum deflections, the amount of rudder needed to balance the adverse yaw may be so large that little rudder is left to overcome additional asymmetrical drag caused by the inactivity of one engine. Many methods are suggested for balancing this adverse yaw, among them being an artifically increased profile drag of the raised aileron, which tends to pull the lowered wing into the turn. Such a profile-drag increase can be obtained either by a special aileron design or by gearing the aileron controls so that the raised aileron has a greater deflection than the depressed one. The latter system is referred to as "differential ailerons." Differential ailerons reduce adverse yaw but are usually accompanied by an overall reduction in maximum rate of roll.

The designer, therefore, notes not only the maximum amount of roll ($C_{l\ max.}$) from graphs such as Fig. 5:21 but also examines

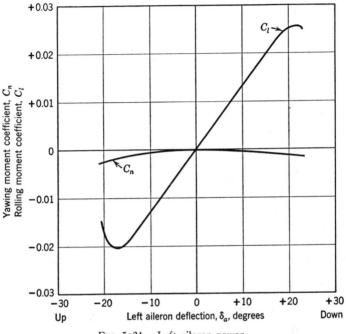

FIG. 5:21.   Left aileron power.

data such as are shown in Fig. 5:22 to observe the amount of adverse yaw, a minimum being desirable. Since nose left yaw is negative and right roll positive, the yaw is adverse when it has an opposite sign to the roll.

Now we come to a point *important* to the tunnel engineer. Referring to Fig. 5:22 again we note that, when the curve appears in the first and third quadrants, favorable yaw is indicated, but it will actually exist only when the airplane does not roll. When rolling occurs the direction of the relative wind over each wing is so altered that a strong adverse yaw is developed, and the results of the static tunnel test may be entirely erroneous.

Under most conditions, the air loads on the ailerons oppose their deflection, producing a moment that must be supplied by the pilot or by some outside means. Methods employed to help the pilots include powered "boosters" and mass and aerodynamic balance. The mass balances may only balance the weight of the surface or may be arranged to provide an inertia force while the ship is rotating. The aerodynamic balances include control surface area ahead of the hinge of various cross-sectional shapes

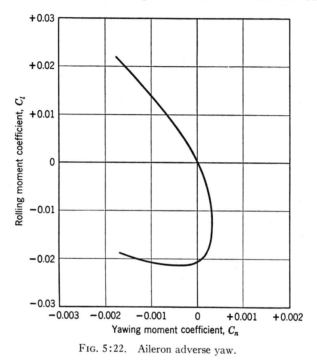

FIG. 5:22. Aileron adverse yaw.

and area disposition such as horns, shielded horns, and internal, medium nose, and sharp nose balances. They may also include various devices aft of the hinge line such as balance tabs and beveled trailing edges.

Aerodynamic balances are simpler and lighter than mass balances or power boost and hence are to be preferred as long as battle damage or icing need not be considered. Unfortunately, most aerodynamic balances are effective for only a portion of the aileron travel, as may be seen by the extent of the decreased slope in Fig. 5:23. A measure of balance superiority is then the range of decreased hinge moments as well as the slope of the balanced part of the curve. Complete aileron data must, of

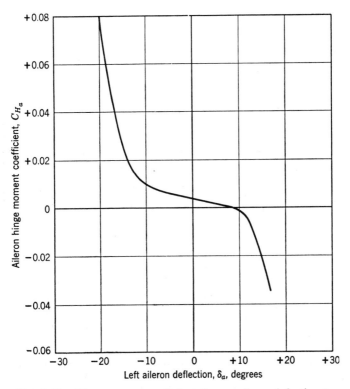

FIG. 5:23. Hinge moment coefficient C_{Ha} vs. aileron deflection δ_a.

course, include the effect of the other aileron as well as the amount of the differential decided upon.

The aileron hinge moment coefficient C_{Ha} is frequently defined by

$$C_{Ha} = \frac{HM}{qS_a c_a} \qquad (5:28)$$

where HM = aileron hinge moment, positive when it aids control deflection; S_a = area of aileron aft of hinge line; c_a = average chord of aileron aft of hinge line.

Another definition of the hinge moment is based on using the root-mean-square chord aft of the hinge as follows:

$$C_{Ha} = \frac{HM}{q\bar{c}_f{}^2 b_f}$$

where $\bar{c}_f$ = root-mean-square chord of flap or aileron aft of the hinge; b_f = flap or aileron span.

The quantity $\bar{c}_f^2 b_f$ is most easily obtained by integrating the area under the curve of local flap chord squared against flap span.

The variance of definitions again demonstrates the necessity of clear and complete statements on every item.

Complete consideration of hinge moments must include the lever ratio of the controls. Various limiting conditions may be imposed. One is that maximum aileron deflection must be obtained from combat speed to stall with a 50-lb stick or wheel force; another, that maximum wheel deflection should be limited to 100 degrees.* The second usually limits the use of gearing as a means of reducing wheel forces.

Sometimes ailerons and even airplanes are compared by the rolling velocity obtained at some particular altitude and airspeed with a 50-lb stick force. Plots of wheel movement vs. rolling velocity at various airspeeds may be made.

In closing this section on ailerons it may be noted that the spoilers used to allow larger flaps areas frequently show negative action for the first few degrees of deflection. A simple cure for this trouble is to arrange the linkage so that about 5 degrees of aileron is realized before the spoiler starts. Its irregularity then only shows up as a wiggle in the total roll and hinge moment curves.

Example 5:7

An airplane has the following specifications:

W = 40,000 lb.	At $-10°$ aileron, C_{Ha} = 0.0188.
S = 755 sq ft.	b = 71.5 ft.
$S_{\text{ail.}}$ = 17.43 sq ft.	Aileron chord aft of hinge = 1.426 ft.
Wheel radius = 0.625 ft.	$\dfrac{\text{Wheel throw}}{\text{Aileron deflection}}$ = 3.33.
Aileron differential = 1:1.	
At $+10°$ aileron, C_{Ha} = -0.0089.	

Calculate the wheel force (one hand) necessary to deflect the ailerons 10 degrees at 262 mph indicated airspeed.

* Owing to aileron cable stretch, the calculated aileron deflection for a given wheel deflection may not be attained. The engineer must consider this in his design.

The total hinge moment coefficient due to both ailerons

$$C_{Ha} = 0.0188 - (-0.0089) = 0.0277$$

$$M_{ail.} = qS_aC_aC_{Ha} = (175.2)(17.43)(1.426)(0.0277)$$

$$= 120.5 \text{ lb-ft}$$

$$\text{Wheel moment} = \frac{120.5}{3.33} = 36.2 \text{ lb-ft}$$

$$\text{Wheel force} = \frac{36.2}{0.625} = 58.0 \text{ lb}$$

5:9. Testing Controls: Rudders. The rudder is supposed to produce a side force that in turn produces a yawing moment about the center of gravity of the airplane. This may or may not produce yaw, for the lateral loading may be asymmetrical and the rudder employed only to maintain a straight course. Some drag, a small moment about the quarter-chord line of the tail itself, some roll, and a rudder hinge moment will also be created. The fact that the drag moment is stabilizing is no argument in favor of a large vertical tail drag, since, in maintaining a straight course with asymmetrical loading, drag is decidedly harmful.

The designer of a vertical tail seeks:

1. A large side force with minimum drag.

2. The steepest slope to the side force curve so that small yaw produces large stabilizing forces.

3. The smallest hinge moment consistent with positive control feel. On a full-scale military ship 180 lb pedal force is considered a maximum.

4. Proper rudder balance so that under no conditions will the pilot be unable to return the rudder to neutral, and preferably it should not even tend to overbalance.

5. A zero trail angle * so that control-free stability is the same as control-fixed stability. It will be seen that the zero trail angle permits smaller pedal forces and rudder movements to return a yawed ship to zero.

6. The largest yawing moments about the airplane's center of gravity. This moment is almost entirely due to the side force. The proportions due to the yawing moment of the vertical tail about its own quarter chord and the yawing moment of the

---

* For zero trail angle the rudder is so balanced that it remains at a zero deflection even when the airplane is yawed.

vertical tail surface due to its drag are quite small but not always insignificant.

The rudder calculations, unlike the aileron panel tests, will require the absolute value of the drag coefficient. (See eq. 5:29.) This is not easily obtained with a panel test, but, in view of the small contribution of the drag effect, an approximation may be made by reading the section drags with a wake survey rake at

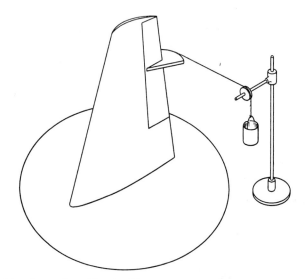

Fig. 5:24.   Set-up for calibrating hinge moment strain gages on a panel model. For quick checks a good spring scale is convenient.

stations along the vertical tail with the rudder angle zero, and by summing them to get the total drag coefficient. This may be subtracted from the minimum drag as read by the balance to get the drag of the endplate. The method as outlined makes the very questionable assumption that the tare drag is unaffected by rudder angle, which is justified only by the peculiar conditions of this set-up in which tare accuracy is not vital.

The signs of the rudder angles are confusing and hence are stated below. They follow the rule for right aileron, elevator, and rudder that positive control angle produces negative airplane movement. Negative movement embraces left roll, nose left yaw, and dive. Another definition for control deflections is that they are positive if the air load on them has a positive direction, that is, if the force increment due to the control deflection is directed up or towards the right wingtip. This rule also holds for tabs as well as complete surfaces.

The rudder set-up to find N (and hence C_n) is shown in Fig. 5:25. The contributing parts are: (1) the moment due to the vertical tail side forces, (2) the moment due to the vertical tail

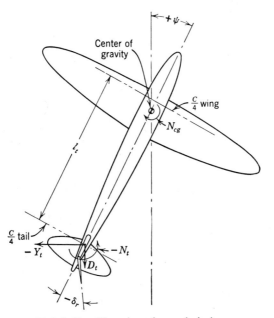

FIG. 5:25. Plan view of yawed airplane.

drag, (3) the moment due to the vertical tail moment about its own quarter chord.

In symbols these factors become:

$$N_{cg} = (N_t)_t - Y_t l_t \cos \psi - D_t l_t \sin \psi$$

$$= qS_t(MAC)_t C_{n\frac{1}{4}t} - qS_t C_{Yt} \cos \psi \cdot l_t - qS_t C_{Dt} \sin \psi \cdot l_t$$

$$C_{ncg} = \frac{S_t(MAC)_t}{S_w b_w} C_{n\frac{1}{4}t} - \frac{S_t}{S_w}\frac{l_t}{b_w} C_{Yt} \cos \psi - \frac{S_t}{S_w}\frac{l_t}{b_w} C_{Dt} \sin \psi \tag{5:29}$$

where N_{cg} = moment of vertical tail about center of gravity.

$\quad\quad S_t$ = vertical tail area.

$\quad C_{n\frac{1}{4}t}$ = vertical tail moment coefficient about its own quarter chord.

$(MAC)_t$ = mean chord of vertical tail.

S_w = wing area.

b_w = wing span.

l_t = distance from tail quarter chord to ship center of gravity.

C_{Yt} = Y_t/qS_t

ψ = yaw angle.

Y_t = side force due to tail.

$(N_t)_t$ = moment of vertical tail about its own quarter chord.

D_t = drag of vertical tail.

It was mentioned in Sect. 5:8 that span loading must be considered in order to apply data properly from an aileron panel test to the complete airplane. In Sect. 5:10 attention is drawn to the proper method of applying the data from an isolated horizontal tail by evaluating the downwash. The vertical tail is less affected by the remainder of the airplane, but some side-wash does exist when the airplane is yawed. Hence 15 degrees of yaw by no means results in the vertical tail angle of attack being 15 degrees. Proper evaluation of the sidewash can be made by equipping the complete model with a vertical tail whose incidence is variable, and by going through a procedure similar to that outlined for the horizontal tail in Sect. 5:10.

Example 5:8

A vertical tail model whose area is 12 ft² is tested at 100 mph. The model MAC = 3.0 ft. The actual airplane, of which the model is 40 per cent scale, has a wing area of 750 ft² and a span of 78 ft. The tail length is 30 ft. Find the tail yawing moment coefficient about the center of gravity if $C_{Yt} = 0.794$, $C_{Dt} = 0.0991$, $C_{n\frac{1}{4}t} = -0.1067$ for $\psi = 6°$. The rudder is deflected 10 degrees.

$$C_{ncg} = \frac{S_t}{S_w}\frac{(MAC)_t}{b_w}C_{n\frac{1}{4}t} - \frac{S_t}{S_w}\frac{l_t}{b_w}C_{Yt}\cos\psi - \frac{S_t}{S_w}\frac{l_t}{b_w}C_{Dt}\sin\psi$$

$$= \frac{12}{(0.40)^2(750)}\frac{3}{(0.4)78}(-0.1067) - \frac{12(0.4)(30)}{(0.40)^2(750)(0.4)(78)}0.794(0.9945)$$

$$- \frac{12}{(0.40)^2(750)}\frac{0.4(30)}{0.4(78)}(0.0991)(0.1045)$$

$$= -0.001025 - 0.0304 - 0.00398$$

$$= -0.0354$$

5:10. Testing Controls: Elevators. The elevators may be also tested by the panel mounting method. With this arrangement, one-half the horizontal tail is usually mounted as shown in Fig. 5:24, and the results are doubled to get the data for the entire tail.

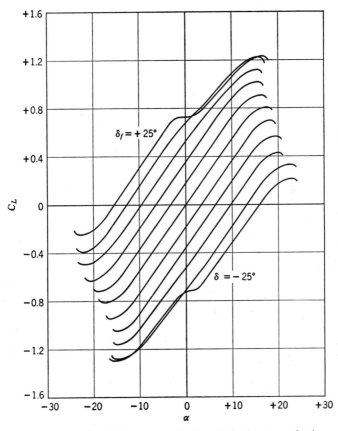

FIG. 5:26. Typical panel lift curves. The breaks in the curves for large flap deflections occur when the flap stalls.

It will be noted that, for airplanes of conventional dimensions, the pitching moment of the horizontal tail about its own quarter chord and the pitching moment about the airplane center of gravity produced by the horizontal tail drag are negligible when compared to the moment produced by the tail lifting force. Hence it will probably be necessary only to measure the lift of the panel model along with the elevator hinge moments in order to evaluate the desired qualities. Occasionally it will be desirable to compare two different methods of trimming to determine which has the lesser drag for a given lift. Then, of course, drag measurements will be necessary.

The tail lift curve slope as determined from the panel model may require adjustment in order to apply the test results. For example, suppose that the complete model has been tested at a constant angle of attack with varying settings of the stabilizer. The pitching moment about the airplane center of gravity due to the horizontal tail

$$M_t = l_t q_t S_t C_{Lt} \qquad (5:30)$$

may be measured, and with the known tail area S_t and tail length l_t the value of C_{Lt} may be determined. In these calculations it is probably better to use $q_t = q_{\text{freestream}}$ than the very questionable $q_t = 0.8 q_{\text{freestream}}$ sometimes arbitrarily employed. From the calculated C_{Lt} and known stabilizer angles the slope of the tail lift curve on the airplane $\left(\dfrac{dC_{Lt}}{d\alpha_t}\right)$ may be established. It then remains to diminish the panel lift curve slope by the factor $\left(\dfrac{dC_{Lt}}{d\alpha_t}\right)_{\text{airplane}} \div \left(\dfrac{dC_{Lt}}{d\alpha_t}\right)_{\text{panel}}$

The procedure followed to align the hinge moment data to the airplane may be traced through Fig. 5:27 as follows:

Let us suppose that the power-off moment curves of our example airplane are a shown in Fig. 5:27 for the model with tail and without tail, some center-of-gravity location * being specified. If lines *abc*, *def*, etc., are drawn between points of equal angle of attack values, the difference between the model plus tail $(M + T)$ and $M - T$ curves is the contribution of the horizontal tail with elevator zero at the specified α_W. The moment due to the tail $\Delta C_{mt} = q_t (C_{Lt}) S_t l_t$ and values of C_{Lt} are readily determined. From the previously prepared tail lift curve we find the tail angles of attack that correspond to the C_{Lt} values, and so label the lines *abc*, *def*, etc., as $\alpha_t = -6.1, -4.2$, etc. This procedure furnishes the relation between the panel tests

---

* If another location is desired for the center of gravity the curves may be rotated about zero lift by the relation

$$\Delta \frac{dC_m}{dC_L} = \frac{\% \ MAC \ \text{change}}{100}$$

and the complete airplane, as values of hinge moment and tail lift coefficient for various angles of attack are available from the panel tests.

To carry this chart to completion, the values of ΔC_m for various elevator deflections are calculated from the C_{Lt} values corre-

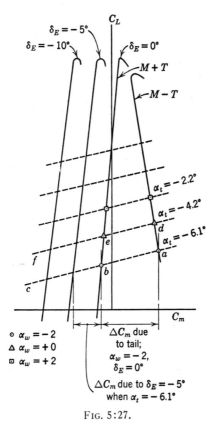

Fig. 5:27.

sponding to the tail angles of attack, and curves of constant elevator deflections may be drawn in. The complete chart may then be used to read the amount of elevator needed to trim at any C_L or the amount of moment available for maneuvering with a specified stick load. The maneuvering investigation requires the hinge moment data and the mechanical advantage, as follows:

1. Assume the chart to indicate that an elevator deflection of $-15°$ is required to trim at $C_L = 1.9$ and $\alpha_{\text{tail}} = +12$. From

the airplane geometry and $C_L = 1.9$, the value of q may be found from $q = W/SC_L$.

2. From the chart of hinge moment vs. α_{tail} we read (say) for $\alpha = +12$ and $\delta_e = -15°$ a $C_{He} = 0.0640$.

3. From the airplane geometry and q (step 1) the elevator hinge moment is calculated from $HM_e = qS_eC_e \cdot C_{He}$.

4. From the curve of mechanical advantage vs. δ_e, and the known linkage lengths, the stick force may then be found.

In this manner the various flight conditions may be investigated and desirable balance changes evaluated. It should be noted that the ability of an elevator to stall the ship may well be a function of the elevator size, for, if the elevator is not large enough to do the job, additional deflection through trim tabs * or power boost will be of no avail.

5:11. Testing Complete Models. The six-component test of a complete model is the most difficult of all wind-tunnel tests. More variables are under consideration than in other tests, for one thing, and the individual tests are more complicated, for another. For instance, each drag run requires *three* additional runs in order to evaluate the tare, interference, and alignment. (See Sects. 4:14 and 4:15.)

The complete testing of an entire model includes the investigation of the effect of all major variables (flaps, gear, etc.) on all forces and moments.

For most tests of complete models the boundary corrections large enough to matter are confined to buoyancy, blocking, wake displacement, downwash, and pitching moment. But it is a good policy to investigate corrections due asymmetrical loading and propeller wake effects just in case any of them are in the range of accuracy.

A list of the runs usually employed for an unpowered model is provided in Table 5:4. The numerical values in this table are, of course, only approximate, exact values being dictated by the particular design in question. Additional runs would be needed to check fillets, alternative tail surfaces, or ground effect.

Attention is drawn to items in Table 5:4 marked "correlation." In many instances correlation runs are added to evaluate separate effects of configurations that would never be flown. For example, a two-motored model usually has a run made with-

---

* When running tabs, use a constant tab angle to surface angle ratio, rather than random tab angles. The data will then be much easier to analyze.

TABLE 5:4. TEST PROGRAM OF UNPOWERED UNSWEPT MODEL *

W = wing.	V = vertical tail.
B = fuselage.	G = gear.
H = horizontal tail.	F = flaps.
"Tare" = dummies in.	Polar plot = C_L vs. α,
"Correlation" refers to	C_D, and C_m from
data accumulated to	$\alpha_{Z.L.}$ through stall.
assist in laying out	Polar run = L, D, M,
new designs.	from $\alpha_{Z.L.}$ through
	stall.

Runs	Model Con- figuration	Data Sought	Run Consists of
1–4	W	Tare, interference, and alignment; final polar plot.	Polars, model normal and inverted, dummies in, dummies out.
5–6	W	Wing lateral stability for future correlation.	Yaw ±30°, at $C_L = 0.3$ and 1.0.
7–10	WB	Tare, interference, and alignment, final polar plot.	Polars, model normal and inverted, dummies in, dummies out.
11–12	WB	Wing and body lateral stability for future correlation.	Yaw ±30° at $C_L = 0.3$ and 1.0.
13	WBH	Polar plot, effect of horizontal tail.	Polar.
14–15	WBH	Lateral stability for evaluating vertical tail and correlation.	Yaw ±30° at $C_L = 0.3$ and 1.0.
16	$WBHV$	Polar plot; effect of vertical tail.	Polar.
17–18	$WBHV$	Directional stability.	Yaw ±30° at $C_L = 0.3$ and 1.0.
19–23	$WBHV$	Tailsetting and downwash.	Polar with tail incidence -4, -3, -2, -1, 1.
24–25	$WBHV$	Effect of yaw on static longitudinal stability.	Polar with $\psi = 5°$, 10°.
26–43	$WBHV$	Rudder equilibrium and power.	Yaw ±30° at $C_L = 0.3$ and 1.0; rudder, 2, 5, 10, -2, -5, -10, -15, -20, -25 degrees.
44–63	$WBHV$	Aileron power.	Yaw ±30° at $C_L = 0.3$ and 1.0 with aileron -25, -20, -15, -10, -5, 5, 10, 15, 20, 25 deg.
64–72	$WBHV$	Elevator power.	Polars with elevators from $-25°$ to 15°, $\psi = 0$.
73–89	$WBHVF$	Effect of flaps on elevator and trim.	Polars with elevators from $-25°$ to 15°, $\psi = 0$, flaps 30°, 55°.
90–95	$WBHVF$	Effect of flaps on lateral stability.	Yaw ±30° at $\alpha = 3.0$ and 10°, flaps 20, 35, and 55.
96–104	$WBHVF$	Effect of flaps on lateral control.	Polars with flaps 55°, $\psi = 0$, ailerons at -25 to 20.
105	$WBHFG$	Effect of gear down.	Polars with flaps 55°, $\psi = 0$. Model inverted to reduce interference between supports and gear, and vertical tail removed to avoid physical interference with tail strut.
106	$WBHFG$	Effect of gear down on lateral stability.	Yaw ±30° with $\alpha = 3°$ and 10°, flaps 55°. Model inverted.

* An airplane with sweep requires more stall studies than are shown in the table, particularly for longitudinal, lateral, and directional stability.

out nacelles. The data from this run compared with those from the run with them in place aid in identifying the effect of the nacelles on the airplane's efficiency, drag, and lift. After several models have been tested the usual effects of a "good" nacelle become known, and, when a "poor" one turns up, it is so identified and attention is directed towards improving it. A standard procedure is to list the important performance parameters in tabular form, noting the change in each as each component is added to the wing. Studies made of such tables can be informative indeed.

Comments on the customary curves and information desired follow.

A. The Lift Curve, Flaps up

Items of interest on the flap-up lift curve include the value of $C_{L\,max}$ for determining flap-up stalling speed and minimum radius of turn; the shape of the curve at the stall (it should be moderately smooth, but rarely is); the angle of zero lift; the slope of the lift curve $dC_L/d\alpha$; and the value of negative $C_{L\,max}$. At the Reynolds numbers usually encountered in the wind tunnel, $C_{L\,max}$ will be from 0.6 to 1.7, and $dC_L/d\alpha$ for unswept wings will be around $0.1R/(R+2)$ per degree where R = aspect ratio. The complete ship values for $C_{L\,max}$ and $dC_L/d\alpha$ will be about 10 per cent greater than the wing alone, the actual value being less than measured model $C_{L\,max}$ since the model will not be trimmed at high α with elevator zero. Construction of the power-off trim lift curve is shown in Fig. 5:28.

Usually the addition of a fuselage increases the angle of zero lift in the positive direction and results in a loss in stability.

B. The Lift Curve, Flaps down

This curve will have very nearly the same slope as the flap-up curve and the same location of the aerodynamic center. The value of flap-down $C_{L\,max}$ is important for determining the increment due to the the flap $\Delta C_{L\,max}$, for this apparently does not change with Reynolds number and may be used to determine full-scale $C_{L\,max}$, flaps down (see Sect. 7:3), which is needed for landing and take-off runs. $C_{L\,max}$, flaps down, will vary from 1.2 to 2.9, the higher value being much sought after but rarely attained.

The angle of $0.9\,C_{L\,max}$ is of interest for landing-gear-length considerations. It will probably be from $\frac{1}{2}$ degree to 3 degrees less for flaps down than for flaps up if the flaps cover the inboard wing area, and 5 to 8 degrees less if they cover the entire span.

Again the sharpness of the stall is of interest as large lift coefficients that are perilously close to a violent stall cannot safely be

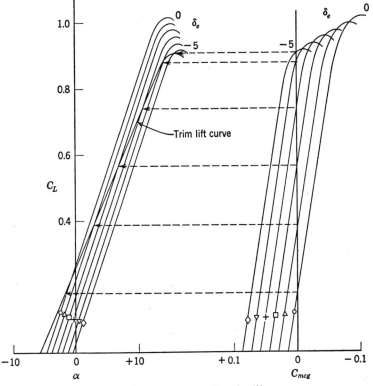

FIG. 5:28. Construction of the trim lift curve.

utilized to their full value. There is usually little need to take the flap-down lift curve as low as the angle of zero lift. The stall should be read in very small steps so that its shape is accurately determined.

Data from tests of a model of a single-engined attack airplane in the 400-mph class are presented in Table 5:5. As is shown, it is customary to list both the fundamental data and the progressive increments, the increments drawing attention to both good and bad items more directly than the total numbers. The data as shown are for an untrimmed model, and the increase of lift curve slope and maximum lift with the addition of the horizontal tail will become a decrease when trim is considered. A pair of nacelles usually reduces the lift curve slope about 0.02. The angle for 0.9 $C_{L \text{ max.}}$ (which is of interest in designing the landing gear) should not be taken too seriously until ground board tests are completed.

TABLE 5:5. LIFT CURVE DATA FROM TESTS OF A SINGLE-ENGINED ATTACK AIRPLANE

Configuration	$\alpha_{Z.L.}$	$\Delta\alpha_{Z.L.}$	$C_{L\alpha}$	$\Delta C_{L\alpha}$	$C_{L \text{ max.}}$	$\Delta C_{L \text{ max.}}$	$\alpha_{C_L \text{ max}}$	$\Delta\alpha_{C_L \text{ max}}$
W	−1.4	...	0.083	.....	1.11	....	16.2	...
WB	−1.2	0.2	0.083	0	1.11	0	16.2	0
WBH	−0.8	0.4	0.089	0.006	1.20	0.09	18.3	2.1
WBHV	−0.9	−0.1	0.091	0.002	1.20	0	18.3	0
WBHVGF$_{30}$	−7.4	−6.5	0.091	0	1.85	0.65	14.0	−4.3
WBHVGF$_{55}$	−10.3	−2.9	0.087	−0.004	1.94	0.09	13.0	−1.0

C. THE DRAG CURVES, FLAPS UP AND DOWN

The designer is particularly interested in $C_{D \text{ min.}}$ for top-speed calculations. In order to insure accuracy in this range the readings should be made every degree. Ship $C_{D \text{ min.}}$ will vary widely with the type of airplane and wing loading, a value of 0.0120 being not unreasonable for a clean fighter.

The airplane drag coefficient, C_D, at $C_{L \text{ max.}}$ is needed for take-off and landing-run calculations. Varying widely, depending on type of airplane and amount of flap, this coefficient may range from 0.1000 to 0.5000.

The shape of the drag curve is important for climb and cruising, a minimum change with C_L being desirable.

Drag data for both a single-engined and a two-engined airplane are included in Table 5:6. Of interest here is the increase of

TABLE 5:6. DRAG DATA FROM TESTS OF BOTH SINGLE- AND TWO-ENGINED PROPELLER-DRIVEN AIRPLANES

Configuration	One Engine			Two Engines	
	$C_{D0} + kC_L^2$	ΔC_{D0}	e	$C_{D0} + kC_L^2$	ΔC_{D0}
W	$0.0066 + 0.0544C_L^2$	......	0.852	$0.0082 + 0.0536C_L^2$	......
WB	$0.0136 + 0.0552C_L^2$	0.0070	0.846	$0.0130 + 0.0531C_L^2$	0.0048
WBH	$0.0148 + 0.0552C_L^2$	0.0012	0.846	$0.0157 * + 0.0567C_L^2$	0.0027 *
WBHV	$0.0154 + 0.0552C_L^2$	0.0006	0.846	$0.0186 + 0.0592C_L^2$	0.0029
WBHVE	....	......	.....	$0.0300 + 0.0588C_L^2$	0.0114
WBHVEG	....	......	.....	$0.0471 + 0.0588C_L^2$	0.0171
WBHVEGF$_{55}$	....	......	.....	$0.0819 + 0.0632C_L^2$	0.0348

* WBN, not WBH. N = 2 nacelles.
E = drag of turrets, oil cooler ducts, desert air scoops, two booster pumps, and ΔC_D = 0.0032 allowance for extrapolation to full scale.

effective induced drag when flaps are down. The increments of drag due to gear, turrets, and other excrescences are presented on a basis of wing area for consideration on the particular airplane at hand. It is also common to see them quoted based on their own frontal area so that their losses may be compared from airplane to airplane.

D. THE PITCHING MOMENT CURVE

The slope of the pitching moment curve must be negative for stability, of course, although definite values for the desired slope have not yet been agreed upon. The usual practice is to test the model mounted at its most rearward center of gravity location and to increase the tail area until the slope of the pitching moment curve dC_m/dC_L is between -0.1 and -0.15 for power off, controls fixed. Assuming a loss of 0.08 due to power and 0.02 for free controls it is seen that the value of $dC_m/dC_L = -0.1$ will be just sufficient to achieve neutral stability $(dC_m/dC_L = 0)$ under the most critical condition. Many of the high-powered airplanes lose more than 0.08, so that dC_m/dC_L power off may occasionally need to be as low as -0.50 for propeller-driven aircraft; less for jets.

Sometimes the stability is stated in terms of the added rearward travel possible without instability. This might be 0.1 MAC, meaning that the ship will still be stable if the center of gravity is moved one-tenth chord aft of the normal rearward location. It should further be stated whether this is for control-free or control-fixed condition.

Actually, the amount of maximum stability is also a function of center-of-gravity travel. If a large travel (say 15 per cent MAC) must be tolerated, excessive stability may be required in the most forward position.

The lift, drag, and moment data are usually presented on one sheet (see Fig. 5:29). The reversal of the moment plus and minus values makes the moment curve appear "normal" when viewed with the page on end.

In general we may say that the stability runs are made to see whether the horizontal tail is large enough to meet the stick-fixed stability requirements of positive static and dynamic stability under the worst condition (usually rated power climbs or approach with flap and gear down, aft center of gravity) and to meet the elevator floating requirements of stability at best climb speed with 75 per cent rated power. These tests require polars with rated power, flaps and gear up, and with 50 per cent rated power, flaps and gear down, both tests encompassing a range of elevator deflections from 0 to −10 degrees.

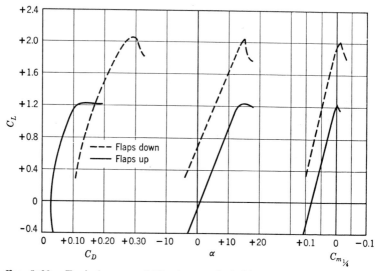

FIG. 5:29. Typical curves of lift, drag, and pitching moment; flaps up and down.

Longitudinal stability data for two airplanes are listed in Table 5:7. Of interest is the customary destabilizing effect of the fuselage and of course the large stabilizing effect of the horizontal tail.

TABLE 5:7. LONGITUDINAL STABILITY DATA FOR TWO PROPELLER-DRIVEN AIRPLANES, POWER OFF

Configuration	Single-Engined Airplane					Twin-Engined Airplane		
	C_{m0}	ΔC_{m0}	C_L trim	$\dfrac{dC_m}{dC_L}$	A C	C_{m0}	ΔC_{m0}	$\dfrac{dC_m}{dC_L}$
W	−0.021	.....	0.50	0.042	25.8	−0.007	.....	0.017
WB	−0.036	−0.015	0.40	0.091	20.9	−0.015	−0.008	0.025
WBH	0.062	0.098	0.53	−0.120	42.0	−0.020 *	−0.005 *	0.085 *
WBHV	0.032	−0.029	0.25	−0.130	43.0	0.024	0.044	−0.102
WBHVF₃₀	0.102	0.070	0.86	−0.118	41.8	.....	.....	.....
WBHVF₅₅	0.167	0.065	1.22	−0.138	43.8	.....	.....	.....

CG at 30.0% MAC, 0.4% above MAC.   CG at 30% MAC, on MAC.
* WBN, not WBH.

For minimum drag, the stabilizer should be set so that $\delta_e = 0°$ for cruise. A large C_{m0} (high camber wing, long fuselage nose) works well for this, as it makes the model-minus-tail $C_{mcg} = 0$

occur at a high (cruise) C_L, especially for airplanes designed for high altitudes. The above conditions also decrease δ_e for landing.

Occasionally the power-on stability is the same tail on or off. For this case a new tail location is obviously necessary.

The slope of the tail lift curve is obtained by holding α_{wing} constant and varying the tail incidence and computing the resulting pitching moment data. The tail lift curve slope should be evaluated early in the program since it is needed for the tail-on wall corrections.

E. The Elevator Power Curve

The plot of ΔC_m against elevator deflection is made at several values of the lift coefficient. It indicates the amount of elevator

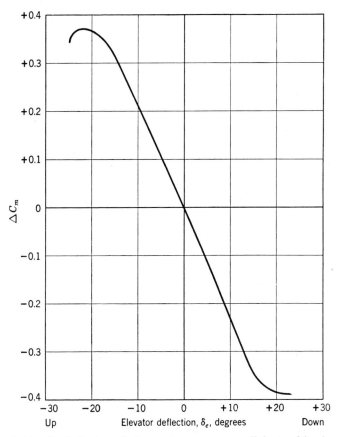

Fig. 5:30. Typical plot of change in moment coefficient with elevator deflection.

deflection needed to produce a certain moment coefficient. Usually the plot is nearly a straight line from plus 15 to minus 20 degrees deflection with a slope of about −0.02. The elevator stalls on one side above that, and further deflection is useless. Some of the newer designs seem to hold good for a slightly greater range.

A further study of the elevator may be made from a plot of C_{mcg} vs. C_L for several elevator angles. The intersections of the

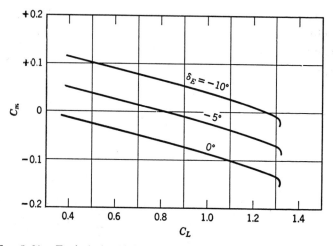

FIG. 5:31. Typical plot of C_{mcg} vs. C_L for several elevator deflections.

curves with the axis indicate trim condition. This plot may also be made against α.

The elevator tests are made to determine whether the elevator is large enough for necessary control under all flight conditions. A successful elevator is powerful enough to develop maximum C_L or allowable load factor at all permissible speeds at all permissible center-of-gravity locations. The most critical condition is normally landing with most forward center of gravity and ground effect, the test usually encompassing polars with propellers windmilling, flaps and gear down, and elevator angles from 0 to −25 degrees.

It is also necessary to determine whether the elevator balance is sufficient to keep the control forces small enough that maximum load factors may be developed with more than 40 lb and less than 150 lb stick force. The control force criteria is usually critical in landing or accelerated flight, flaps and gear up, props windmilling.

For a jetplane, 10 lb of stick force per g and 20 lb per degree of elevator are reasonable figures.

F. THE AILERON POWER CURVES

The aileron criteria are usually determined at zero yaw and may be considered from the plots of C_l vs. C_n (Fig. 5:22), C_l and

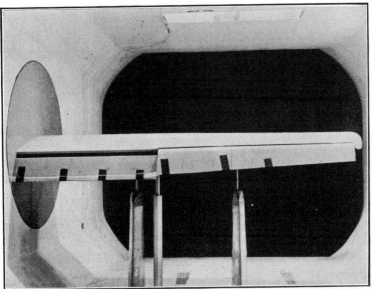

Courtesy University of Wichita.

FIG. 5:32. A semi-span mount using the external balance.

C_n vs. δ_a (Fig. 5:21), and C_{Ha} vs. δ_a (Fig. 5:23). The important qualities of good ailerons are high rolling moment and low hinge moments—the latter usually not obtainable from tests of a complete model. (See Sect. 5:8.) The maximum rate of roll and the maximum helix angle are determined from $C_{l\,max.}$ (see Sect. 5:8), a $C_{l\,max.}$ of 0.03 being satisfactory for one aileron. The maximum rate of roll (taking due account of the stick forces) will vary from 50 degrees per second for a medium bomber to 150 degrees per second for a very maneuverable fighter.

Sometimes the criteria may be stated in terms of the helix angle (Sect. 5:8), typical needs being (for military aircraft): (1) a helix angle of at least 0.09 at 0.7 $V_{max.}$ with rudder zero, flaps and gear up, normal rated power; and (2) a helix angle of at least 0.07, rudder zero, power off, flaps and gear down, at 1.2 V_{stall}.

Requirements for commercial airplanes are usually satisfied with less than the above amounts.

Tests required to obtain the above information embrace runs at the proper angles of attack, $\psi = 0$. The rolling moments are measured for various aileron deflections and the helix angles computed as per Sect. 5:8. (See runs 45–63 of Table 5:4.) A discussion of aileron hinge moments is also presented in Sect. 5:8.

When taking aileron or rudder data a small amount of rolling and yawing moment and side force is usually found even when the controls are neutral and there is zero yaw. This delta is due to either asymmetrical flow in the tunnel or model asymmetry, and both the appearance of the data and their use are improved if aileron and rudder zero moments are subtracted from the data so that only deflected controls have any value, as of course they should.

It is a nice refinement to run aileron tests with the horizontal tail off, for two reasons. The first (and minor one) is that it saves several columns of calculating in the work-up since tunnel-wall effect on the horizontal tail is then non-existent. The second is that when the ailerons are deflected in flight the airplane normally rolls and the inboard aileron trailing vortices are swept away from the horizontal tail by the helix angle. When the model is immobile in the tunnel these vortices stream back quite close to the horizontal tail and induce a loading on it that does not occur in rolling flight.

G. RUDDER POWER AND EQUILIBRIUM CURVES

In most single-engined aircraft the rudder is not a critical component. It must furnish adequate control on the ground and in the air, but no criteria similar to "rate of roll" or "pounds of stick force per g" have been established. The problem of the high-powered single-engine aircraft becomes difficult under the high-power low-airspeed (wave-off) condition. Here it is not unusual to require full rudder to overcome torque to maintain straight flight. The criteria become more those of hinge moments (Sects. 5:8 and 5:9) than those usually obtainable from the complete model. Particular attention must be paid to avoiding overbalance at high rudder deflections.

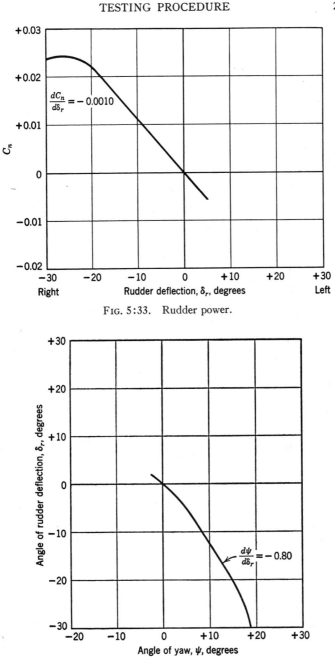

FIG. 5:33.   Rudder power.

FIG. 5:34.   Rudder equilibrium.

The modern high-performance multiengined airplane must possess sufficient directional stability to prevent it from reaching excessive angles of yaw or developing rudder forces that tend to

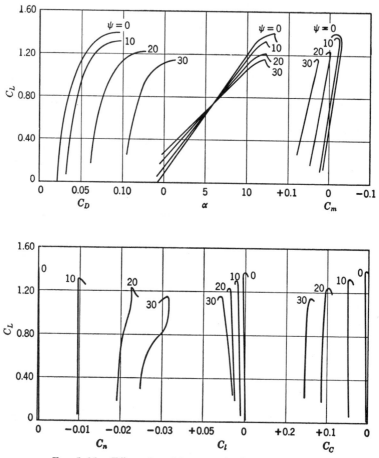

Fɪɢ. 5:35.   Effect of model yaw on basic characteristics.

keep the plane yawing. Further, it must also be able to be balanced directionally at the best climb speed with asymmetric power (one engine out, other at full power for a two-engined airplane), rudder free and trim tab neutral, without exceeding a 15-degree angle of bank.

The most critical condition for the criterion of decreasing pedal force occurs at high thrust coefficient, flaps and gear down, at large angles of right sideslip, and test runs must be made accordingly.

The asymmetric power condition requires yaw runs at the attitude corresponding to $1.2 V_{stall}$ gear down, flaps at take-off setting, take-off power on right engine, left engine windmilling.

Usually the rudder information is grouped into two curves. The first, rudder equilibrium, is a plot of rudder deflection against angle of yaw, or in other words δ_r for $C_n = 0$. This need be taken for yaw in only one direction, for it will be similar in the other owing to symmetry. The slope $d\psi/d\delta_r$ can be around 1.2 for maneuverable airplanes on down to 0.5 for the more stable types.

The second curve, rudder power, is a plot of C_n vs. δ_r. A slope of $dC_n/d\delta_r = -0.001$ is reasonable, varying widely with airplane specifications. Again the curve need be plotted only for either plus or minus rudder.

The rudder hinge moment should be such that 180 lb pedal force is never exceeded. No help from a trim device is assumed.

The effect of yaw on the characteristics of an airplane is shown in Fig. 5:35.

TABLE 5:8. DIRECTIONAL STABILITY FOR A SINGLE-ENGINED ATTACK PLANE, LOW AND HIGH ANGLES OF ATTACK

Configuration	$C_{n\psi}$	$\Delta C_{n\psi}$	$C_{l\psi}$	$\Delta C_{l\psi}$	dC_l/dC_n
W	−0.00012 *	....	0.00056	....	.....
	−0.00014	....	0.00037	....	.....
WB	0.00118	0.00130	0.00058	0.00002	.....
	0.00082	0.00096	0.00037	0	.....
WBH	0.00063	−0.00055	0.00070	0.00012	.....
	0.00027	−0.00055	0.00087	0.00050	.....
WBHV	−0.00165	−0.00228	0.00120	0.00050	−0.727
	−0.00186	−0.00213	0.00087	0	−0.467
$WBHVF_{45}$	−0.00230	....	0.00040	....	−0.174
	−0.00250	....	0.00012	....	−0.480
$WBHVF_{55}$	−0.00230	....	0.00040	....	−0.174
	−0.00250	....	0.00	....	0

* The upper value is for $\alpha = 2.5$ degrees; the lower, for $\alpha = 11.1$ degrees.

H. The Amount of Lateral Stability as Compared with
the Amount of Directional Stability

Information about the roll axis is needed to determine whether
sufficient dihedral is incorporated in the design to provide lateral
stability at the most critical condition. This will be, for most
airplanes, the approach with flaps down and power on where
power and flaps combine to reduce the dihedral effect. The
ailerons should be free if possible.

The tests for lateral stability embrace yaw runs at the approach attitude, flaps and gear down, and 50 per cent normal
power. (See runs 90–95 in Table 5:4 for gear-up data; add runs
with gear down.) The angle of attack for the approach should
be chosen on the basis of tunnel $C_{L \max}$. (used to get 1.2 V_{stall}),
but the thrust coefficient should be based on full-scale conditions.

Too much lateral stability for a given amount of directional
stability results in an objectionable motion called a "Dutch
roll." Too little lateral stability for a given amount of directional stability results in spiral instability. However, the advantages in general control and handling characteristics are so great
with a relatively large vertical tail that some spiral instability
is acceptable. Hence dihedral investigations are usually more
concerned with avoiding Dutch roll than escaping spiral instability.

For most airplanes the critical condition will occur at high
speed, where dihedral effect will be a maximum and directional
stability a minimum owing to small power effects. The test runs
therefore embrace yaw runs at high speed, flaps and gear up,
with propeller windmilling or at high-speed thrust coefficient.

Tests have indicated that a value of roll to yaw that will give
what pilots call satisfactory stability is

$$\frac{dC_l/d\psi}{dC_n/d\psi} \cong -0.8 \qquad (5:31)$$

A value of $dC_n/d\psi = -0.0010$ for controls fixed and -0.0007
for controls free is reasonable for a large transport.

A very rough idea of the proper distribution of dihedral and
fin area may be obtained from Fig. 5:36, which is an adaptation
from Fig. 4 of Ref. 5:3. This figure is for a lightly loaded high-
wing monoplane; for low-wing airplanes, γ should be replaced by
γ_L, where

$$\gamma_L = \gamma + 3° \qquad (5:32)$$

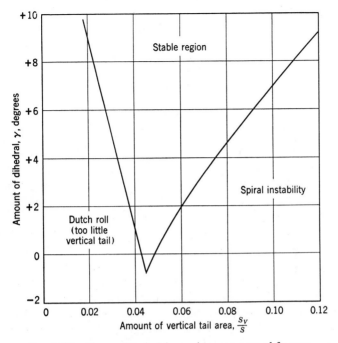

F<small>IG.</small> 5:36. Proper dihedral for various amounts of fin area.

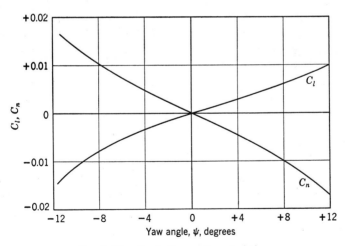

F<small>IG.</small> 5:37. Typical yaw characteristics.

The airplane should have enough vertical tail to be near or within the boundary of spiral instability.

It is convenient at this point to draw attention to an alteration that may have to be made to the ordinary wind-tunnel data when the model is yawed.

The majority of the wind-tunnel balances read pitching moment about a horizontal axis perpendicular to the wind-tunnel

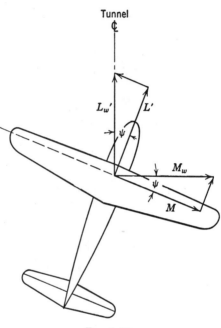

FIG. 5:38.

jet axis and passing through the balance resolving center. The rolling moment is read about the centerline of the wind tunnel test section, and the yawing moment perpendicular to roll and pitch. Hence, when the model is yawed, the indicated rolling moment L_w' and pitching moment M_w are for axes parallel and perpendicular to the relative wind (wind axis) and not for axes parallel and perpendicular to the centerline of the airplane. (See Fig. 5:38.)

In some cases the aerodynamicist needs data relative to *body* axes which move with the airplane and are fixed to it; in others the data are needed relative to axes yawed but not pitched—the so-called *stability* axes.   Transferring from wind axes to either system is indicated in Table 5:9.*

TABLE 5:9a.   WIND AXES TO BODY AXES

$$C_{LB} = C_L \cos \alpha + C_D \cos \psi \sin \alpha + C_Y \sin \psi \sin \alpha$$
$$C_{DB} = C_D \cos \psi \cos \alpha - C_L \sin \alpha - C_Y \sin \psi \cos \alpha$$
$$C_{mB} = C_m \cos \psi - (b/c)C_l \sin \psi$$
$$C_{lB} = C_l \cos \psi \cos \alpha + (c/b)C_m \sin \psi \cos \alpha - C_n \sin \alpha$$
$$C_{nB} = C_n \cos \alpha + C_l \cos \psi \sin \alpha + (c/b)C_m \sin \psi \sin \alpha$$
$$C_{YB} = C_Y \cos \psi + C_D \sin \psi$$

TABLE 5:9b.   WIND AXES TO STABILITY AXES

$$C_{LS} = C_L$$
$$C_{DS} = C_D \cos \psi - C_Y \sin \psi$$
$$C_{mS} = C_m \cos \psi - (b/c)C_l \sin \psi$$
$$C_{lS} = C_l \cos \psi + (c/b)C_m \sin \psi$$
$$C_{nS} = C_n$$
$$C_{YS} = C_Y \cos \psi + C_D \sin \psi$$

The yaw tests will also yield the value of the side force $Y = qSC_Y$.   No particular slope or values to C_Y are required. The only use of C_Y is to calculate the side force for asymmetrical flight and hence the necessary angle of bank to counteract said side force with a tangent component of lift.   The side force needed to overcome the torque reaction at low speed while maintaining straight flight may also be evaluated.

I. TAILSETTING AND AVERAGE DOWNWASH ANGLE

In order to avoid the drag of cruising with elevators deflected, and the loss of maximum ΔC_m due to elevator if partial elevator is needed for trim, it is usually desirable to set the stabilizer incidence so that the ship is trimmed at cruising with $\delta_e = 0$.   For stability considerations as well as correlation for future designs, it is necessary to know the angle of downwash at the tail for each wing angle of attack.   The procedure is as follows:

1. Run the model with the horizontal tail removed, probably obtaining a tail-off stability curve as shown in Fig. 5:39.

2. Next run the model with the horizontal tail on, using tail incidence, i_t, angles of, say, -8, -4, 0, 4, 8°.   Curves as indicated in Fig. 5:39 will be obtained.

* Many engineers prefer to use symbols other than those presented above in order to leave "lift" and "drag," etc., properly unique for reference to the relative wind. See Sect. 11:7.

Now the intersections of the horizontal tail-on curve with the tail-off curve are points where, for a given wing angle of attack, α_w, the tail-on pitching stability equals the tail-off pitching stability; i.e., the tail is at zero lift, and hence

$$\alpha_T = \alpha_w + i_t - \epsilon_w = 0 \qquad (5{:}33)$$

where ϵ_w = downwash angle at the tail; α_T = tail angle of attack.

Since α_w and i_t are known for the points of intersection, ϵ_w may be determined from eq. 5:33, and a plot of ϵ_w against α_w or C_L may be made. This plot and the usual effect of flaps on downwash are shown in Fig. 5:40. Not infrequently the curve of ϵ_w vs. α_w is a straight line.

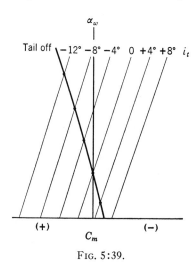

Fig. 5:39.

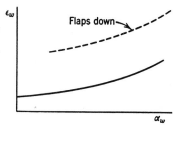

Fig. 5:40.

Methods shortcutting the above lengthy procedure have been devised based on the assumption that the wing downwash is zero at zero lift. Though this is true enough for the complete wing, the tail occupies only a fraction of the wing span and hence quite often shows a value of downwash existing when the wing is at zero lift. This makes the short methods open to question.

J. Power Effects

An important phase of complete model testing is the determination of the power-on effects. Though for light planes this could be safely neglected or "estimated," the low power loadings on many modern airplanes lead to differences in power-on and power-off flight characteristics that are impossible to ignore and very difficult to predict.

The effects of the power are divided into two classes:

(a) The effects due primarily to the power. These include the thrust moment, torque reaction, and force due to yawed propeller.

(b) The effects due to the resulting slipstream. These effects depend very largely on when and how completely the tail is immersed in the slipstream and on the flight condition, which in turn determines the ratio of the dynamic pressure in the slipstream q_s to the freestream dynamic pressure q.* Also important are the rotation of the slipstream and the change of downwash at the tail.

In a conventional single-engine aircraft, the application of power is accompanied by a rolling moment due to torque and slipstream over the wings. When ailerons are applied to correct this effect, a nose left yawing moment is incurred. The twist of the slipstream striking the vertical fin produces a large side force and more left yaw. The yawed propeller adds still a further small amount of nose left yaw. At the same time, depending on the location of the horizontal tail, changes in longitudinal trim occur, owing to both thrust moment and slipstream. All these changes keep the pilot very busy, and it becomes important that the loss of stability about any of the axes should not be added to his troubles.

Fortunately, the above effects may be evaluated in the wind tunnel, and the aircraft may be revised or the pilot forewarned.

The model engine-propeller combination should be chosen to duplicate the full-scale conditions as nearly as possible. In order to preserve the proper ratio of q_s/q, it is important that the thrust of the model propeller be proportionately the same as in the full-scale ship. To preserve the same twist, the torque should also be the same. These conditions lead at once to the necessity of having the model propeller similar to the full-scale propeller. The blade setting that most nearly aligns the model and full-scale thrust is that of equal V/nd ratios. For convenience this may be put in coefficient form as follows:

Define

$$T_C = \frac{T}{\rho V^2 d^2}$$

and

$$Q_C = \frac{Q}{\rho V^2 d^3}$$

* q_s/q varies from about 1.05 at top speed to 1.8 at take-off.

where T and Q are thrust and torque respectively, and d the propeller diameter. Then letting subscript S = full-scale airplane and subscript M = model, we have for similarity

$$\frac{V_S}{n_S d_S} = \frac{V_M}{n_M d_M} \qquad (5{:}34)$$

also

$$T_{CM} = \frac{T_M}{\rho V_M{}^2 d_M{}^2} \qquad \text{and} \qquad T_{CS} = \frac{T_S}{\rho V_S{}^2 d_S{}^2}$$

Dividing,

$$\frac{T_{CM}}{T_{CS}} = \frac{T_M}{\rho V_M{}^2 d_M{}^2} \frac{\rho V_S{}^2 d_S{}^2}{T_S}$$

Substituting from eq. 5:34 and clearing

$$\frac{T_{CM}}{T_{CS}} = \frac{T_M}{T_S} \frac{n_S{}^2 d_S{}^4}{n_M{}^2 d_M{}^4}$$

Now it can also be shown that the thrust

$$T_S = \rho n_S{}^2 d_S{}^4 C_{TS} \qquad \text{and} \qquad T_M = \rho n_M{}^2 d_M{}^4 C_{TM}$$

and that, for a given V/nd, if the two propellers are geometrically similar, $C_{TS} = C_{TM}$ (this omits scale effect). Hence

$$\frac{T_M}{T_S} = \frac{n_M{}^2 d_M{}^4}{n_S{}^2 d_S{}^4} \qquad \text{and} \qquad \frac{T_{CM}}{T_{CS}} = 1$$

or, if the model is tested at $T_{CM} = T_{CS}$, similarity of thrust will be preserved. In a similar manner, Q_{CM} should equal Q_{CS}.

Obtaining equal model and full-scale values of T_C and Q_C, however, is a little more complicated than duplicating equal lift and drag coefficients, and a proper procedure must be followed. This includes calibrating the model motor-propeller combination and arranging some suitable procedure for duplicating desired values of T_C and Q_C while the tests are being run.

1. *Calibration of the motor and propeller.* Since it usually takes every last fraction of allowable space to house the motor in the model (see Fig. 5:41), there is rarely sufficient room left for the installation of devices for reading the torque as the tests are proceeding. Hence it is necessary to calibrate the motor and obtain various thrusts and torques in the tunnel by regulating the power supplied at various blade angles.

Courtesy Aerolab Development Corp.

FIG. 5:41. Interior view of model having cast aluminum fuselage, fillets, and flaps, showing drive shaft for 110-hp electric motor.

The motor-propeller calibration is as follows:

(*a*) Set the motor in a dynamometer and obtain curves of bhp for various values of kw input and rpm. The plot will appear as Fig. 5:42.

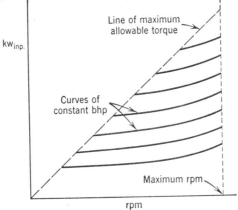

FIG. 5:42.

(b) With thrust line at zero angle of attack, install the model with motor and propeller in the tunnel. For various rpm and motor outputs, read the thrust for various blade angles. Plot this as T_C vs. Q_C for constant blade angle. See dotted curves in Fig. 5:43.

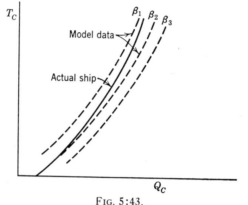

FIG. 5:43.

(c) From the actual airplane-performance calculations, read the thrust and torque for a given power condition. It will be observed that constant power does not result in constant thrust because the propeller efficiency varies. Plot the thrust and torque as T_C vs. Q_C on the same plot as the model T_C and Q_C. See solid line, Fig. 5:43. From this combined plot select the model blade angle that most nearly matches the required T_C vs. Q_C curve.

As the airplane curve includes many blade angles due to the constant-speed propeller, no one fixed blade angle on the model will be suitable throughout the range. Usually one angle can be picked for low speeds and another for high speeds.

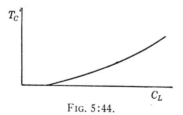

FIG. 5:44.

2. *Running the tests.* Now, although the calibration has defined various values of thrust and torque, the tunnel operators are not yet in a position to know what thrust to apply. The thrust output of the airplane's motor varies with C_L (forward speed). To isolate this variation, a plot of T_C vs. C_L is made for the airplane (Fig. 5:44). From Fig. 5:43 the corresponding Q_C for the model is read, and from a plot of T_C vs. rpm (not

shown) the rpm is read. After the rpm and torque are known, the bhp is calculated, and the kw input is found from Fig. 5:42. The airplane C_L is used to calculate the corresponding model lift, and an operating chart of kw input vs. model lift in pounds is prepared. By watching his lift scale, the tunnel operator is able to set the kw input to the model motor that will yield the proper T_C and Q_C.

The necessity of approximating full-scale V/nd leads to unusually high rpm for the model propeller. This condition follows from the fact that the tunnel speed may approach the airplane

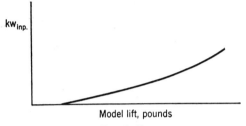

FIG. 5:45.

speed though the diameter of the model propeller may well be $\frac{1}{10}$ scale. Normally this scale relation would indicate a model rpm of 10 times the actual airplane rpm, but a second effect tends to diminish the exceedingly high rpm on many models, particularly those of low power loading. It is shown in Chapter 6 that to a large degree the size of the wind tunnel limits the size of the model to be tested. In turn the size of the model dictates the maximum size of the electric motor to be installed for driving the propeller. If no motor can be found that supplies enough power to drive the propeller at design V/nd when the tunnel is at full speed, the tunnel velocity must be diminished until the proper V/nd can be realized. Very often the final tunnel speed is around 60 mph for the power on tests, and a low Reynolds number must be tolerated.

The need for meeting the requirements of wind-tunnel model motors has brought about the introduction of special electric motors combining small frontal area and high rpm and requiring in turn water cooling and a current source of variable frequency. See Fig. 5:46. Some of the motors available are listed in Table 5:10. In many set-ups both the power and cooling water enter the tail of the model through the rear support.

In view of the small size of hydraulic motors and the high rpm they develop, it is reasonable to ask why they have not been used as model propeller drives. The answer seems to lie in the large tube sizes needed to meet the power requirements. Work is

Courtesy Aerolab Development Corp.

FIG. 5:46. High-speed model motor and gear train for propeller drive.

TABLE 5:10. DIMENSIONS OF SOME WIND-TUNNEL-MODEL MOTORS

Hp	Diameter, in.	Length, in.	Rpm
9	2.2	7.5	27,000
20	3.2	7.0	18,000
35	4	10.0	18,000
75	4.5	12	18,000
130	8	16	5,400
150	7.5	14	8,000
200	10	33	5,000
1000	28	38	2,100

TABLE 5:11. SOME WIND-TUNNEL-MODEL PROPELLER SIZES AND WEIGHTS

Propeller Diameter, in.	Weight per Blade, lb	Centrifugal Load under Operating Conditions, lb
7	0.02	600
14	0.10	...
22	1.00	...

Courtesy Boeing Airplane Co.

FIG. 5:47. Powered model tests of the Boeing Stratocruiser.

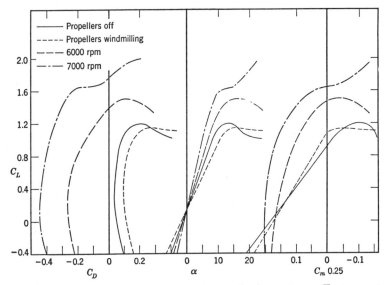

FIG. 5:48. The effect of power on a four-engined transport. Test run at $q = 8.0$ lb per sq ft. Note windmilling propeller data for approach condition. The power effect for other types of aircraft, single-engined for instance, could be widely different.

currently being done on the use of steam drives for an internal pump to simulate the jet exhaust from a turbo-prop installation.

The effect of power varies widely with many factors, the results of one test being shown in Fig. 5:48 to illustrate a method of presenting the data. Power effects for turbo-prop installations are likely to be particularly bad since the light engine weight usually results in a forward propeller location which coupled with the great thrust produces a very large destabilizing moment at high pitch angles.

Propeller failures seem most likely to occur when the model is at high angles of yaw, and, accordingly, yaw tests of powered models should be last on the schedule.

5:12. Testing Fuselages, Nacelles, and Bodies of Revolution. Tests of fuselages alone are rarely made, for the interference effect of the wing on the fuselage is of such prime importance and magnitude that fuselage tests without the presence of the wing are of very questionable value. When a fuselage alone is tested the buoyancy effects (see Sect. 6:9) are usually important. Blocking corrections are commonly moderate to large.

Nacelle tests are much more valuable than fuselage tests because usually entirely different items are being investigated. Generally the nacelle tests are concerned only with cooling pressure drops and cooling drags and not with the total nacelle drag, which would be largely dependent on the wing-nacelle interference.

For a wing plus fuselage and/or a horizontal tail on, Sects. 6:21 and 6:22 should be consulted.

If a power-driven propeller is to be utilized in the set-up, extreme consideration should be given to the control and measurement of the rpm. For nacelles simulating modern high-powered units, the loss of a single revolution per minute can represent a large thrust decrement and, in turn, invalidate any drag measurements that may be made. It is usually advantageous to fix the rpm by means of a synchronous driving motor and to vary the tunnel speed and propeller blade angle to get various flight conditions. Such an arrangement corresponds to the customary constant-speed set-up of most airplanes.

The usual nacelle (Fig. 5:49) is of such dimensions that buoyancy, constriction, and propeller corrections are important. For clarity, let us assume that a model is to be tested at 100 mph. The constriction effect of the closed jet increases the velocity over the model so that the results are similar to those encountered in free air at a slightly higher speed, say 102 mph. The effect on the propeller is opposite, however, yielding the results expected in free air at 96 mph. It is therefore necessary to increase the

Courtesy United Aircraft Corp.

Fig. 5:49. Propeller test rig in United Aircraft wind tunnel. A cooling test would, of course, have a simulated engine nacelle, and probably a stub wing as well.

tunnel speed to approximately 104 mph, at which time the propeller slipstream is the same as in free air at 100 mph. The propeller coefficients are then based on 100 mph.

The buoyancy effect is assumed to be the same as expected at 100 mph without the propeller.

Drag coefficients for a nacelle may be based either on nacelle frontal area or on engine disk area. The choice should be clearly stated. The quantity of cooling air per second Q is usually defined by

$$Q = KS \sqrt{2\Delta p/\rho}$$

where K = engine conductivity; S = nacelle or engine frontal area, ft^2; Δp = baffle pressure drop, lb/ft^2; ρ = air density, slugs/ft^3.

Bodies of revolution or fuselages are best tested on their sides, using a single strut and yawing the model to simulate angles of attack. This procedure both reduces the tare and interference and makes their determination easier. For accurate angle determination the torsional deflection of the strut under torque load should be calibrated and allowed for in the setting or work-up.

5:13. Testing Propellers. Propellers are frequently investigated in wind tunnels either alone or in conjunction with a fuselage or nacelle. If an entire model is tested, the propeller diameter will be small compared to the tunnel jet diameter, and the corrections to be described will become small also. For tests in which propeller characteristics are to be determined, the propeller diameter may well be 60 per cent of the jet diameter, and the corrections are not only large but unfortunately not as accurate as those for wings. An approach to the problem has been made by Glauert; boundary corrections for propellers may be found in Sect. 6:28.

Numerous coefficients have been advanced for presenting propeller data, each type perhaps being advantageous for particular applications. One of the more popular forms is

$$C_P = \frac{P}{\rho n^3 d^5} = \text{Power coefficient} \qquad (5{:}35)$$

$$C_T = \frac{T}{\rho n^2 d^4} = \text{Thrust coefficient} \qquad (5{:}36)$$

where P = power input, ft-lb/sec; n = rps; d = propeller diameter, ft; T = thrust, lb. The "variable" of propeller testing is usually the advance ratio, $J = V/nd$, where V is in feet per second and n in revolutions per second. A form using more conventional quantities is $J = 88V/Nd$, where V is in miles per hour and N in revolutions per minute. It will be seen that the two are numerically identical.

Plots of C_P and C_T against J for a typical propeller are in Fig. 5:50.

Some notes on propeller structural criteria are in Sect. 11:6. Not mentioned therein is that propeller erosion can be held to a minimum by using a rubber-base paint on the blades.

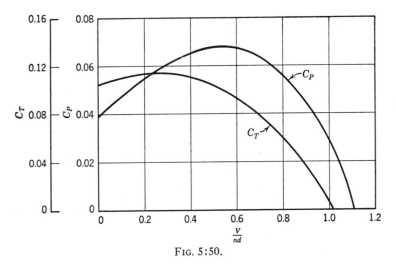

Fig. 5:50.

5:14. Testing for Cavity Resonance. One of the newer problems that besets the modern high-speed aircraft is cavity resonance, a high-intensity vibration of wheel wells, bomb bays, or
cockpits that arises when their covers are removed and the high-
speed airstream moves by (and into) the opening. Frequently
the resonance reaches alarming proportions, causing unsteady
bombing platforms, dizziness and nausea of the crews, or, if left
unheeded, failure of parts or all of the airplane.

This phenomenon has been located by means of tunnel tests,
and overcome by means of Helmholtz resonators, tuned chambers
which are opened into the offending cavity. The procedure for
the tunnel test is to open the various cavities one at a time and to
pick up their natural frequencies with a pressure pickup fed into
a scope or recording oscillograph. The resonance, if any, will
occur close to the same speed at which it will occur on the airplane, but at a frequency increased by the scale factor. If space
is available for Helmholtz resonators they may be tried; if not,
scoops or lips may be added to the cavities intuitively until the
intensity is down.

A second approach, if the natural frequency has already been
determined by flight test, is to mount the model on strain gages
selected so that their spring constant and the mass of the model
results in the natural frequency value already known. Decreased
amplitudes of vibration then indicate the success of the cure
being considered.

5:15. Testing Jet-Engined Models. The need for power-on tests is far less acute for a jet-engined airplane than for a propeller-driven one. The effect of the thrust moment is easily calculable, and there is no large slipstream of high rotation which strikes the fuselage and tail with a wide variety of effects. Indeed, the sting mounting (see Chapter 11) usually employed helps simulate the jet stream for the single-engined airplane.*

There are two schools of thought as regards the simulation of the power-off jet engine. One prefers to fair both front and back with smooth-fitting blocks; the other simply leaves a clear passage. Of the two, the tunnel seems a bit closer to actual conditions, although for most models the "free" space is usually sorely needed for an internal balance.

When it is decided to simulate the jet flow, added difficulties arise. First of all, although the jet engine itself has a subsonic velocity, a supersonic cold air stream will be needed to obtain the proper thrust. This arises since normal jet velocities run around 1400 ft per sec and remain subsonic only because their temperature is so high. The difference in temperature is of little account, producing no measurable effect as long as the proper mass flow is maintained. That the freestream air is not employed produces more serious effects: the drag of the engine nacelle will be in error because some of the air on the full-scale ship goes through it instead of around it, and, if the same thrust coefficient is maintained for model and full-scale ship, the change of mass flow at the model's tail due to the addition of outside air will not reproduce true conditions. A solution to this problem is to adjust the flow from the model jet so that the same thrust coefficient is maintained for both model and full-scale ship, defining the coefficient:

$$T_c' = \frac{\text{Thrust}}{(\rho/2)SV_0^2} \tag{5:37}$$

but subtracting from the model thrust the momentum mV_0 due to the freestream air. This will make the flow at the tail of the model simulate that developed by the actual airplane. Definitions used above include:

  m = mass flow per second from model jet.
  V_0 = freestream velocity.
  S = wing area.

* See Sect. 12:6 for the supersonic case.

Not infrequently the entrance loss is under scrutiny and the wind-tunnel engineer need consider duplication of the entering flow only. This greatly simplifies the problem: in many cases no air need be added, nor is a pump or source of high-pressure air required. If the ratio of intake air velocity to freestream is below 1.0, simple variations of the exit passage may suffice. If inlet velocity ratios above 1.0 are required an enlarged exist passage will act as a pump and draw in the added air, up to an inlet velocity ratio of about 1.4. Checking inlet velocity ratios much higher than this, say around 3 or 4, is advisable for the go-around flight condition. These ratios will require a pump or a tailpipe venturi.

One may reasonably expect 2 or 3 per cent more ram recovery full scale than model scale.

Augenstein in Ref. 5:7 discusses a method of simulating the exhaust from a jet engine.

5:16. Aeroelasticity. It is a great mistake to attempt to compare the performance of a rigid wind-tunnel model and that of a

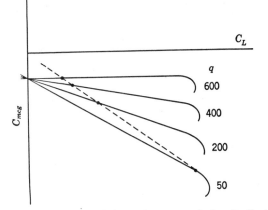

FIG. 5:51. Effect of airplane deformation on static longitudinal stability, swept-wing bomber.

modern high-performance airplane without making due allowance for the deformations of the real airplane under loads. This is particularly important for airplanes with swept wings, as they lose stability with increasing dynamic pressure as the tips "wash out" under load. A typical example is shown in Fig. 5:51, where a swept-wing bomber showed good stability with the rigid model (nominally called $q = 0$) but less stability as the dynamic pressure increased. Actually the airplane does not fly at constant q, and the effective stability curve (for this airplane at one altitude) is a curve such as the one shown dotted.

There are some factors that may act to ameliorate the difficulties usually arising from deformations. For instance, the deformation may not be as serious during maneuvers as it is statically, since inertia forces may well act to resist the deformation. Also one may "luck out," as in the event of loss of aileron power due to wing twist, by having a corresponding decrease in the damping due to roll.

Models for examining the aeroelastic effects must be carefully constructed to duplicate to scale the deformations of the full-scale airplane. Usually this precludes a continuous wing structure, and separate sections having a span of only a few inches are fastened to a spar which is carefully selected to provide the proper deformation due to torque and normal loads, chord loads normally being inconsequential. A typical installation used balsa wings sections on an aluminum spar, with chordwise joints sealed with thin rubber sheeting (called "dental dam" and available at most surgical supply houses). Engines and concentrated loads were simulated with small lead weights.

The model was then placed on the usual wind-tunnel balance, and runs were made with varying q. The results appeared somewhat like those shown in Fig. 5:51. Excellent correlation has been obtained between elastic models and flight test of the full-scale airplane.

5:17. Testing for Dynamic Stability. Problems of dynamic stability have become of great interest, particularly at high speed where it is not uncommon to find oscillations beyond the capabilities of a human pilot. Before discussing testing methods, however, it might be well to define the difference between static and dynamic stability. An airplane is statically stable if upon being displaced from a trimmed condition it tends to return to the trimmed condition. If the oscillations that ensue damp out, the airplane is said to be dynamically stable also. Airplanes normally have two modes of oscillation in the plane of symmetry: a short-period oscillation lasting a few seconds, and a longer period, of around a minute, or "phugoid" motion. Interest centers around the short-period oscillation, which could become

catastrophic before the pilot could handle it.   The long-period
oscillation is annoying but controllable.

Many wind-tunnel rigs have been used to get dynamic stability
data.   Most of them allow for one degree of freedom at a time,
and to a fair approximation this seems to be conservative; if the

Courtesy Boeing Airplane Co.

FIG. 5:52.   Flexible model of the Boeing B-47 being flown on the dynamic
stability rig in the Boeing wind tunnel.   Deflection of the wings indicates that
a high-g condition is being simulated.

model is dynamically stable in pitch it will probably be dynamically stable in pitch plus vertical displacement.   Finned
bodies of revolution stable in pitch are usually stable in free
flight.   Roll-pitch coupling and Dutch roll of course cannot be
examined without an adequate number of freedoms.

The mount shown in Fig. 5:52 can be used for determining
several types of dynamic stability.   The model is mounted at the
center of gravity on a bearing that permits pitch.   A rod running
vertically through the model allows yaw.   Motion up and down

the vertical rod is permitted by a bearing on the rod. (The model is slotted to allow clearance for the rod when the model pitches.)

One would naturally assume that the model, being free to pitch and plunge, would be admirably suited to duplicate the phugoid or long-period oscillation in the wind tunnel, but such is not the case. When the airplane follows the phugoid there are wide changes in velocity while the tunnel operates at a constant speed. On the other hand, the model may be clamped out of trim, the tunnel brought up to speed, and the model suddenly released. The ensuing motion defines the short-period oscillation which takes place so rapidly in the real case that the airplane does not have time to change speed, and the tunnel representation is a true one. Limits should be provided on the vertical "fly rod" so that the model does not inadvertently reach the floor or ceiling and get subjected to large deflections. Figure 5:52 shows the B-47 dynamic model being subjected to a several g pullout.

The instrumentation for such tests usually embraces some visual and photographic techniques plus a high-speed oscillograph which gets an input from strain gages on very flexible beams or from a differential transformer.

One procedure is to bring the tunnel gradually up to its maximum speed while watching the behavior of the model through its record on the oscillograph. Sometimes the model needle will write a record of light stable actions until high subsonic Mach number is reached. Then, in perhaps 2 or 3 seconds violent instability will appear. It goes without saying that a brake in the model trunnion is a necessary adjunct.

A second procedure is to hold the tunnel speed constant and "kick" the model into a displaced attitude from which it is released. The data sought usually embrace (1) the time to complete a single oscillation (i.e., the "period," T); (2) the time to damp to one-half amplitude, $t_{1/2}$; (3) the number of oscillations to damp to one-half amplitude, $n_{1/2}$; and (4) the damping factor, DF. The derivation of the theory for dynamic stability is beyond the scope of this book, and the reader may consult Ref. 5:4 for the basic dynamic stability theory.

In greatly condensed form it may be stated that the theory for dynamic stability requires more than the usual tunnel parameters for fixed models such as C_L, C_D, C_m, $dC_L/d\alpha$, dC_D/dC_L^2. Additional information needed includes moments of inertia and damping coefficients that are unattainable with a fixed model.

As for longitudinal stability it may be said that the uncertain time lag between flow changes at the wing and their corresponding effect at the tail is one of the problems not soluble from model-fixed tests.

In closing this brief summary of dynamic stability testing methods perhaps it will be useful to discuss the effect of scale. Density will be assumed constant.

First of all, since the areas of the model will be decreased by the $(scale)^2$, the aerodynamic forces at constant velocity and air density will also. Similarly, the aerodynamic moments will decrease by $(scale)^3$.

The tangential velocities of the model are important since they combine with the translational velocities to produce effective angles of attack. Tangential velocities on a model rotating at the same angular velocity as the full-scale job will obviously be reduced by the scale, or, correspondingly, to achieve the same angles of attack on the tail surfaces of the model its angular velocity must be increased by the scale. In other words, the frequency must increase as the scale. Thus the time to perform a specific maneuver will be reduced by the scale.

In order that angular velocities increased by the scale can be obtained in a time reduced by the scale, the angular acceleration must go up as the $(scale)^2$. In order for this to be possible with $1/(scale)^3$ of the aerodynamic moment, it will be necessary to reduce the model moment of inertia by $(scale)^5$.

Now the path of the model will be similar to that of the prototype, and hence linear displacement distances will occur in a time reduced by the scale. Thus the linear accelerations must be increased by the scale. To get the increased acceleration with the force decreased by $(scale)^2$ requires that the mass be reduced by the $(scale)^3$.

Thus a 0.1-scale model tested at the same speed and in the same air as the prototype should weigh 1/1000 of the full scale and have 1/100,000 of its moment of inertia. (This will automatically accrue if similar construction is feasible.)

It will oscillate with 10 times the frequency, but if stable dynamically full scale will be stable dynamically model scale, reaching similar amplitudes, but doing so in $\frac{1}{10}$ the time. It will damp to $\frac{1}{2}$ amplitude in $\frac{1}{10}$ the time.

5:18. Testing Spin Models. The number of turns required for an airplane to recover from a tailspin can be determined with good accuracy from a test of a properly scaled model in a vertical spin tunnel, one in which a dish-shaped velocity gradient is used to keep a spinning model in the center of the stream.

Models for these spin tests are reduced in weight by the cube of the scale factor, and in moment of inertia by the fifth power of the scale factor.

If it is desired to add in altitude, the airplane density may be further reduced by the density ratio for the particular altitude desired. Normal limits for the errors in the above are ±1 per cent in full-scale weight, ±1 per cent in center-of-gravity location, and ±5 per cent in moment of inertia. The requirements of such models dictate balsa construction for light planes and mahogany for some of the heavier fighters.

The model is tossed into the vertically rising stream in such a manner that it starts spinning, usually with the controls locked into the spin. Adjustment of the tunnel velocity keeps the model in the field of the cameras, and at a selected time the controls are moved to stop the spin by a gauss ring about the test section or a timer. Sometimes a little piece of paper is simultaneously released to give the picture a time pip reference.

From reading the films the following maybe obtained: angle of attack, angle of bank, revolutions per second, and number of turns to recover. The tunnel speed yields the rate of vertical descent. The most important factors—number of turns to recover and vertical distance to recover—may be obtained within a 5 per cent error.

5:19. Testing Windmill Generators. The need for a power source to operate when a jet-engined airplane has a high-altitude flame-out has reactivated the interest shown many years ago in wind-driven generators, and not infrequently the tunnel engineer is called upon to evaluate a particular generator by an operational test. When this is so, the special precautions that are paid to models such as rotors, propellers, and the like whose possibility of failure is higher than that of rigid models should be applied.

Corrections to the data from a windmill test are subject to boundary corrections as outlined in Chapter 6, specifically wake blocking, and propeller corrections with a negative sign. However, in most cases the windmill is so small relative to the tunnel and the interest in very accurate data as compared to proof testing is so slight that corrections may be neglected.

It is of interest to look into the mechanism of a windmill from the theoretical side in order to gain an understanding of how it works. Of course the device takes energy from the air, but surprisingly the total stream energy is not available to the windmill. In words, the slowing of the stream makes a portion of the air go around the windmill instead of through it, and a point may be reached beyond which an attempt to take more energy from the stream is fruitless.

Looking at the problem from a momentum standpoint we find that, if the velocity at the windmill is $V(1 - a)$, the final velocity will be $V(1 - 2a)$, and, letting the windmill radius be R, the power-out will be

$$P_o = V(1 - a)[\rho\pi R^2 V(1 - a) \cdot V - \rho\pi R^2 V(1 - a) \cdot V(1 - 2a)]$$

$$= 2\pi\rho R^2 V^3 a(1 - a)^2$$

Differentiating and solving, we find the maximum power-out occurs when $a = \frac{1}{3}$. Substituting this value, and comparing the maximum power-out with the total in a freestream of the same radius P_s, we have

$$\frac{P_o}{P_s} = \frac{0.296\rho\pi R^2 V^3}{0.5\rho\pi R^2 V^3} = 0.594$$

or even with no-drag blades the windmill can only hope for 59.4 per cent of the stream energy. A good figure in estimating windmill sizes seems to be about one-half of that theoretically available, or roughly 30 per cent of the total stream energy. During testing, stalled blades should be avoided, as when they unstall a runaway may occur.

5:20. Testing with a Ground Plane. When an airplane is in the landing attitude and close to the ground the effect of the ground on the horizontal tail surfaces is very pronounced. Sometimes 10 more degrees of elevator deflection are required to stall the airplane when it is close to the ground than when it is at altitude. As landing is frequently the critical condition for the determination of elevator size an accurate test must be performed in the wind tunnel for the information of the design group. Such a test may be performed in conjunction with a flat panel that spans the tunnel beneath the model. (See Figs. 5:53 and 5:54.) This panel, called a ground plane, is superior to mounting the model near the tunnel floor, as the thick boundary layer found there would impair the results.

As far as the dimensions of the ground plane are concerned, it is better to err on the large side than the small. For wing-alone tests a groundboard extending three chords ahead of the quarter chord and six chords behind it is adequate; for complete models the board must extend a tail length ahead of the model nose and a tail length behind the model tail. A groundboard 3 in. thick is reasonable for a 10-ft test section, and one or two boundary

Courtesy North American Aircraft Corp.

FIG. 5:53. Groundboard tests of a new jetplane. Note the fairings around the strut slots.

layer removal slots (activated by a flap on the groundboard lower surface) improve the simulation of the ground, which of course would have no boundary layer. No boundary-induced upwash corrections are necessary.

5:21. Testing for Local Loads. Quite often the structures group needs local loads in order to design an item whose pressure distribution cannot be computed. For bomb-bay-door motor loads a hinge and a strain gage system is superior to integrated pressures, but if skin loads are needed a particular item may be equipped with a number of pressure orifices and loads determined from pressure diagrams. Normally the multiple manometer is referenced to tunnel static pressure and the pressure increments are expressed as a fraction of the freestream dynamic pressure. During the work-up the reference may be changed to airplane cabin pressure (if relevant) or other internal pressure.

Courtesy Lockheed Aircraft Corp.

FIG. 5:54. Groundboard mounting detail.

5:22. Testing Low-Aspect-Ratio Wings. The advantages of using low aspect ratios for supersonic airplanes are quite impressive, and not infrequently the tunnel engineer finds himself testing such configurations for low-speed characteristics.

Low-aspect-ratio lift curves may look quite different from those at high aspect ratio. Below $AR = 2.0$ the curve is usually concave upwards (Figs. 5:55 and 5:56). The lift curve slope at zero lift may be approximated by

$$dC_L/d\alpha = 0.008 + 0.018(AR) \quad \text{(per degree)} \quad (5{:}38)$$

below $AR = 3.0$. For greater aspect ratios, eq. 5:1 should be employed.

5:23. Testing Engines. The actual operation of piston or jet engines in a wind tunnel for development reasons is a very specialized type of test possible in only a very few wind tunnels. Of the two, the piston engines present less of a tunnel problem since their exhaust is smaller in quantity than that from a jet engine. The jet engine requires a huge scavenging system sometimes using half as much power as the tunnel itself in order to keep contamination low. This problem, incidentally, has an interesting facet in high-speed work, where the presence of rather small amounts of exhaust changes the values of γ and hence confuses the operating Mach number. In some low-speed tunnels the air exchangers can handle the exhaust problem.

Owing to the relative rarity of engine tests, a complete discussion of proper methods will not be presented.

5:24. Jettison Tests. It is frequently necessary to determine the satisfactory release capabilities of tip tanks, underwing stores, bombs, or other devices. This type of test is concerned mostly with duplicating a flight condition and a trajectory, and accordingly the most important parameters to simulate are the linear accelerations which are basically associated with the model density ρl^3.

Using W for weight, and subscripts M for model and FS for full scale, the following simple relations are obtained:

$$W_M = W_{FS} \frac{\rho_M}{\rho_{FS}} \left(\frac{l_M}{l_{FS}}\right)^3 \quad (5{:}39)$$

and

$$q_M = q_f \frac{W_M}{W_{FS}} \left(\frac{l_{FS}}{l_M}\right)^2 \quad (5{:}40)$$

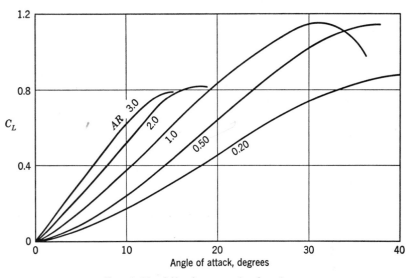

FIG. 5:55. Lift of rectangular flat plates.

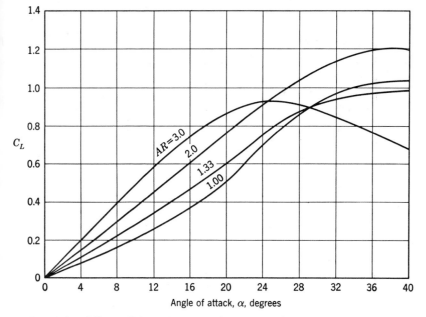

FIG. 5:56. Lift coefficients for delta wings of various aspect ratios, NACA
0012 profile.

The trajectory obtained by model work needs to be multiplied by the scale factor to equal the full-scale trajectory. If the models are caught in a safety net in the diffuser one may reasonably figure on five drops for each bomb model and one drop for an empty tank before the model is destroyed.

PROBLEMS

5:1. Outline five procedures that should be followed in any research program.

5:2. The results from a wind-tunnel test of a wing of aspect ratio = 5.5 are in the following table. Find e.

C_L	C_D	C_L	C_D
0.1	0.0068	0.5	0.0224
0.2	0.0073	0.6	0.0294
0.3	0.0104	0.7	0.0375
0.4	0.0160	0.8	0.0470

5:3. For the wing of problem 2 find dC_D/dC_L at $C_L = 0.7$ by eq. 5:12, and check by the mirror method.

5:4. Locate the center of pressure for a wing whose moment center is at the 25 per cent chord point. $C_{mtr} = -0.300$, $C_L = 1.375$, $C_D = 0.0969$, and $\alpha = 0.0°$.

5:5. Explain why wings of finite aspect ratio show a smaller $C_{L\ max.}$ than wings of "infinite" aspect ratio.

5:6. A wing has a constant chord center-section of 2-ft chord and 3-ft semi-span. The panel is then tapered 2:1 and has a 4-ft span. The tip which is outside the panel is a semicircle. Find the ratio between panel and complete wing lift coefficients, assuming no twist. Use Schrenk's method.

5:7. What two steps can be taken during a run to catch errors?

5:8. What is the greatest advantage of two-dimensional testing?

5:9. Draw a plot of C_L, C_D, and C_{mcg} for a reasonable airplane, showing values on the plot, and show (dotted) the same qualities with flaps down.

5:10. What full-scale propeller parameter is duplicated during powered model testing, and how does this affect model rpm?

5:11. What serious factor is missing when adverse yaw is determined in a wind tunnel?

REFERENCES

5:1. B. Lockspeiser, Ventilation of 24 ft Wind Tunnel, *R&M* 1372, 1930.

5:2. C. C. Clymen, Power Requirements for Wind Tunnel Motors, *Aero Digest*, December, 1941.

5:3. Gotthold Mathias, Supplemental Data and Calculations of the Lateral Stability of Airplanes, *TM* 742, 1934.

5:4. C. H. Zimmerman, An Analysis of Longitudinal Stability in Power-off Flight with Charts for Use in Design, *TR* 521, 1935.

5:5. H. J. Goett, Tunnel Procedure for Determining Critical Stability Procedure, *TR* 781, 1943.

5:6. G. Chester Furlong and Thomas V. Bollech, Effect of Ground Interference on the Aerodynamic Characteristics of a 42° Swept Wing, *TN* 2487, 1951.

5:7. B. W. Augenstein, The Simulation of Combustion Models in Wind Tunnels, *JAS*, March, 1949.

5:8. O. Schrenk, A Simple Approximation Method for Obtaining the Spanwise Lift Distribution, *TM* 948, 1940.

5:9. H. A. Pearson, Span Load Distribution for Tapered Wings with Partial-Span Flaps, *TR* 585, 1937.

5:10. A. H. Flax and H. R. Lawrence, The Aerodynamics of Low-Aspect-Ratio Wings and Wing-Body Combinations, Anglo-American Aeronautical Conference, 1951.

5:11. William Milliken, Dynamic Stability and Control Research, Anglo-American Aeronautical Conference, 1951.

5:12. Archibald R. Sinclair and A. Warner Robins, A Method for the Determination of the Time Lag in Pressure-Measuring Systems Incorporating Capillaries, *TN* 2793, 1952.

5:13. Time Lags Due to Compressible-Poiseuille Flow Resistance in Pressure-Measuring Systems, *NOL Memo* 10,677, 1950.

Chapter 6

WIND-TUNNEL-BOUNDARY CORRECTIONS

The conditions under which a model is tested in a wind tunnel are not the same as those in free air. There is absolutely no difference traceable to having the model still and the air moving instead of vice versa, but the longitudinal static-pressure gradient usually present in the test section and the open or closed jet boundaries in most cases produce extraneous forces that must be subtracted out. These may be summarized as follows:

The variation of static pressure along the test section produces a drag force known as "horizontal buoyancy." It is usually small and in the drag direction in closed test sections, and negligible in open jets where in some cases it becomes thrust.

The presence of the lateral boundaries produces:

1. A lateral constraint to the flow pattern about a body known as "solid blocking." In a closed wind tunnel solid blocking is the same as an increase of dynamic pressure, increasing all forces and moments at a given angle of attack. It is usually negligible with an open test section since the airstream is then free to expand in a normal manner.

2. A lateral constraint to the flow pattern about the wake known as "wake blocking." This effect increases with an increase of wake size (drag), and in a closed test section increases the drag of the model. Wake blocking is usually negligible with an open test section since the airstream is then free to expand in a normal manner.

3. An alteration to the local angle of attack along the span. In a closed test section the angles of attack near the wingtips of a model with large span are increased excessively, making the tip stall start early. The effect of an open jet is just the opposite (tips unstalled), and in both cases the effect is diminished to the point of negligibility by keeping model span less than 0.8 tunnel width.

268

4. An alteration to the normal curvature of the flow about a wing so that the wing moment coefficient, its lift, and angle of attack are increased in a closed wind tunnel, decreased with an open jet.

5. An alteration to the normal downwash so that the measured lift and drag are in error. The closed jet makes the lift too large and the drag too small at a given geometric angle of attack. An open jet has just the opposite effect.

6. An alteration to the normal downwash behind the wing so that the measured-tailsetting and static stability is in error. In a closed jet the model has too much stability and an excessively high wake location, the opposite being noted in an open jet. This stability effect is large.

7. An alteration to the normal flow pattern so that hinge moments are too large in a closed test section, too small in an open one.

8. An alteration to the normal flow about an asymmetrically loaded wing such that the boundary effects become asymmetric and the observed rolling and yawing moments are in error.

9. An alteration to the normal free air flow about a thrusting propeller so that the pressure in the slipstream is too high when a closed test section is employed. This effect is negligible when an open jet is used.

Fortunately, it is a rare test indeed when all the above corrections must be applied. We should note, however, that the additional effects due to the customary failings of wind tunnels—angularity of flow, local variations in velocity, tare, and interference—are extraneous to the basic wall corrections discussed in this chapter, and it is assumed that the errors due to these effects have already been removed before wall effects are considered. Methods governing their removal have been discussed in Chapters 3 and 4.

Since the manner in which the two- and three-dimensional walls affect the model and are simulated is quite different, they will be individually considered in the sections to come.

Treatment of data from nearsonic, transonic, and supersonic tests is covered in Chapters 11 and 12.

6:1. The Method of Images. It is well known that the flow pattern about a wing may be closely simulated mathematically by replacing it with a vortex system composed of a lifting line vortex and a pair of trailing vortices. Similarly, a solid body may be represented by a source-sink system, and a wake by a source. Thus the entire airplane or component may be simulated by "artificial" means almost to any degree of accuracy desired, depending of course on the complexity of calculations that can be tolerated.   Fortunately, a very simple first-order set-up usually suffices.

Students of fluid theory are well acquainted with the simulation of a boundary near a source, sink, doublet, or vortex by the addition of a second source, sink, doublet, or vortex "behind" the boundary to be represented.   Solid boundaries are formed by the addition of an image system which produces a zero streamline matching the solid boundary.   An open boundary requires an image system which produces a zero velocity potential line which matches the boundary in question.   After the image system is established, its effect on the model is the same as that of the boundary it represents.

We may see how to make up an image system by considering the following case for a vortex in a closed rectangular tunnel; and we may as well note herewith that it is usually only necessary to satisfy the conditions in the plane of the lifting line.   A three-

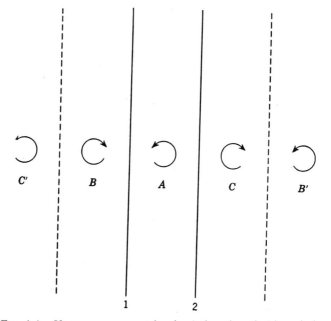

FIG. 6:1.   Vortex arrangement for simulation of vertical boundaries.

dimensional image system is only necessary to get the boundary induced upwash aft of the wing, the streamline curvature effect, or the corrections for a wing with a lot of sweepback.

Consider a single vortex A which we wish to contain within the solid walls 1 and 2 (Fig. 6:1). To simulate wall 1, we need a vortex B of sign opposite to that of A, and for wall 2, a vortex C of the same sign as B. Now, however, vortex B needs a vortex B' to balance it from wall 2, and vortex C needs a vortex C' to balance it from wall 1, and so on out to infinity with vortices of alternating sign.

The containment of a wing or vortex pair similarly becomes that shown in Fig. 6:2a for vertical walls and in Fig. 6:2b for horizontal walls.

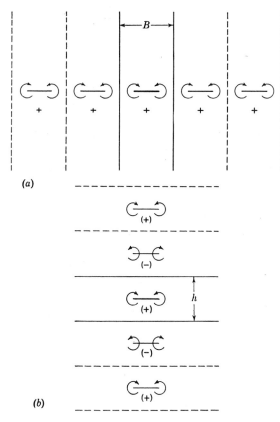

(a)

(b)

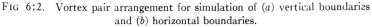

Fig 6:2. Vortex pair arrangement for simulation of (a) vertical boundaries and (b) horizontal boundaries.

The image system for a closed rectangular test section thus becomes a doubly infinite system of vortices. Figure 6:3 shows the image system needed for a wing in a closed rectangular tunnel when the three-dimensional quantities are required.

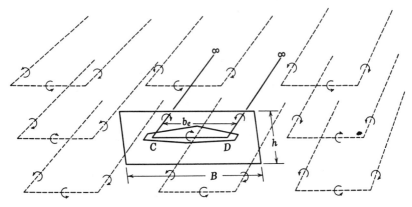

FIG. 6:3. Image system for a closed rectangular test section.

We may through elementary vortex theory and logic develop the form that corrections for boundary-induced upwash will take for an arbitrarily shaped test section. The only mathematical tools needed are the expression for the induced velocity w due to a vortex of strength Γ at a distance r

$$w = \Gamma/4\pi r \qquad (6:1)$$

and the relation between lift and circulation for a uniformly loaded wing

$$\Gamma = (SV/2b)C_L \qquad (6:2)$$

Combining the two we get

$$w = (SV/8\pi rb)C_L \qquad (6:3)$$

Now r represents the vortex spacing in the image system which we may express as some constant times a tunnel dimension, say the tunnel height h, and the model wing span may be expressed in terms of the tunnel width B. The induced angle at the centerline of the test section is then

$$\Delta(\Delta\alpha_i) = \frac{w}{V} = \frac{S}{8\pi k(b/B)(hB)} C_L$$

for any one image, and, summing the whole field, setting $B/8\pi kb$ = δ, and noting that hB is the test-section area C, we have

$$\Delta\alpha_i = \delta(S/C)C_L \qquad (6:4)$$

for the complete system.

It develops that δ is completely determined by the shape of the test section, the size of the model relative to the test section, the type of spanwise load distribution over the model, and whether or not the model is on the centerline of the test section. Equation 6:4 is hence a general form useful for all wings and test sections as long as the wing is small (less than $0.8B$) relative to the test section so that the upwash at the tunnel centerline may be taken as the average upwash.

Since the induced drag coefficient may be written as

$$C_{Di} = \alpha_i C_L$$

where α_i = induced angle, the change in induced drag caused by the boundary induced upwash becomes

$$\Delta C_{Di} = \Delta\alpha_i C_L = \delta(S/C)C_L{}^2 \qquad (6:5)$$

Equation 6:5 is also a general form. The manner in which the downwash affects larger models, and how it must be handled for the special cases of asymmetrical loadings, is covered in later pages.

We will turn now to image systems and other corrections for two-dimensional testing. Later, the corrections for three-dimensional tests will be covered in detail.

6:2. Wall Corrections for Two-Dimensional Testing. In order to study effects primarily concerned with airfoil sections, it is customary to build models of constant chord which completely span the test section from wall to wall.* The trailing vortices are then practically eliminated, and the image system for a *small* wing consists of a vertical row of vortices (having alternately plus and minus signs) above and below the model. Usually, however, when two-dimensional tests are made, the models are made of large chord to obtain the highest Reynolds number possible, and the wing must be represented by a distribution of vortices instead of a single one. The effect of the floor

---

* There is no occasion in this type of test to have the model off the tunnel centerline, and the corrections mentioned in this section will cover only the symmetric cases.

and ceiling of the tunnel is to restrain the naturally free air curvature of the flow so that the model acts like one with extra camber.

The effects of the walls on the model thickness and wake are subject to solid and wake blocking, and buoyancy if the tunnel has a longitudinal static-pressure gradient. These effects will be considered separately.

The wall corrections for two-dimensional testing have been discussed by Allen and Vincenti in Ref. 6:1, and it seems logical to follow their treatment in general. Since the trailing vortices that escape in the boundary layer are quite weak, no downwash corrections are needed.

6:3. Buoyancy (Two Dimensions). Almost all wind tunnels with closed throats have a variation in static pressure along the axis of the test section due to the thickening of the boundary layer as it progresses toward the exit cone and to the resultant effective diminution of the jet area. It follows that the pressure is usually progressively more negative as the exit cone is approached, and there is hence a tendency for the model to be "drawn" downstream.

Glauert finds that the magnitude of the gradient may be expressed as a non-dimensional factor k defined by

$$\frac{dp}{dl} = -k\frac{(\rho/2)V^2}{B}$$

where l = jet length, ft; p = pressure, lb/ft^2; B = jet width, ft. The factor k is from 0.016 to 0.040 for a closed square jet of width B, but should be experimentally measured for a given tunnel.

The amount of "horizontal buoyancy" is usually insignificant for wings, but for fuselages and nacelles it is larger and becomes important. Corrections may be calculated as follows:

Suppose that the static-pressure variation along a jet is as shown in Fig. 6:4 and that the model to be tested has the cross-section areas S as shown in Fig. 6:5. It will be seen that the variation of static pressure from, say, station 2 to station 3 is $p_2 - p_3$ and that this pressure differential acts on the average area $(S_2 + S_3)/2$. The resulting force for that segment of the fuselage is therefore

$$\Delta D_B = (p_2 - p_3)(S_2 + S_3)/2$$

This equation is most simply solved by plotting local static pres-

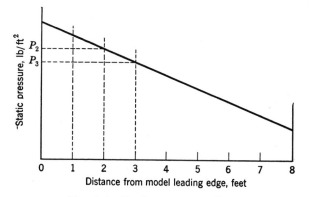

FIG. 6:4. Static-pressure gradient.

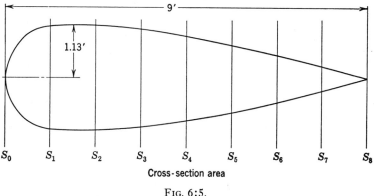

FIG. 6:5.

sure against body section area, the buoyancy then becoming the area under the curve.*

For the case where the longitudinal static pressure gradient is a straight line the equation becomes:

$$\Delta D_B = -\Sigma S_x (dp/dl) dl$$

where S_x = fuselage cross-section area at station x; l = distance from fuselage nose; dp/dl = slope of longitudinal static-pressure curve.

Since $\Sigma S_x dl$ = body volume, we have

$$\Delta D_B = -(dp/dl) \text{ (body volume)} \qquad (6:6)$$

* Or by plotting the local static pressure coefficient against body section area divided by wing area to get the buoyancy drag coefficient directly.

Now the existence of a falling static-pressure gradient implies that the test section is getting effectively smaller, or in other words the streamlines are being squeezed by the contracting tube. Adding the squeezing effect to the pressure-gradient effect Glauert (Ref. 6:2) found that the total drag increment (for a two-dimensional body) is

$$\Delta D_B = -(\pi/2)\lambda_2 t^2(dp/dl) \quad \text{lb per ft of span}$$

where t = body thickness and λ_2 = body-shape factor from Fig. 6:6.

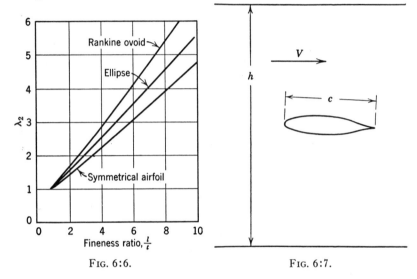

Fineness ratio, $\frac{l}{t}$

FIG. 6:6.   FIG. 6:7.

Allen and Vincenti in Ref. 6:1 replace $\lambda_2 t^2$ by $\frac{1}{4}\Lambda c^2$ and hence get

$$\Delta D_B = -\frac{\pi}{8}\Lambda c^2\frac{dp}{dl} = -\frac{6h^2}{\pi}\Lambda\sigma\frac{dp}{dl} \qquad (6:7)$$

where h = tunnel height, c = model chord, and $\sigma = (\pi^2/48)(c/h)^2$; and

$$\Lambda = \frac{16}{\pi}\int_0^1 \frac{y}{c}\sqrt{(1-P)\left(1+\frac{dy}{dx}\right)}\,d\frac{x}{c} \qquad (6:8)$$

x and y are the airfoil coordinates, c its chord, and P its no-camber (basic) pressure distribution.

Values of Λ for a number of airfoils are in Fig. 6:8; more are available in Ref. 6:1, or by direct integration of the above equation.   Reference 6:3 may be consulted if the integration is used.   Application of the buoyancy correction is covered in example 6:1.

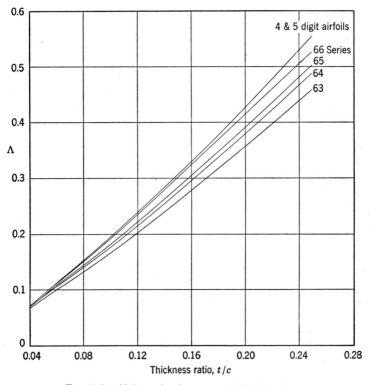

Fig. 6:8.   Values of Λ for several airfoil families.

6:4. Solid Blocking (Two Dimensions).   The presence of a model in the test section reduces the area through which the air must flow, and hence by Bernoulli's principle increases the velocity of the air as it flows over the model.   This increase of velocity, which may be considered constant over the model for customary model sizes, is called "solid blocking."   Its effect is a function of model thickness, thickness distribution, and model size and is independent of the camber.   The solid-blocking velocity increment at the model is much less (about one-fourth) than the increment one obtains from the direct area reduction since it is the streamlines far away from the model that are most displaced. The average velocity in the lateral plane of the model *is* proportionately increased, of course.

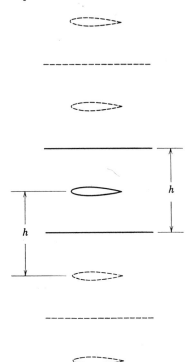

To understand the mathematical approach, consider solid blockage for a right circular cylinder in a two-dimensional tunnel. The cylinder which may be simulated by a doublet of strength $\mu = 2\pi V a^2$ (Ref. 6:39, p. 46), where $a =$ cylinder radius, is "contained" by an infinite vertical series of doublets of the same strength as the one simulating the model. The axial velocity due to the first doublet (Ref. 6:39, p. 73) is

$$\Delta V = \mu/2\pi h^2$$

so that

$$|\Delta V/V_u = a^2/h^2$$

where V_u is uncorrected velocity.

Since the velocity produced by a doublet varies inversely with the square of the distance from the doublet, the doubly infinite doublet series may be summed as

Fig. 6:9. Image system for simulating floor and ceiling.

$$\epsilon_{sb} = \left(\frac{\Delta V}{V_u}\right)_{\text{total}} = 2 \sum_1^\infty \frac{1}{n^2} \frac{a^2}{h^2}$$

$$\epsilon_{sb} = (\pi^2/3)(a^2/h^2)$$

It is seen that a large 2-ft-diameter cylinder in a tunnel 10 ft high would act as though the clear jet speed were increased by 3.3 per cent.

Now, the blockage due to a given airfoil of thickness t may be represented as that due to an "equivalent" cylinder of diameter $t \sqrt{\lambda_2}$, and using this approach the solid blocking for any two-dimensional body may be found from simple doublet summation.

Glauert in Ref. 6:2 wrote the solid-blocking velocity increment as

$$\epsilon_{sb} = \frac{\pi^2}{3} \frac{\lambda_2}{4} \frac{t^2}{h^2} = 0.822\lambda_2 \frac{t^2}{h^2} \tag{6:9}$$

Values of λ_2 may be found in Fig. 6:6. For an open jet the constant becomes -0.411.

Allen and Vincenti in Ref. 6:1 rewrite eq. 6:9 by introducing σ as per eq. 6:8, and $\Lambda = 4\lambda_2 t^2/c^2$. Their result is then

$$\epsilon_{sb} = \Lambda\sigma \tag{6:10}$$

where Λ and σ have the same values as in eq. 6:7. The manner of using this increment will be held until a later time.

A simpler form * for the solid blocking correction for two-dimensional tunnels has been given by Thom in Ref. 6:4. It has the merit of showing the parameters upon which the correction depends a little more clearly than eq. 6:10. Thom's solid blocking correction is

$$\epsilon_{sb} = \frac{K_1 \text{ (model volume)}}{C^{3/2}} \tag{6:11}$$

where $K_1 = 0.74$ for a wing spanning the tunnel breadth and 0.52 for one spanning the tunnel height. (A good approximation for airfoil model volume is $0.7 \times$ model thickness $\times$ model chord $\times$ model span.)

The term C above is the tunnel test section area, which, if a little greater accuracy is desired, may be properly taken as the geometric area less the boundary-layer displacement thickness taken around the perimeter. Usually, the approximation that the displacement thickness is one-sixth of the boundary-layer thickness works well, since it is inevitable that the boundary layer be turbulent. (For the laminar case, as a matter of interest, one-third would be a good approximation for the displacement thickness.) It is not possible to give an approximate value for the boundary-layer thickness in a wind tunnel since it varies with roughness, cracks, leaks, Reynolds number, and Mach number. In one 8 by 12 ft tunnel it is 3 in. thick.

The boundary-layer displacement thickness, when it is desired, may be figured from

$$\delta^* = \int_0^Y \frac{u}{V_0} dy$$

* Corrections for very large models are given in Ref. 6:41.

where u = local velocity in boundary layer at a height y above the surface, Y = boundary-layer thickness, and V_0 = free-stream velocity.

Several wind tunnels of the 7 by 10 ft general size seem to have boundary-layer displacement thicknesses of about ½ to ¾ in.

A fundamental source of error in the above solid blocking method is the simulation of the body by a doublet or a doublet system. This error may be circumvented if the pressure at the tunnel wall is measured model in and model out; the resultant velocity increment computed; and the image system theory used to compute the ratio between blocking at the wall and at the tunnel centerline. The new difficulty is in having a smooth enough wall for trustworthy pressure measurements. For a two-dimensional tunnel the velocity increment at the tunnel wall is three times that at the tunnel centerline.

6:5. Wake Blocking (Two Dimensions). Any real body without suction-type boundary-layer control will have a wake behind it, and this wake will have a mean velocity lower than the free-stream. According to the law of continuity, the velocity outside of the wake in a closed tunnel must be higher than freestream in order that a constant volume of fluid may pass through the test section (Fig. 6:10). The higher velocity in the main stream has,

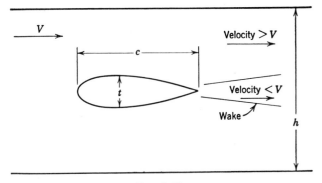

FIG. 6:10.

by Bernoulli's principle, a lowered pressure, and this lowered pressure, arising as the boundary layer (which later becomes the wake) grows on the model, puts the model in a pressure gradient and results in a velocity increment at the model.

In order to compute this wake effect we must first mathematically simulate the wake and the tunnel boundaries. The wake simulation is fairly simple. In the two-dimensional case a source at the wing trailing edge emitting, say, "blue" fluid will result in a "blue" region quite similar to a wake. Since the only drag existent is represented by this wake, the proper quantity Q to be emitted may be determined by

$$D = \rho Q V$$

In order to preserve continuity, a sink of the same absolute strength should be added far downstream.

The simulated wake may be contained within the floor and ceiling by an infinite vertical row of source-sink combinations. The image sources produce no axial velocity at the model, but the image sinks will induce a horizontal velocity in the amount

$$\Delta V = \tfrac{1}{2} Q / h$$

where h = spacing between sources.

The factor $\tfrac{1}{2}$ arises since half of the sink effect will be upstream and the other half downstream. Thus, an incremental velocity is produced at the model by the walls which should be added to the tunnel-clear results to allow for "wake blocking." A useful form of the above is

$$\epsilon_{wb} = \Delta V / V_u = \tau c_{du} \qquad (6{:}12)$$

where

$$\tau = \tfrac{1}{4} c / h \qquad (6{:}13)$$

Thom's paper yields the same relation as eq. 6:12 for two-dimensional wake blocking.

The wake gradient effect, from eq. 67 of Ref. 6:1, is

$$\Delta c_{dwb} = \Lambda \sigma$$

Wake blockage may be neglected for the open-jet case.

6:6. Streamline Curvature (Two Dimensions). The presence of ceiling and floor prevents the normal curvature of the free air that occurs about any lifting body, and—relative to the straightened flow—the body appears to have more camber (around 1 per cent for customary sizes) than it actually has. Accordingly, the airfoil in a closed wind tunnel has too much lift and moment about the quarter chord * at a given angle of attack,

---

* The moment about the half chord is independent of the camber and has no curvature effect.

and, indeed, the angle of attack is too large as well. This effect is not limited to cambered airfoils, since, using the vortex analogy, any lifting body produces a general curvature in the airstream.

We may gain an insight into the streamline curvature effect, and calculate values as well, by assuming that the airfoil in question is small and may be approximated by a single vortex at its quarter-chord point. The image system necessary to contain this vortex between floor and ceiling consists of a vertical row of vortices above and below the real vortex. The image system extends to infinity both above and below and has alternating signs according to the logic of Sect. 6:1. Let us start by considering the first image pair as shown in Fig. 6:11. It is apparent that they induce no horizontal velocity since the horizontal components cancel, but, as will also be seen, the vertical components add.

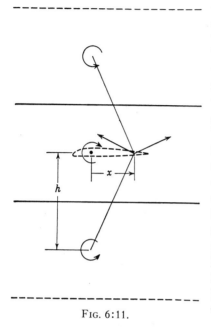

Fig. 6:11.

From simple vortex theory, the vertical velocity at a distance x from the lifting line will be

$$ w_v = \frac{\Gamma}{2\pi} \frac{1}{\sqrt{h^2 + x^2}} \frac{x}{\sqrt{h^2 + x^2}} = \frac{\Gamma}{2\pi} \frac{x}{h^2 + x^2} $$

Substitution of reasonable values for x and h into the above equation reveals that the boundary-induced upwash *angle* varies almost linearly along the chord, and hence the streamline curvature is essentially circular.

The chordwise load for an airfoil with circular camber may be considered as a flat plate loading plus an elliptically shaped loading.* The magnitude of the flat plate load is determined from the product of the slope of the lift curve (2π per radian) and the boundary-induced increase in the angle of the tangent at the

* See p. 110 of Ref. 6:39.

half-chord point because for circular camber the curve at this point is parallel to the line connecting the ends of the camberline. This load is properly computed as an angle-of-attack correction.

The elliptical loading is determined by the product of the slope of the lift curve and the angular difference between the zero lift line (i.e., the slope of the curve at the three-quarter chord point) and the chord line (the angle at the half chord). The lift, pitching-moment, and hinge-moment corrections are due to this elliptic component of the load.

Considering the flat plate loading first, the upwash induced at the half chord by the two images closest to the real airfoil is

$$ w_v = 2 \frac{\Gamma}{2\pi} \frac{c/4}{h^2 + (c/4)^2} $$

Since $\Gamma = c c_l V/2$, the angular correction needed for the nearest images becomes

$$ \Delta\alpha = \frac{w_v}{V} = \frac{1}{8\pi} \frac{c^2}{h^2 + (c/4)^2} c_l $$

Assuming that $(c/4)^2$ is small compared to h^2, and again using

$$ \sigma = (\pi^2/48)(c/h)^2 $$

we get

$$ \Delta\alpha = (6\sigma/\pi^3) c_l $$

The second pair of vortices being twice as far away will be roughly one-fourth as effective, and the third pair one-ninth, so that for the images above and below the real wing we have

$$ \Delta\alpha_{sc} = (6\sigma/\pi^3)(1 - \tfrac{1}{4} + \tfrac{1}{9} - \tfrac{1}{16} \cdots) c_l $$

$$ = \frac{6}{\pi^3} \frac{\pi^2}{12} \sigma c_l = \frac{1}{2\pi} \sigma c_l $$

since the alternating series shown above equals $\pi^2/12$ when summed to infinity. The additive lift correction is

$$ \Delta c_{lsc} = -2\pi(\tfrac{1}{2}\pi)\sigma c_l $$

$$ = -\sigma c_l \qquad\qquad (6:14) $$

and the additive moment correction is

$$ \Delta c_{m\frac{1}{4}sc} = (-\sigma/4)\Delta c_{lsc} \qquad\qquad (6:15) $$

Allen and Vincenti in Ref. 6:1 spread the vorticity out along the airfoil chord instead of concentrating it at the quarter chord. The lift and moment values of the simple analysis remain the same, but the angle-of-attack correction becomes

$$\Delta\alpha_{sc} = (57.3\sigma/2\pi)(c_{lu} + 4c_{m\frac{1}{4}u}) \qquad (6:16)$$

If the chord is kept less than 0.7 tunnel height (and it usually is), wall effects on the *distribution* of lift may be neglected.

Since there is no drag in theoretical two-dimensional flow, there is no streamline curvature correction for drag.

6:7. Summary of Two-Dimensional Boundary Corrections. The complete low-speed wall effects for two-dimensional wind-tunnel testing are summed below for ease in use. The data with the subscript u are uncorrected data based on clear stream q, with the exception of drag which must have the buoyancy due to a longitudinal static-pressure gradient removed before final correcting.

Velocity (from eqs. 6:10 and 6:12):

$$V = V_u(1 + \epsilon) \qquad (6:17)$$

where $\epsilon = \epsilon_{sb} + \epsilon_{wb}$.

Dynamic pressure (from expanding eq. 6:17, and dropping higher-order terms):

$$q = q_u(1 + 2\epsilon) \qquad (6:18)$$

Reynolds number (from eq. 6:17):

$$R = R_u(1 + \epsilon) \qquad (6:19)$$

α, c_l, and $c_{m\frac{1}{4}}$ (from eqs. 6:14, 6:15, 6:16):

$$\alpha = \alpha_u + \frac{57.3\sigma}{2\pi}(c_{lu} + 4c_{m\frac{1}{4}u}) \qquad (6:20)$$

$$c_l = c_{lu}(1 - \sigma - 2\epsilon) \qquad (6:21)$$

$$c_{m\frac{1}{4}} = c_{m\frac{1}{4}u}(1 - 2\epsilon) + (\sigma c_l/4) \qquad (6:22)$$

c_{d0} (from the dynamic-pressure effect plus the wake gradient term):

$$c_{d0} = c_{d0u}(1 - 3\epsilon_{sb} - 2\epsilon_{wb}) \qquad (6:23)$$

For the above,

$$\sigma = (\pi^2/48)(c/h)^2$$

The case of the free two-dimensional jet (floor and ceiling off, but wingtip walls in place) requires an additional factor that accounts for the downward deflection of the airstream as follows (both flow curvature and downwash deflection are included):

$$\Delta\alpha = -\left[\frac{1}{4}\left(\frac{c}{h}\right)c_l + \frac{\pi}{24}\left(\frac{c}{h}\right)^2(c_l)\right](57.3) \quad (6\!:\!24)$$

$$\Delta c_{d0} = -\frac{1}{4}\left(\frac{c}{h}\right)c_l^2 \quad (6\!:\!25)$$

$$\Delta c_{m\frac{1}{4}} = -\frac{\pi^2}{96}\left(\frac{c}{h}\right)^2 c_l \quad (6\!:\!26)$$

These values should be added to the observed data.

It is noted that a drag correction is present here, and further that these corrections are extremely large. Since the jet is free to expand, blocking corrections are not necessary.

The case where a wing completely spans a free jet without lateral restraining walls is not of much value in practice. Such a set-up is rarely used except in small tunnels for preliminary tests. The spillage around the wingtip makes the wing area less effective so that the coefficients as obtained should be increased. One test (unpublished) indicates that, for $c/h = 0.2$, the measured lift was 18 per cent low. This amount should be applied over and above the free jet correction with lateral walls.

Example 6:1

Find the corrected data for the following two-dimensional test:

Model 65-209 airfoil; test speed 100 mph; test section 2 by 7 ft; model chord 2.5 ft, standard sea-level air; $\alpha_u = 4.0°$; lift 61.30 lb; drag 7.54 lb; moment about quarter chord -7.98 ft-lb; tunnel longitudinal static pressure gradient -0.02 lb per sq ft per ft. Neglect area reduction by boundary layer.

From Fig. 6:8, $\Lambda = 0.163$, and from page 283, $\sigma = 0.0262$. From eq. 6:7 the buoyancy is

$$\Delta D_B = -\frac{6(7)^2}{\pi}(0.163)(0.0262)(-0.02)$$

$$= 0.008 \text{ lb}$$

The uncorrected coefficients are

$$c_{lu} = \frac{61.30}{25.58 \times 5.0} = 0.48$$

$$c_{d0u} = \frac{7.54 - 0.008}{25.58 \times 5.0} = 0.00589$$

$$c_{m\frac{1}{4}u} = \frac{-7.98}{25.58 \times 5.0 \times 2.5} = -0.025$$

The corrected coefficients are

$$\alpha = 4.0° + \frac{(57.3)(0.0262)}{2\pi}[0.48 + 4(-0.025)] = 4.09°$$

$$c_l = 0.48[1 - 0.0262 - 2(0.163)(0.0262) - 2(0.0893)(0.00589)]$$

$$= 0.472$$

$$c_{d0} = 0.00589[1 - 3(0.163)(0.0262) - 2(0.0893)(0.00589)]$$

$$= 0.00577$$

$$c_{m¼} = (-0.025)[1 - 2(0.163)(0.0262) - 2(0.0893)(0.00589)]$$

$$+ (0.0262)(0.472/4)$$

$$= -0.0216$$

6:8. Experimental Verification of Two-Dimensional Wall Corrections. By testing models of several sizes at the same Reynolds number, data were obtained that have yielded an excellent check on the wall corrections presented. These (from Ref. 6:1) are shown in Fig. 6:12, uncorrected, and Fig. 6:13, corrected. It is seen that the method given brings the data into beautiful agreement.

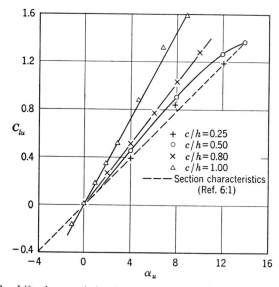

FIG. 6:12. Lift characteristics for NACA 0012 airfoil section uncorrected for tunnel-wall interference.

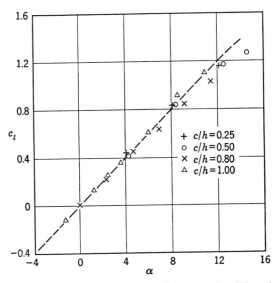

FIG. 6:13.   Data of Fig. 6:12 corrected for tunnel-wall interference.

6:9. Buoyancy; Three Dimensions.   The philosophy behind the buoyancy correction has been covered in Sect. 6:3 and need not be repeated here.   For the three-dimensional case the total correction (pressure-gradient and streamline squeezing effect) has been given by Glauert in Ref. 6:2 as

$$\Delta D_B = -(\pi/4)\lambda_3 t^3 (dp/dl) \qquad (6:27)$$

where λ_3 = body-shape factor for three-dimensional bodies from Fig. 6:14 and t = body maximum thickness.

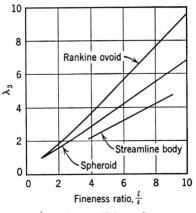

FIG. 6:14.   Values of λ_3.

Example 6:2

Calculate the drag due to buoyancy for the model of Fig. 6:5 when tested in a closed round tunnel of 9-ft diameter at 100 mph. The static-pressure gradient is -0.026 lb per sq ft per ft.

1. The volume of the body is 16.62 ft³. Neglecting the virtual mass

$$\Delta D_B = -\frac{dp}{dl}\,(\text{volume}) = (0.026)(16.62) = 0.43 \text{ lb}$$

2. From Fig. 6:14 for an $l/t = 3.98$, $\lambda_3 = 2.2$ (estimated), $t = 2.26$ ft

$$\Delta D_B = -(\pi/4)\lambda_3 t^3 (dp/dl)$$

$$= -(\pi/4)(2.2)(2.26)^3(-0.026)$$

$$= 0.519 \text{ lb}$$

As seen from example 6:2, neglecting the virtual mass may change the buoyancy drag as much as 20 per cent, but this in turn would be about 1 per cent of the total model drag for models of ordinary dimensions.

6:10. Solid Blocking (Three Dimensions). The solid blocking corrections for three-dimensional flow follow the same philosophy described in Sect. 6:4 for two dimensions. According to Herriot (Ref. 6:25), the body is again represented by a source-sink distribution, and contained in the tunnel walls by an infinite distribution of images.

Summing the effect of the images, the solid blocking velocity effect for a wing is

$$\epsilon_{sbW} = \frac{\Delta V}{V_u} = \frac{K_1 \tau_1 \,(\text{wing volume})}{C^{3/2}} \qquad (6:28)$$

where K_1 = body-shape factor from Fig. 6:15, and τ_1 = a factor depending on the tunnel test section shape, and model span to tunnel width ratio, from Fig. 6:16.

For bodies of revolution a similar approach results in

$$\epsilon_{sbB} = \frac{\Delta V}{V_u} = \frac{K_3 \tau_1 \,(\text{body volume})}{C^{3/2}} \qquad (6:29)$$

where K_3 = body-shape factor from Fig. 6:15; τ_1 = a fac or depending on the tunnel test-section shape, and model span (*assumed zero*) to tunnel width ratio from Fig. 6:16.

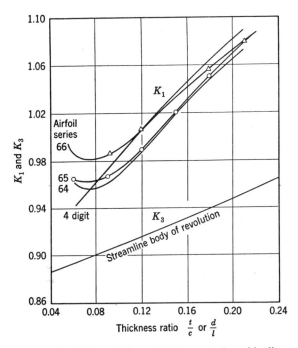

FIG. 6:15.   Values of K_1 and K_3 for a number of bodies.

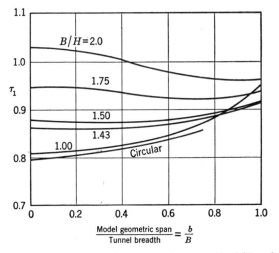

FIG. 6:16.   Values of τ_1 for a number of tunnel types.   Use $b/B = 0$ for bodies of revolution.

Thom's short-form equation for solid blocking for a three-dimensional body is

$$\frac{\Delta V_{sb}}{V_u} = \epsilon_{sb} = \frac{K \text{ (model volume)}}{C^{3/2}} \qquad (6:30)$$

where $K = 0.90$ for a three-dimensional wing and 0.96 for a body of revolution. (A good approximation for the volume of a streamline body of revolution is $0.45ld^2$, where l = length and d = maximum diameter.)

Solid blocking for a wing-body combination is simply the sum of each component as determined from the above relations.

The velocity ratio method (see Sect. 6:4) yields that the velocity increment at the wall of a round closed wind tunnel is 2.2 times that at the tunnel centerline for bodies of revolution, and about 2.0 for typical airplane models.

For open jets the solid blocking may be taken as one-fourth of the above values. Normally this results in a quantity that is quite negligible.

6:11. Wake Blocking (Three Dimensions). The corrections for wake blocking again follow the logic of Sect. 6:5 for the two-dimensional case in that the wake is simulated by a source of strength of $Q = D/\rho V$ which is matched by a downstream sink, but for the three-dimensional case the image system consists of a double infinite source-sink system spaced a tunnel height h apart vertically and a tunnel width B horizontally.

The axial velocity induced at the model by the image source system is again zero, and that due to the image sink system is

$$\Delta V = \tfrac{1}{2}Q/Bh$$

The incremental velocity is then

$$\epsilon_{wb} = \Delta V/V_u = (\tfrac{1}{4}S/C) \, C_{Du} \qquad (6:31)$$

The increase of drag due to the pressure gradient may be subtracted by removing the wing wake pressure drag

$$\Delta C_{Dw} = \frac{K_1 \tau_1 \text{ (wing volume)}}{C^{3/2}} \, C_{Du} \qquad (6:32)$$

and the body wake pressure drag

$$\Delta C_{DB} = \frac{K_3 \tau_1 \text{ (body volume)}}{C^{3/2}} \, C_{D0(u)} \qquad (6:33)$$

Thom in Ref. 6:4 gets the same value as eq. 6:31 for the wake corrections, but no corrections for the pressure-gradient drag are given.

Again the total velocity increment

$$\epsilon = \epsilon_{sb} + \epsilon_{wb} \qquad (6:34)$$

It is of interest to note that the above corresponds closely to assuming that the model frontal area is one-fourth effective, or

$$\epsilon = \frac{1}{4} \frac{\text{Model frontal area}}{\text{Test section area}} \qquad (6:35)$$

Equation 6:35 yields a correction quite close to the theoretical development, and may be used for rough mental calculations or when the model shape defies a theoretical approach.

Blocking applies to everything in the test section, of course, and hence corrections to the free jet conditions must allow for the windshields and struts or other items necessarily in the test section during test. If the image system method of evaluating tare and interference is used the blocking contribution of the mounting system is automatically evaluated. That is, putting the image system in increases the model drag by the tare and interference *plus* the wake and solid blocking of the image windshields and support struts. When T and I are subtracted the windshield goes with it.

On the other hand, when for some reason an image system is not to be used, ϵ should be taken as

$$\epsilon = \epsilon_{\text{model+struts}} + \epsilon_{\text{windshields}}$$

The windshield term will be a constant that can be evaluated with the help of eqs. 6:28 and 6:31. For tests without yaw, the strut blocking may be included in the windshield term. An alternative method is to make a pitot-static survey with the windshields in, and use its values for "freestream," allowing for model blockage only in the work-up.

Wake blockage in open test sections is customarily taken as negligible.

6:12. Streamline Curvature (Three Dimensions). The corrections for streamline curvature for three-dimensional testing follow the same philosophy as those for the two-dimensional case (Sect. 6:6) in that they are concerned with the variation of the boundary-induced upwash along the chord. Once again the variation turns out to be essentially a linear increase in angle so that the streamline curvature effect may be treated as the loading on a circular arc airfoil.   Similarly, the loading is treated as a flat-plate effect based on the flow-angle change between the quarter and half chord, and an elliptic load based on the flow-

Courtesy Office National d'Études et de Recherches Aeronautique.

FIG. 6:17.   The ONERA 26-ft nearsonic wind tunnel, largest and most power-ful wind tunnel in the world.   This tunnel was originally designed by the Ger-mans and was under construction by them at Otztal, Austria, at the close of World War II.   It was subsequently moved to France.   Of great interest is the direct hydraulic drive, without the usual electrical interstep.

angle change between the half and three quarter chord.   But for the three-dimensional case the image system is vastly different from the simple system for two dimensions.

The three-dimensional image system is shown in Fig. 6:3. Basically it consists of the real wing with its bound vortex CD and trailing vortices $C\infty$ and $D\infty$.   The vertical boundaries are simulated by the infinite system of horseshoe vortices and the horizontal boundaries by the infinite lateral system.   Linking the two systems is the infinite diagonal system.

The effect of the doubly infinite image system at the lifting line of the real wing is the main boundary upwash effect, and it may be found in the familiar δ values for any particular condition. Here as mentioned previously we are interested in the *change* of upwash along the chord and, in some cases, along the span as well.

The amount of correction needed is most easily handled as a "τ_2" effect (see Sect. 6:21), where the "tail length" is, as per the two-dimensional discussion in Sect. 6:6, one-quarter of the wing chord length.

The τ_2 factor represents the increase of boundary-induced upwash at a point P behind the wing quarter chord in terms of the amount *at* the quarter chord. The total angle effect is then

$$\Delta\alpha_{total} = \Delta\alpha + \tau_2\,\Delta\alpha \qquad (6:36)$$

where $\Delta\alpha$ = additive correction required for upwash at the quarter chord and τ_2 = streamline curvature effect on angle.

Values of τ_2 may be found in Figs. 6:52 to 6:57, using $c/4$ as the tail length needed to determine τ_2.

Another form of the same correction may be derived by assuming that the τ_2 curves are linear for the short "tail length" of the wing streamline curvature corrections. We then have

$$\Delta\alpha_{sc} = \tau_2\delta(S/C)C_L$$

$$= \frac{c}{4B}\frac{d\tau_2}{d(l_t/B)}\,\delta\frac{S}{C}\,C_L(57.3)$$

For a particular tunnel, both B and $\dfrac{d\tau_2}{d(l_t/B)}$ will be known, so that

$$\Delta\alpha_{sc} = kc(\Delta\alpha)(57.3) \quad \text{degrees}$$

and once k is determined no charts are needed to find $\Delta\alpha_{sc}$ for various models.

The additive lift correction is

$$\Delta C_{Lsc} = -\Delta\alpha_{sc}\cdot a \qquad (6:37)$$

where a = wing lift curve slope.

The additive correction to the moment coefficient is

$$\Delta C_{msc} = -0.25\,\Delta C_{Lsc} \qquad (6:38)$$

It should be noted that many tunnel engineers prefer to apply the correction entirely to the angle rather than to the angle and the lift. To make the correction to angle only, τ should be determined by using $c/2$ as a tail length instead of $c/4$. The moment correction will then be

$$\Delta C_{msc} = +0.125 \; \Delta\alpha_{sc(2)} \cdot a \qquad (6{:}39)$$

6:13. General Downwash Corrections. Very early in the century experimenters using open-throat wind tunnels found

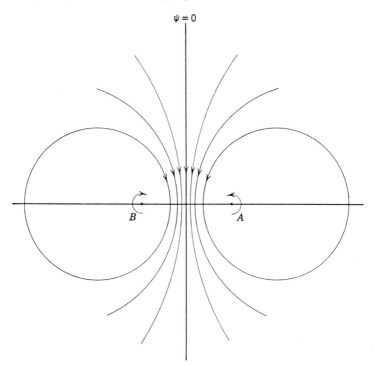

$\psi = 0$

B A

FIG. 6:18.   Field of bound vortices.

their tunnels giving very pessimistic results. The measured minimum drag and rate of change of drag with lift were too large, and the slope of the lift curve was too small. The minimum drag effect was largely due to the very low Reynolds numbers then found in the low-speed tunnels, but the other two effects were due to the tunnel boundaries. The discovery of a way to represent the walls mathematically led to a calculation of their effect. We may now present the theory and numerical values of the correction factors needed when a three-dimensional tunnel is used.

Consider the free-air streamlines caused by a pair of vortices such as are made by a uniformly loaded wing (Fig. 6:18). These streamlines extend to infinity in free air, but when the wing is enclosed in a round duct, they become contained, the wall itself becoming a streamline through which no fluid can pass. As in the two-dimensional case, the problem becomes that of finding the mathematical device that will simulate the walls by making a streamline that coincides with the walls. If we let the wing be small relative to the tunnel size, the problem becomes the simplest of all boundary problems; a streamline with the same radius as

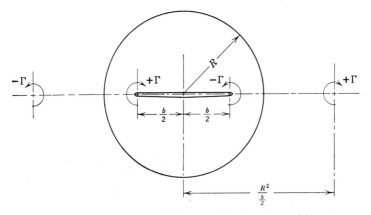

FIG. 6:19. Location of added vortices, closed round jet.

the tunnel test section is created by a pair of vortices placed out a distance $x = 2R^2/b$ on each side of the tunnel (Fig. 6:19). They must have the same strength as the wing vortices.

The streamlines due to the added vortices are shown in Fig. 6:20. (It will take but a moment for the student to trace Fig. 6:18 and place it on Fig. 6:20, and to see for himself how the $\psi = 0$ streamline coincides with the tunnel wall [Fig. 6:21].)

Another way to look at the effect of the added vortices is to consider their velocity field at the wing, as shown in Fig. 6:22. The upflow tends to offset the downflow caused by the wing trailing vortices, and the wing then has too little induced angle and too little induced drag. The exact amount may be found as follows:

The lift of a uniformly loaded wing may be written

$$L = (\rho/2)SV^2C_L = \rho V\Gamma b$$

so that the circulation

$$\Gamma = SVC_L/2b$$

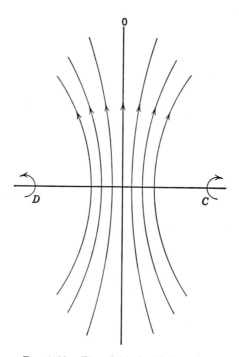

FIG. 6:20.   Flow field of added vortices.

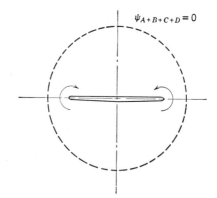

FIG. 6:21.   Total flow field of both bound and added vortices; $\psi = 0$.

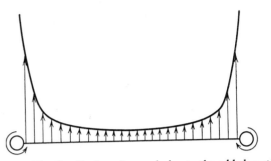

FIG. 6:22.   The distribution of upwash due to the added vortices.

The upwash at a distance r from a semi-infinite vortex is

$$w = \Gamma/4\pi r$$

and for two vortices at a distance $R^2/(b/2)$ this becomes

$$w = \Gamma b/8\pi R^2$$

Substituting for Γ we get

$$w = \tfrac{1}{8}(SV/\pi R^2)C_L$$

and the induced angle due to the boundaries (let the tunnel cross-sectional area be C) is

$$\Delta\alpha_i = w/V = \tfrac{1}{8}(S/C)C_L$$

The induced drag increment due to the boundaries is

$$\Delta C_{Di} = \Delta\alpha_i C_L$$
$$= \tfrac{1}{8}(S/C)C_L{}^2$$

Both these effects reduce the free-air induced angle and induced drag attributable to a given C_L, making the wing appear to have a larger aspect ratio than it really has. The true values become (as per the development in Sect. 6:1)

$$\alpha = \alpha_u + \delta(S/C)C_L(57.3) \tag{6:40}$$

and

$$C_D = C_{Du} + \delta(S/C)C_L{}^2 \tag{6:41}$$

where $\delta = 0.125$ for a round closed test section when the wing is small and has uniform loading.

But wings are seldom small and *never* have uniform loading. We shall have to re-examine these assumptions and see whether they induce serious errors.

The factor δ, it develops, is a function of the span load distribution, the ratio of model span to tunnel width, the shape of the test section, and whether or not the wing is on the tunnel centerline. δ may be found for almost all conditions somewhere in this chapter, and eqs. 6:40 and 6:41 are general; once δ is found they may be used to find the boundary effects. For most tunnels, however, only the δ's for uniform loading have been provided.

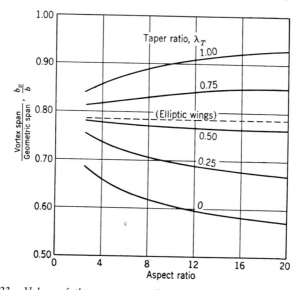

Fig. 6:23. Values of the vortex span for elliptic, rectangular, and tapered wings.

This seems odd until one realizes that the shed vortices rapidly roll up into a single pair of vortices which exactly duplicate the trailing vortex pattern of uniform loading. They then have a vortex span b_v (which is given for a large number of wings in Fig. 6:23), and it is proper to use the uniform loading correction. However, since b_v is developed somewhat downstream, it is suggested that it is more reasonable to take an effective vortex span *

$$b_e = (b + b_v)/2 \qquad (6:42)$$

for use at the wing. The values of δ for elliptic loading are rarely used.

* Values from eq. 6:42 agree excellently with those suggested by Swanson and Toll in Ref. 6:5.

Thus, in summary, to find δ for a given wing, find b_e from eq. 6:42 and use the proper δ for uniform loading. For wings not covered in Fig. 6:23, the approximation

$$b_e = 0.9b$$

will not result in a serious error.

If elliptic loading corrections are to be used, the geometric span b should be used in computing $k = $ span/tunnel width.

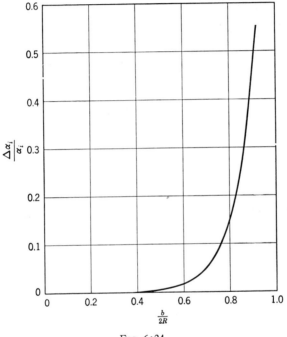

Fig. 6:24.

The theory for open test sections will not be outlined other than to mention that the condition for a free boundary is that no pressures can be supported ($\phi = 0$, where ϕ is the velocity potential). For open jets, δ normally has a negative sign. Values of δ for open jets are given in the following sections.

The special effects of very large models are covered in the next two sections.

6:14. Lift Distribution Interference (Round Jets). The variation of spanwise distribution due to the walls of a closed-throat wind tunnel is small unless the wing has large span. If this condition exists, the data become pessimistic, tip stall starting earlier and being more severe than it actually would be in free air.

Lift distribution interference in a round closed tunnel is discussed by Stewart (Ref. 6:6), who finds that span-tunnel width ratios greater than 0.8 will indicate early tip stall. An interesting numerical example shows that, for a wing of $AR = 7$, span/tunnel width = 0.9, and $C_L = 1.2$, an effective wash-in amounting to 1.44 degrees is caused by the tunnel walls.

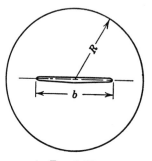

Fig. 6:25.

The designer of wind-tunnel models cannot correct for this in the model design since the effect of the walls varies with C_L. The amount of twist induced by a round closed tunnel on wings of elliptic planform is shown by Stewart to be

$$\frac{\Delta\alpha_i}{\alpha_i} = \frac{4R^2}{b^2}\left[\left(1 - \frac{b^4}{16R^4}\right)^{-\frac{1}{2}} - 1 - \frac{b^4}{32R^4}\right] \qquad (6:43)$$

where $\Delta\alpha_i$ = induced wash-in of wing due to wind-tunnel-wall interference; α_i = induced angle of attack = $C_L/\pi AR$; r = wind-tunnel radius; b = wing span. A plot of eq. 6:43 is shown in Fig. 6:24.

6:15. Lift Distribution Interference (Elliptic Jets). Gavin and Hensel (Ref. 6:7) have discussed the effect of the tunnel walls on the spanwise distribution of lift for closed elliptic jets with wings of aspect ratio = 8.0. Though the example discussed is very limited, further calculations using their method are possible. Their calculations may be summarized as follows:

1. At high lift coefficients when the wing tips lie outside the focal points of the elliptic jet the variation of the induced angle of attack along the span is no longer negligible. This amounts to apparent wash-in which becomes severe as the wing tip approaches the stall. As a result, when the wing span approaches the tunnel major diameter, determination of stall characteristics in the tunnel are conservative; i.e., the wing tips will stall at higher angles in free air.

2. Other things being constant, tunnel-wall interference is less for lift distributions in which the lift is concentrated toward the centerline. That is, for untwisted wings, those with high

taper ratio have tunnel-induced upwash of smaller magnitude than wings with low taper ratios.

3. Tunnel-wall interference is less for wings of high aspect ratio, other conditions being held constant.

4. For wings with normal lift distributions, the mean upwash factor is a minimum when the wing tips are approximately at the tunnel foci.

6:16. Downwash Corrections for Circular Jets. The corrections for uniform loading in a circular jet have been completed by

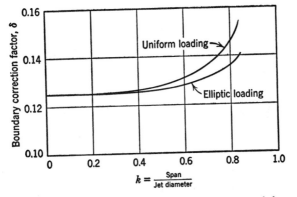

FIG. 6:26. Values of δ for a wing with elliptic loading and for one with uniform loading in a closed round jet. For an open round jet the sign of δ is negative.

Kondo (Ref. 6:8), and those for elliptic loading by Glauert (Ref. 6:9) following a method proposed by Rosenhead (Ref. 6:10). They are both based on the ratio of span to tunnel diameter $k = b/2R$, actual values being presented in Fig. 6:26. Glauert's data have been corrected to more modern units.

Owing to model length or mounting, it is sometimes necessary to place the model with its wing not on the jet centerline. This places the trailing vortices closer to one wall than to the other, altering the flow pattern and hence the proper value of δ. This condition has been examined by Silverstein

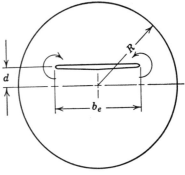

FIG. 6:27.

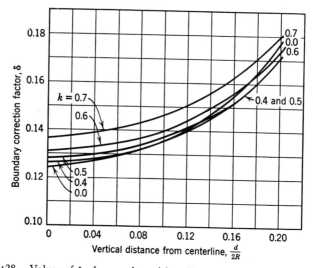

FIG. 6:28. Values of δ when a wing with uniform loading is displaced above or below the centerline of a closed round jet. δ is negative for the open jet.

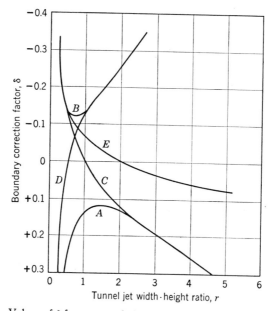

FIG. 6:29. Values of δ for open and closed rectangular jets, very small wings only. *A*. Closed tunnel. *B*. Free jet. *C*. Jet with horizontal boundaries only. *D*. Jet with vertical boundaries only. *E*. Jet with one horizontal boundary.

(Ref. 6:11), who finds the values of δ with a displaced wing of uniform loading in a round jet to be as shown in Fig. 6:28. The nomenclature is described in Fig. 6:27.

6:17. Downwash Corrections for Rectangular Jets. Van Schliestett (Ref. 6:12) has discussed basic rectangular jet corrections for very small wings, correcting a mathematical error that appears in *TR* 461 (Ref. 6:13). His results are given in Fig. 6:29.

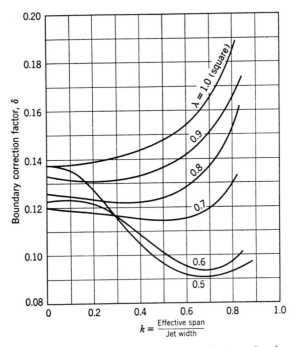

Fig. 6:30. Values of δ for a wing with uniform loading in a closed rectangular tunnel.

The boundary corrections for wings of moderate span compared to the tunnel width have been worked out for uniform loading by Terazawa (Ref. 6:14) and for elliptic loading by Glauert (Ref. 6:15). Figures 6:30, 6:31, and 6:32 give the values for δ.

$$\lambda = \frac{\text{Tunnel height}}{\text{Tunnel width}}$$

Values of δ for the square and duplex tunnel when the wing of uniform span loading is above or below the centerline are found in Figs. 6:33 to 6:36.

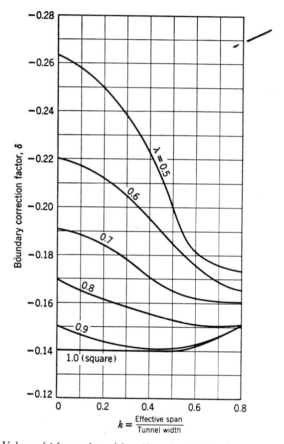

FIG. 6:31. Values of δ for a wing with uniform loading in an open rectangular jet.

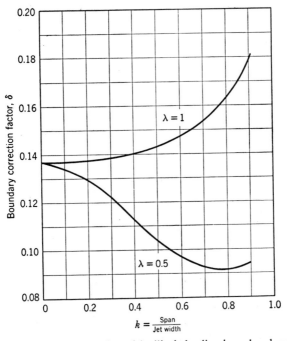

$$k = \frac{\text{Span}}{\text{Jet width}}$$

FIG. 6:32. Values of δ for a wing with elliptic loading in a closed rectangular jet.

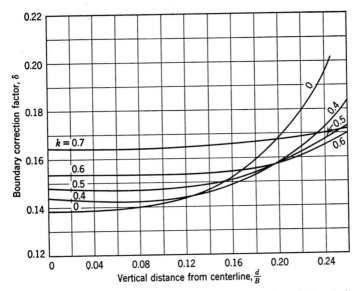

FIG. 6:33. Values of δ when a wing with uniform loading is displaced above or below the centerline of a closed square jet.

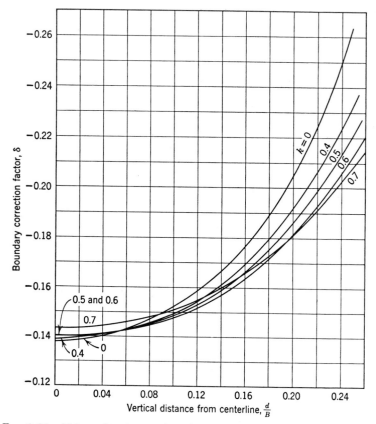

Fig. 6:34. Values of δ when a wing with uniform loading is displaced above or below the centerline of an open square jet.

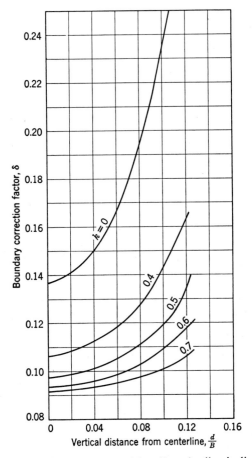

F IG. 6:35. Values of δ when a wing with uniform loading is displaced above or below the centerline of a closed 2:1 rectangular jet.

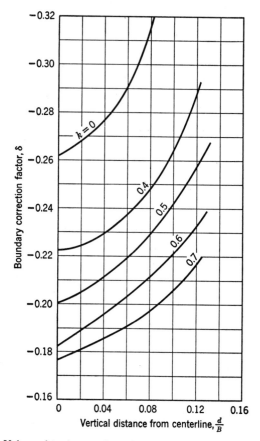

FIG. 6:36. Values of δ when a wing with uniform loading is displaced above or below the centerline of an open 2:1 rectangular jet.

6:18. Downwash Correction for Circular-Arc Jets. The testing of panels as discussed in Sects. 5:7 to 5:10 requires special corrections that mathematically simulate the tunnel boundaries and the image wing which theoretically exists on the other side on the mounting plate. This condition has been considered by Kondo (Ref. 6:8) for a test section whose original shape was round before the addition of the mounting plate.

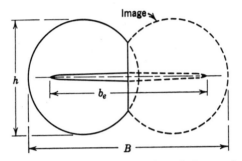

FIG. 6:37.   A model b_e in a tunnel whose boundaries are circular arcs.

The variables are the wing area S, the area of the *original circle before the plate was added* S_0, the ratio of tunnel radius to tunnel height

$$\lambda = h/B \qquad (6:44)$$

and the ratio of span to tunnel height

$$k = b_e/B \qquad (6:45)$$

The additive corrections as usual take the form

$$\Delta\alpha = \delta(S/C)C_L(57.3)$$

$$\Delta C_D = \delta(S/C)C_L^2$$

but a word of caution is necessary. In Ref. 6:8 some confusion exists in the definition of "wing area" and "tunnel area." The wing area to be used is the *actual wing area including the image area*, and the tunnel area is the area of the original circle *not including the image circle*.

Values of δ for variations of k and λ may be found in Fig. 6:38 for closed circular-arc jets and in Fig. 6:39 for open circular-arc jets.

It will be noted that these corrections are not strictly applicable to aileron tests as in practice the "image" wing would have the

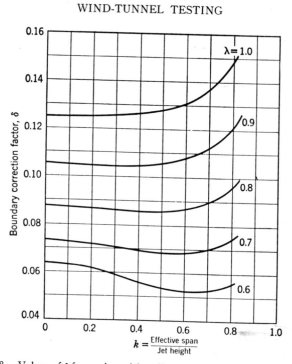

FIG. 6:38.   Values of δ for a wing with uniform loading in a closed circular-arc
wind tunnel.

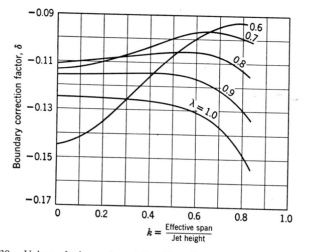

FIG 6:39.   Values of δ for a wing with uniform loading in an open circular-arc
wind tunnel.

control surface deflected oppositely. See Sect. 6:26. Further corrections for circular-arc jets are given in Ref. 6:30.

6:19. Downwash Corrections for Elliptic Jets. The corrections for wings with uniform loading in an elliptic jet have been completed by Sanuki (Ref. 6:16) and those for elliptic loading by Rosenhead (Ref. 6:17).

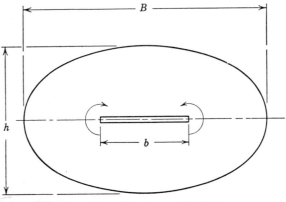

FIG. 6:40. Wing in an elliptic jet.

Sanuki bases his values for δ (uniform loading) on the ratio of the minor to the major axis of the jet λ, and the ratio of the span to the major axis k (Fig. 6:40).

$$\lambda = h/B \qquad (6:46)$$

$$k = b_e/B \qquad (6:47)$$

Values of δ are shown in Figs. 6:41 and 6:42.

The values for the wing not on the tunnel centerline (uniform loading) may be found in Figs. 6:44 and 6:45.

Rosenhead bases his values for δ (elliptic loading) on the ratio of the axis containing the wing to the other axis of the jet λ and on the ratio of the span to the focal length b/c. For presentation here, however, the latter has been reconverted to the ratio of span to tunnel width $k = b_e/B$. The values of δ are shown in Figs. 6:47 and 6:48.

Additional corrections for wings with uniform loading in $1:\sqrt{2}$ partly open elliptic test sections have been given by Riegels in Ref. 6:42. In view of the improbability of using these values they are not presented, although their existence and derivation are of interest.

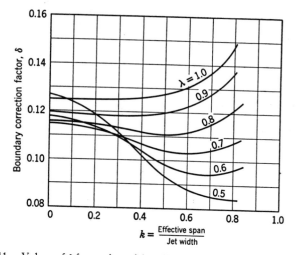

FIG. 6:41.   Values of δ for a wing with uniform loading in a closed elliptic jet.

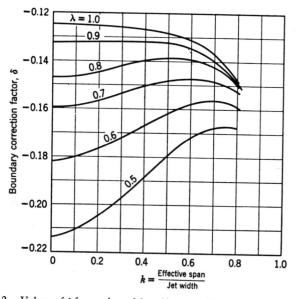

FIG. 6:42.   Values of δ for a wing with uniform loading in an open elliptic jet.

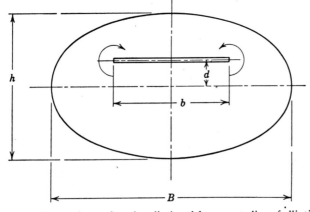

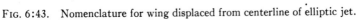

Fig. 6:43. Nomenclature for wing displaced from centerline of elliptic jet.

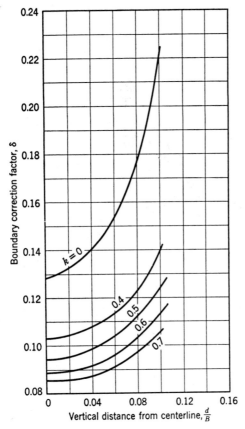

Fig. 6:44. Values of δ when a wing with uniform loading is displaced from the centerline of a closed 2:1 elliptic jet.

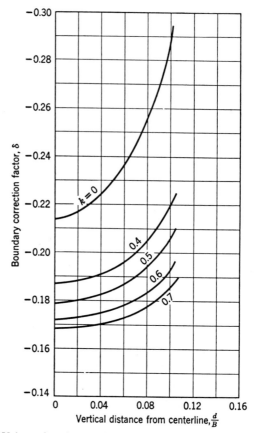

FIG. 6:45. Values of δ when a wing with uniform loading is displaced above or below the centerline of an open 2:1 elliptic jet.

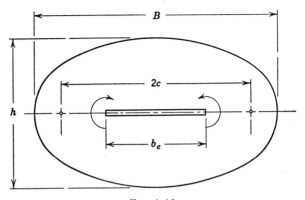

Fig. 6:46.

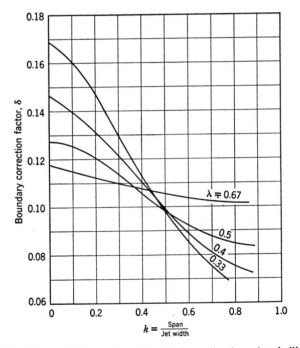

Fig. 6:47. Values of δ for a wing with elliptic loading in a closed elliptic jet.

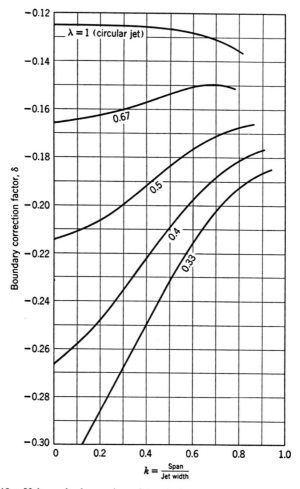

FIG. 6:48.   Values of δ for a wing with elliptic loading in an open elliptic jet.

6:20. Downwash Correction for Closed Octagonal Jets.
Wings with elliptic loading in octagonal test sections have been
considered by Batchelor (Ref. 6:18) and Gent (Ref. 6:19). The
conclusion is that, for regular octagonal test sections (Fig. 6:49),
the corrections for circular sections may be used, the maximum
error being 1.5 per cent in δ or well under 0.2 per cent in C_D for
the most critical case.

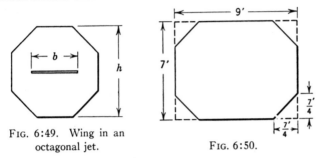

FIG. 6:49. Wing in an
octagonal jet.

FIG. 6:50.

The octagonal test section formed by tempering the corners
of a rectangular jet has been discussed only for the case where a
7 ft by 9 ft rectangular jet is reduced by 45-degree flat fillets
whose vertical height reduces the amount of side wall exposed by
one-half (Fig. 6:50). The effect of these fillets is to make the
basic rectangular jet more nearly approach the elliptic jet. The
wind-tunnel boundary factor is hence reduced.

The correction factors for both the 7 by 9 rectangular and
octagonal test sections are shown in Fig. 6:51. As may be sur-

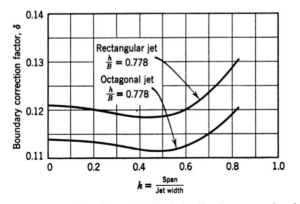

FIG. 6:51. Values of δ for wings with elliptic loading in octagonal and rectangular test sections with tempered corners.

mised, the corrections of the octagonal jet are essentially those of an elliptic jet of the same height-width ratio.

6:21. Downwash Corrections for the Flow behind the Wing. The method of simulating the boundaries by an image system in a plane taken through the wing quarter chord perpendicular to the axis of symmetry of the airplane has been covered in Sect. 6:13. However, the amount of velocity induced by a vortex

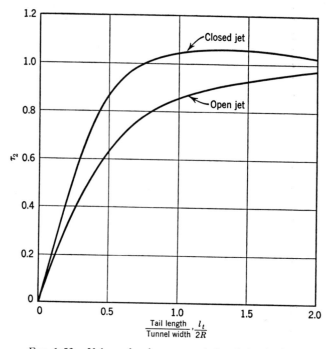

FIG. 6:52. Values of τ_2 for open and closed circular jets.

increases rapidly as one moves from the end of the vortex, so that, looking at the three-dimensional picture (Fig. 6:3), the amount of upwash at the tail of a model in a tunnel is very much more than that at the wing. Thus, for instance, at a time when the walls are reducing the wing angle of attack by 2 degrees, they could conceivably be reducing the tail angle of attack by 3 degrees. This large discrepancy, proportional to the lift coefficient, makes complete models in a closed test section appear very much more stable than they would in free air, while in an open jet the opposite effect is true.

This problem has been discussed by Lotz (Ref. 6:20), and the boundary-induced upwash velocity at a distance l_t behind the quarter-chord line has been presented as

$$w_k = \delta(S/C)C_L(1 + \tau_2)V \qquad (6:48)$$

where w_k = upwash velocity in the plane of symmetry at distance l_t behind the quarter chord (w_k does not vary greatly along

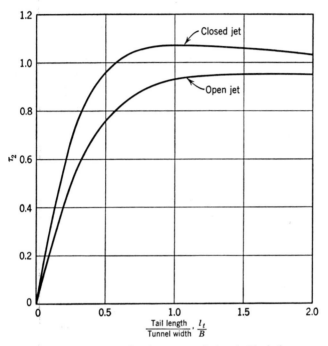

FIG. 6:53. Values of τ_2 for open and closed elliptic jets.

the span); C = jet cross-section area; V = tunnel velocity; τ_2 = downwash correction factor.

Values of τ_2 for a number of tunnels are given in Figs. 6:52 to 6:57, and values of δ for the relevant model may be found in Sects. 6:16 through 6:20.

Some doubt exists about the validity of the downwash corrections for open-throat wind tunnels as regards the values behind the lifting line since they were derived for an infinitely long test section and not for one about a diameter long. This finite length does change δ and τ_2, but, as far as wing corrections and corrections for streamline curvature go, the change is not serious.

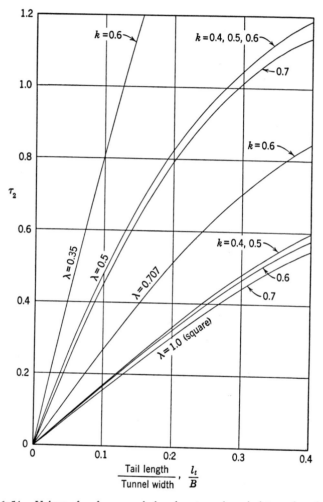

FIG. 6:54. Values of τ_2 for several closed rectangular wind tunnels; wing on tunnel centerline; and horizontal tail on wing centerline. Values for $\lambda = 0.35$ are by extrapolation.

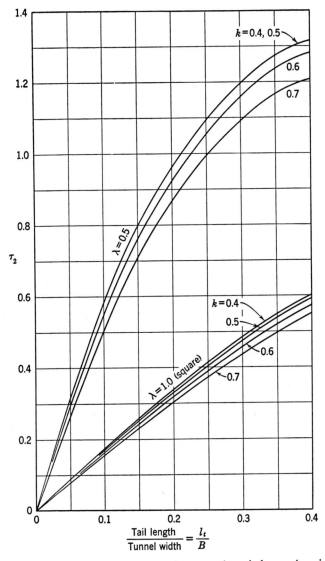

FIG. 6:55. Values of τ_2 for two closed rectangular wind tunnels, wing on tunnel centerline, but horizontal tail 0.1 b_e above or below w'ng centerline.

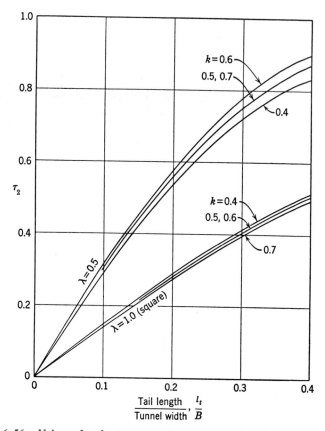

FIG. 6:56. Values of τ_2 for two open-throat rectangular wind tunnels, wing
on tunnel centerline, horizontal tail on wing centerline.

For stability corrections for complete models in open test sections
it would be in order to consult Ref. 6:45 if the tail length is more
than 0.4 B, where B is the tunnel width.

Example 6:3

It is desired to measure the downwash angles 1.425 chords behind a
wing in the full-scale tunnel at Langley Field. A yawhead will be used.
How should the data be treated to reduce it to free-air conditions? Wing
dimensions: area 231 sq ft; span 28.5 ft; taper ratio 0.5; $MAC = 8.1$ ft.
Tunnel dimensions, 30 by 60 ft open elliptic jet. The aspect ratio of
this wing is a low 3.5.

1. From Fig. 6:23 the vortex span of this wing is $0.78 \times 28.5 = 22.2$
ft. From eq. 6:42 the effective span is 25.35 ft. For a span to width

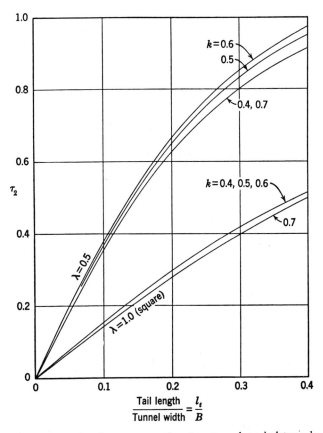

FIG. 6:57. Values of τ_2 for two open-throat rectangular wind tunnels, wing on tunnel centerline, but horizontal tail $0.1b_e$ above or below wing centerline.

ratio of $25.35/60 = 0.423$, and a $\lambda = 0.5$, we have from Fig. 6:42 that $\delta = -0.187$.

2. From Fig. 6:53 using $l_t/B = 1.425 \times 8.1/60 = 0.192$ we get that $\tau_2 = 0.39$.

3. From eq. 6:48 we have finally that

$$\Delta\epsilon = w_k/V = (-0.187)(231/1410)(1 + 0.39)(57.3)C_L$$

$$= -2.45C_L \quad \text{degrees}$$

This amount should be added to the measured downwash where downwash angles are positive and upwash angles negative. It is independent of sweep.

A parallel correction may be worked out for the static stability as follows:

The moment coefficient about the center of gravity due to the tail is

$$C_{mcgt} = \frac{q_t S_t l_t}{qSc} C_{Lt} \qquad (6:49)$$

where the subscript t means "horizontal tail." The change of moment coefficient due to the change of angle * at the tail is

$$\Delta C_{mcgt} = \frac{q_t S_t l_t}{qSc} \frac{dC_{Lt}}{d\alpha_t} \Delta\alpha_t$$

$$= \frac{q_t S_t l_t}{qSc} \frac{dC_{Lt}}{d\alpha_t} \frac{\Delta w_k}{V}$$

$$= \frac{q_t S_t l_t}{qSc} \frac{dC_{Lt}}{d\alpha_t} \frac{S}{C} C_{LW} \tau_2 \delta \qquad (6:50)$$

The subscript W is added to point out that the wing lift coefficient is being used. Equation 6:50 may be differentiated to give an additive correction directly as

$$\Delta \frac{dC_{mcgt}}{dC_{LW}} = \left[\frac{q_t}{q} \frac{dC_{Lt}}{d\alpha_t} \right] \frac{S_t l_t}{Sc} \tau_2 \delta \frac{S}{C} \qquad (6:51)$$

The term in the bracket is usually evaluated as a unit during the first runs of a program by changing the tail incidence i_t ($=\alpha_t$ in this discussion), and it follows that every model should have a variable-incidence tail whether the real airplane will have one or not. In eq. 6:51 the tail lift curve slope should be per radian and the additive correction to the pitching moment curve slope normally works out around $+0.02$ to $+0.04$. Since the curve will have a negative slope for stability of -0.10 to -0.20 the correction is seen to be very large. It is not uncommon for complaints to be heard about applying this large correction, especially when measured slopes are coming out less then estimated values, but flight tests have amply demonstrated its validity.

* The change referred to here is the difference between the boundary-induced angle at the wing and that at the tail.

If it is impossible to evaluate $(q_t/q)(dC_{Lt}/d\alpha_t)$, the relation

$$\frac{q_t}{q}\frac{dC_{Lt}}{d\alpha_t} = \frac{0.1AR_t}{AR_t + 2}(0.8)(57.3) \qquad (6:52)$$

may be used. It will be seen that this is the well-known approximate lift curve slope formula reduced by the factor 0.8. It is common to hear the factor 0.8 spoken of as a loss in dynamic pressure. Though there is some loss in average dynamic pressure over the horizontal tail due to the fuselage boundary layer it is far less than 20 per cent, and the correction is more properly thought of as being due to the blanketing of the horizontal tail by the fuselage and its boundary layer, and the resultant loss in lift across the fuselage, than as a loss in average dynamic pressure.

The amount that the wake is displaced by the tunnel boundaries may be found by calculating the induced velocities at several stations back of the wing and by making a step-by-step integration, solving for the time for each increment by dividing the distance between stations by the tunnel velocity.

The wake location is of great importance when considering tail buffeting due to wing flaps and dive brakes.

Example 6:4

A rectangular wing of 6-ft span and 1-ft chord is tested in a closed round jet (9-ft diameter) at 100 mph. Find the approximate wake displacement caused by the tunnel walls 2 ft behind the wing quarter chord at $C_L = 1.0$.

1. For this wing and tunnel (Eq. 6:42),

$$k = 0.629$$

From Fig. 6:26, $\delta = 0.132$.
From Fig. 6:52, $\tau_2 = 0.475$ for $l/2R = 0.222$.

2. $w_k = \delta \dfrac{S}{C} C_L(1 + \tau_2)V$

$\qquad = (0.132)(6/63.8)(1.0)(1 + 0.475)(147)$

$\qquad = 2.69$ ft/sec

That is, the wall effect 2 ft behind the quarter chord is an upward velocity of 2.69 ft/sec.

3. The time required for a particle of air to travel from the quarter chord to the station 2 ft farther back is

$$\Delta t = \tfrac{2}{147} = 0.0136 \text{ sec}$$

The average upwards velocity during this period is $(0 + 2.69)/2 =$ 1.345 ft/sec. Hence the displacement is

$$h = \overline{V} \Delta t$$

$$= (1.345)(0.0136)$$

$$= 0.018 \text{ ft}$$

This amount is probably negligible. For larger models, however, the wake correction must be considered. Greater accuracy in making this correction may be obtained by considering the process in a series of short steps, summing up to get the total correction.

6:22. Downwash Corrections for Wing-Body Combinations. Smith, in Ref. 6:21, points out that the simple simulation of a round closed jet by a pair of added vortices set out from the tunnel centerline is not realistic when a wing-body combination is in the tunnel, and a rather complex vortex pattern is then required.

The effect of this new vortex pattern is to increase δ (around 10 per cent for most airplane models) so that an error of around 0.2 degree in the stall angle and 1 per cent in drag may thereby be incurred. A second effect is that the boundary-induced upwash, which for a wing alone tends to make an early tip-stall, now makes for an early root-stall. It should hence be noted that stall observations of average-sized models should be shaded towards the tip (by about a degree) when the stall studies are evaluated.

For the case of highly loaded, low-aspect-ratio missiles, the effect may be more noticeable. δ may then be found from:

$$\delta = \tfrac{1}{16}(F_1 + (R/r)F_2) \tag{6:53}$$

where

$$F_1 = \frac{1}{1 + P_1} + \frac{1}{1 - P_1} - \frac{1}{(b_e/2r)^2 - P_1}$$

$$- \frac{1}{(b_e/2R)^2 + P_1} \tag{6:54}$$

$$F_2 = \frac{1}{P_2 - (b_e/2R)^2} - \frac{1}{P_2 + (b_e/2R)^2}$$

$$- \frac{1}{P_2 - (r/R)^2} + \frac{1}{P_2 + (r/R)^2} \tag{6:55}$$

where r = fuselage radius, feet; R = test section radius, feet;

$P_1 = b_e \zeta / 2R^2$; $P_2 = b_e \zeta / 2r^2$; b_e = wing effective span, feet (see eq. 6:42); ζ = wing station, feet.

The above equations assume no dihedral, and wing and body on the tunnel centerline. The final δ is an average of δ across the span weighted for the local chord.

6:23. Downwash Corrections for Power-on Tests. The slip-stream due to a thrusting propeller increases the lift over the inboard part of the wing, and to a minor amount changes the spanwise load distribution. It also blows back the downwash so that the normal power-off roll-up is not quite attained, and the image system must have added to it a stream function to allow for the slipstream. Generally it is sufficient to use the power-off (normal span loading) value of δ and the power-on lift coefficients.

6:24. Downwash Corrections for Sweptback Wings. The downwash corrections for sweptback wings are more difficult to calculate than those of straight wings, since the vortex pattern is then more complex. The added variables of sweep and span make graphs such as have been presented for straight wings quite impractical. However, there is an ameliorating circumstance: planes with swept wings are usually quite fast and models of them are hence usually tested at high Mach numbers. This, in turn (see Chapter 11), requires small models, and the downwash corrections for angle of attack are then usually negligible, and for drag small enough so that using the same corrections as for straight wings will not result in errors of serious magnitude. Indeed, even when the models are of more customary size, the straight-wing corrections are not seriously off. In one example, that of a wing swept 47.7 degrees, 6.56-ft span with a 0.383 taper in a 10-ft circular tunnel, the straight wing value of $\Delta \alpha_i = 0.813 C_L$ and $\Delta C_{Di} = 0.0140 C_L^2$. The swept wing corrections by a fairly laborious procedure, yield $\Delta \alpha_i = 0.905 C_L$ and $\Delta C_{Di} = 0.0139 C_L^2$. This degree of agreement is not always found, but a good agreement usually is.

References given at the end of this chapter will enable those interested to look into the problems of corrections for swept wings, if they so desire.

6:25. Downwash Corrections for Flapped Models. When the flaps are down on a model the spanwise distribution of lift is changed considerably from the no-flap condition. It is a nice refinement to make allowance for this change when computing the boundary corrections. This is done by separating the lift due to the wing alone from that due to the flaps. The wing-alone δ is selected as outlined heretofore using b_e, and the flap-down δ is selected using the flap span. It is not necessary to consider roll-up of the flap vortices. The boundary correction equations become

$$\Delta\alpha_i = (\delta_W C_{LW} + \delta_F C_{LF})(S/C) \text{ (57.3)} \qquad (6{:}56)$$

$$\Delta C_{Di} = (\delta_W C_{LW}{}^2 + \delta_F C_{LF}{}^2)(S/C) \qquad (6{:}57)$$

6:26. Corrections for Reflection Plane Models. The main purpose of testing reflection plane models is to get the largest model size and hence the largest model Reynolds number. In turn the large model size may need special attention paid to wall corrections. Another special effect is that the reflection plane reflects, and under some conditions (aileron down, or vertical tail, for instance) an undesirable reflection for which special allowances must be made is obtained.

Reflection plane tests are conveniently divided into four classes:

1. Small symmetrical models (less than $0.6h$) such as halves of flapped wings, or horizontal tails.

2. Small unsymmetrical models such as aileron panels.

3. Small vertical tail models where a reflection is not desired.

4. Large reflection plane models of all kinds.

The first three may be reasonably treated in the space available, but detailed studies of large models will require consulting the work by Swanson and Toll (Ref. 6:5).

1. *Small symmetrical models.* The data for a small reflection plane model which is half of a symmetrical model may be corrected by treating the upwash and blocking as though the entire

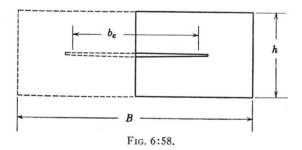

FIG. 6:58.

model were in a tunnel of double the width. (See Fig. 6:58.) The values of δ for such a set-up are in Fig. 6:30, and those for a circular-arc tunnel are in Fig. 6:38. One normally gets a slightly lower lift curve slope and slightly higher induced drag than in the complete-model, complete-tunnel case, owing to some vortex shedding in the root boundary layer. Using panel area and *MAC* the final data are directly applicable to the airplane if the split is along the plane of symmetry with an added amount of span to allow for the boundary-layer displacement thickness. Sections 5:7 through 5:10 should also be consulted.

2. *Small unsymmetrical models.* When the model is unsymmetrical (aileron deflected, for instance), additional troubles accrue since the reflection will be symmetrical. Thus in this case the tunnel data include a small carry-over from the reflection and will show from one-tenth to one-fourth more increment of lift, drag, and pitching moment, yawing moment, and rolling moment than it should. Since tunnel data will be high for ailerons on account of the failure to simulate aileron cable stretch and wing twist some engineers plot up span loadings with ailerons zero and deflected and reduce their measured data by the proper carry-over increment.

The only time this effect can be misleading in comparing different ailerons on the same basic panel is when one aileron has more span than another. As seen in Fig. 6:59 the reflection effects increase with span and the aileron of greatest span yields the data most erroneously high.

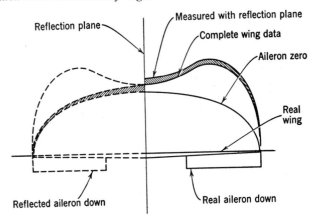

Fig. 6:59.   Effect of reflection plane on panel with aileron down.

Difficulties arising from the doubled increment of lift, drag, and moment have been covered in Sect. 5:8, which must be consulted for proper interpretation of the results.

3. *Small vertical tail models.* The small vertical tail models present a number of additional difficulties since the degree of endplating given by the fuselage and horizontal tail is very difficult to predict. One approach is to consider it a completely reflected symmetrical semi-span wing and, after determination of the slope of the vertical tail lift curve from the complete model tests, to reduce the panel test data to conform. Normally the vertical tail drag is of so little interest that an increase of panel drag to allow for the reduced aspect ratio is not required.

Another approach, and perhaps the best one, is to determine the slope of the lift curve of the vertical tail from complete model tests and use the hinge moment data from panel tests at the same lift coefficient. This neglects the difference of span loading for panel and actual vertical tail installation. Still another alternative is to build a tail assembly model such as that shown in Fig. 6:60. Here the model is large enough for high Reynolds

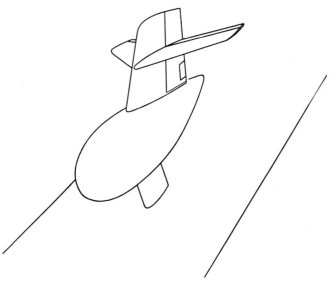

Fig. 6:60.

number, and actual endplating is well simulated. The effects of sidewash must be obtained from the complete model tests and incorporated in the data. The tail assembly model should have a fuselage stub nose at least one *MAC* ahead of the tail quarter chord.

4. *Large models.* The analysis for large models is complicated fundamentally because the boundary-induced upwash cannot be considered constant along either the chord or span. One is therefore justified in taking greater pains for the upwash corrections, but variation of the blocking along the model almost never is large enough to be considered.

Besides the streamline curvature effects, the variation of boundary-induced upwash along the span of the model tends to load up the tips. Some test-section shapes do this to a smaller extent than others, or, if a split fuselage is included, its effect usually compensates for the tip loading and standard wall corrections are satisfactory. (See Sect. 6:22.)

6:27. Jet Arrangements with Zero Corrections. Figure 6:29 indicates that rectangular jets may have several arrangements that yield zero boundary effects. Such arrangements include jets with one horizontal boundary and a width-height ratio of 2.0, with two horizontal boundaries and a width-height ratio of 1.0, and with two vertical boundaries and a width-height ratio of 0.5. But is must be remembered that Fig. 6:29 applies to very small wings only.

In practice, nearly every wing requires its own specific downwash correction factor δ, and it is obvious that each wing would require its own specific jet configuration in order to have zero boundary effect.

It so happens that the downwash correction *may* be neglected for one type of test—that of wings or complete models when they are tested in the tunnel for ground effect. This type of test utilizes a groundboard (see Sect. 5:20) close to the model to simulate the ground. The effect of the board is opposite in sign to the boundary effect of a closed jet and practically cancels it out. Data from tests of this type made with the wing within one chord of the ground plane may be used directly without downwash corrections (Ref. 6:22.)

The set-up is similar to that of a wing far off the tunnel centerline. However, when considering the wall effect of the three remote walls (in a rectangular tunnel) by subtracting out the interference of the fourth wall which represents the ground and hence should have its "interference" in, it develops that the effect of the remote walls is quite small and may be neglected as far as pitch stability is concerned.

6:28. Boundary Correction for Propeller Tests. Glauert (Ref. 6:2) has examined the problem of testing propellers in a wind tunnel and suggests that the propeller diameter be kept small relative to the jet diameter and that an open-throat tunnel be employed. Under these conditions no boundary corrections are needed.

Unfortunately, for various practical reasons it is not always possible to adhere to the above stipulations. An approach to

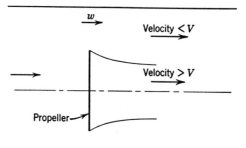

FIG. 6:61.   Propeller in a closed-throat wind tunnel.

the wall corrections for propeller tests in a closed-throat tunnel may be made as follows:

In a closed jet the propeller slipstream under conditions of positive thrust will have a velocity u greater than the velocity in the jet without the propeller V. Since the same volume of air that passes section x ahead of the propeller must pass section y behind it, it follows that the velocity w outside the slipstream will be less than V. In free air, w would, of course, equal V. The lower-velocity outside air has a higher static pressure, and it follows that the slipstream also has too high a static pressure. This reacts back to the propeller so that it develops the thrust that might be expected at a lower speed V'. The test should therefore be run at a speed above V in order to develop the proper forces for V.

The amount of correction for this "continuity" effect may be found from

$$\frac{V'}{V} = 1 - \frac{\tau_4 \alpha_1}{2\sqrt{1 + 2\tau_4}} \qquad (6:58)$$

where $\tau_4 = T/\rho A V^2$; $\alpha_1 = A/C$; A = propeller disk area; C = jet cross-section area; T = thrust.

One approach is to place a pitot-static tube in the plane of the propeller and to operate the tunnel at constant w, basing the coefficients on w, also. The difficulty of finding the average w, however, makes this seem less valuable than reading the thrust and correcting V by eq. 6:58. See Chapter 10.

Values of V'/V may be obtained from Fig. 6:62.

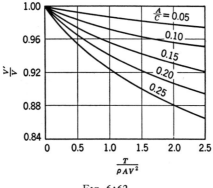

Fig. 6:62.

If the tunnel utilized has an open jet, the airstream surrounding the propeller slipstream is free to contract; hence no correction is necessary.

6:29. Downwash Corrections for Asymmetrical Loading. When the ailerons of a model are deflected, the downwash is no longer symmetrical, and the effect of the jet boundaries becomes asymmetrical also. The effect on the rolling moment is small and is frequently neglected. Biot (Ref. 6:23) shows that for full-span ailerons of customary model size it amounts to about 3 per cent. Stewart (Ref. 6:24) has considered the correction to the yawing moment coefficient necessary for round jets. He reaches the conclusion * that the total yawing moment correction may be found from

$$\Delta C_n = \Delta C_{n1} + \Delta C_{n2} + \Delta C_{n3} \qquad (6:59)$$

where

$$\Delta C_{n1} = C_l C_L \frac{SR^2}{b^2(a_2{}^2 - a_1{}^2)}\left[F_1\left(\frac{ba_2}{2R^2}\right) - F_1\left(\frac{ba_1}{2R^2}\right)\right]$$

$$F_1(x) = -\frac{2}{\pi}\ln\left(1 + \sqrt{1 - x^2}\right) \qquad (6:60)$$

* Verified by W. L. Koch in a Caltech thesis, 1939.

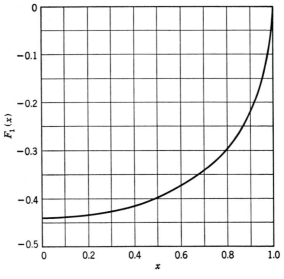

Fig. 6:63.

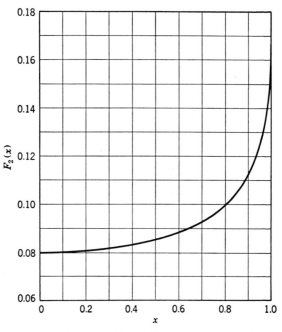

Fig. 6:64.

and may be found from Fig. 6:63, wherein

$$x = ba_1/2R^2 \qquad \text{or} \qquad ba_2/2R^2$$

$$\Delta C_{n2} = C_l C_L \frac{S}{a_2{}^2 - a_1{}^2}\left[F_2\left(\frac{ba_2}{2R^2}\right) - F_2\left(\frac{ba_1}{2R^2}\right) \right]$$

where

$$F_2(x) = \frac{1 - \sqrt{1 - x^2}}{2\pi x^2} \tag{6:61}$$

and may be found from Fig. 6:64.

$$\Delta C_{n3} = -C_l{}^2 \frac{Sbr}{2\pi(a_2{}^2 - a_1{}^2)} F_3\left(\frac{a_2}{R}, \frac{a_1}{a_2}\right)$$

where $F_3(a_2/R, a_1/a_2)$ may be found from Fig. 6:65.

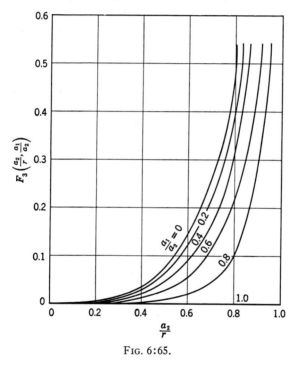

FIG. 6:65.

The symbols not readily apparent are

a_1 = distance from wing centerline to inner tip of aileron.
a_2 = distance from wing centerline to outer tip of aileron.
b = wing span.
R = tunnel radius.

The correction Δc_n should be subtracted for a closed wind tunnel and added for an open one. Further, Δc_{n3} should be omitted when both ailerons are deflected. Though it may seem surprising that correction of one aileron only is even mentioned, this is not an unusual case. When two aileron designs are under consideration it is customary to build one into the right aileron and one into the left aileron, testing each separately.

The sign conventions for ailerons are such that down aileron is "plus," regardless of whether the right or left aileron is under consideration. It should therefore be mentioned, with the signs employed, which aileron is being tested.

Stewart gives a numerical example, which may be readily checked, as follows:

Suppose that the left aileron of a model with an 8-ft span is tested in a closed round jet, 10 ft in diameter. The left aileron extends from 2 to 3.5 ft out. The wing area is 8 ft; the lift coefficient $C_L = 1.5$; and the rolling moment coefficient so developed is $C_l = 0.0300$. Find the yawing moment correction.

$$\Delta C_{n1} = C_l C_L \frac{SR^2}{b^2(a_2{}^2 - a_1{}^2)} \left[F_1\left(\frac{ba_2}{2R^2}\right) - F_1\left(\frac{ba_1}{2R^2}\right) \right]$$

$$= (0.0300)(1.5) \frac{(8)5^2}{8^2(3.5^2 - 2^2)} \left[F_1 \frac{(8)(3.5)}{(2)(5^2)} - F_1 \frac{(2)(8)}{(2)(5^2)} \right]$$

$$= 0.00069$$

$$\Delta C_{n2} = C_l C_L \frac{S}{a_2{}^2 - a_1{}^2} \left[F_2\left(\frac{ba_2}{2R^2}\right) - F_2\left(\frac{ba_1}{2R^2}\right) \right]$$

$$= (0.0300)(1.5) \frac{8}{(3.5^2 - 2^2)} \left[F_2 \frac{(8)(3.5)}{(2)(5^2)} - F_2 \frac{(8)(2)}{(2)(5^2)} \right]$$

$$= 0.00024$$

$$\Delta C_{n3} = -C_l{}^2 \frac{SbR}{2\pi(a_2{}^2 - a_1{}^2)} F_3\left(\frac{a_2}{R}, \frac{a_1}{a_2}\right)$$

$$= -(0.0300)^2 \frac{(8)(8)(5)}{2\pi[(3.5)^2 - 2^2]} F_3\left(\frac{3.5}{5}, \frac{2}{3.5}\right)$$

$$= 0.00008$$

$$\Delta C_n = 0.00069 + 0.00024 + 0.00008 = 0.00101$$

ΔC_n should be subtracted from the observed yawing moment.

6:30. Summary of Three-Dimensional Boundary Effects (Closed Test Section). Data from a wing test in a closed three-dimensional wind tunnel may be corrected to free-air conditions according to the following relations: *

The corrected velocity is

$$V = V_u(1 + \epsilon) \qquad (6:62)$$

where

$$\epsilon = \epsilon_{sb} + \epsilon_{wb} \qquad (6:63)$$

The dynamic pressure, from eq. 6:62, is

$$q = q_u (1 + 2\epsilon) \qquad (6:64)$$

The Reynolds number, from eq. 6:62, is

$$R = R_u(1 + \epsilon) \qquad (6:65)$$

The lift coefficient, from eq. 6:64, is

$$C_L = C_{Lu}(1 - 2\epsilon) - \tau_2 \, \Delta\alpha \cdot a \qquad (6:66)$$

The angle of attack, from eqs. 6:40 and 6:36, is

$$\alpha = \alpha_u + [\delta(S/C)C_L(57.3)](1 + \tau_2) \qquad (6:67)$$

The pitching moment coefficient, from eqs. 6:64 and 6:38, is

$$C_{m\frac{1}{4}} = C_{m\frac{1}{4}u} (1 - 2\epsilon) + 0.25\tau_2 \, \Delta\alpha \cdot a \qquad (6:68)$$

The drag coefficient, from eqs. 6.64, 6:32, 6:33, and 6:41, is

$$C_D\dagger = C_{Du}(1 - 2\epsilon) - \Delta C_{DW} - \Delta C_{DB} + \delta(S/C)C_L{}^2 \qquad (6:69)$$

Applying eqs. 6:62 through 6:69, it develops, is a very complicated procedure since the wake blocking term contains the profile drag coefficient which (a) is not readily obtainable and (b) is a variable with angle of attack. One may fight this procedure through, but a far simpler approach is to assume the wake blocking constant, *and* to run the tunnel at "blocked *q*." The running and work-up are then as follows:

1. Calculate ϵ by eq. 6:34. The minimum drag coefficient including bayonet and pitch strut drag should be used in eq. 6:31.

2. The blocked dynamic pressure is then

$$q_b = q_u(1 + 2\epsilon)$$

---

* The boundary corrections have been added to the blocking corrections of Ref. 6:25.

† It is assumed that the buoyancy correction has already been applied.

3. The tunnel is set at q_u, and the coefficients become:

$$C_L' = \text{Lift}/q_b S$$

$$\alpha = \alpha_u + \Delta\alpha + \Delta\alpha_{sc} \qquad (6\!:\!36,\ 6\!:\!40)$$

$$= \alpha_u + (1 + \tau_2)\delta(S/C)C_L'(57.3)$$

$$C_L = C_L' + \Delta C_{Lsc} \qquad (6\!:\!37)$$

$$= C_L'[1 - \tau_2\delta(S/C)(57.3)\cdot a]$$

$$C_m = \frac{\text{Pitching moment}}{q_b Sc} - 0.25\Delta C_{Lsc} \qquad (6\!:\!38)$$

$$C_D = \frac{\text{Drag} - \Delta D_B}{q_b S} + \delta\frac{S}{C}C_L^2 \qquad (6\!:\!27,\ 6\!:\!41)$$

The streamline curvature corrections usually become negligible for wings of high aspect ratio but are worth including for delta wings and panel models.

The jet-boundary corrections for wing-body combinations, horizontal tail on, and other special cases may be found in the appropriate sections.

The tunnel static pressure will be needed for pressure tests but will normally not be available from the static pressure piezometer ring because of model effects. Letting the subscript b indicate blocked conditions and u the uncorrected (clear jet) values we may write

$$p_u + \tfrac{1}{2}\rho V_u^2 = p_b + \tfrac{1}{2}\rho V_b^2$$

Since

$$V_b = V_u + \epsilon V_u$$

$$p_b = p_u - 2\epsilon q_u$$

Unfortunately, no systematic study verifying the three-dimensional wall corrections (similar to that of Ref. 6:1 for the two-dimensional case) has been reported.

Example 6:5

Correct the following data to free-air conditions:
    Closed tunnel test section 7 by 10 ft.
    Longitudinal static pressure gradient 0 per foot.
    Clear jet speed 200 mph (indicated).
    Boundary-layer displacement thickness 0.5 in.

Model dimensions:

Wing area 6.33 sq ft, $MAC = 0.897$ ft.

Wing span 7.3 ft, taper ratio 0.5, aspect ratio 8.4.

Average airfoil section 65-012, wing lift curve slope = 0.088 per degree.

Fuselage maximum diameter 9.20 in.

Fuselage overall length 5.24 ft.

Tail area 2.16 ft².

Tail length 3.1 ft.

Tail aspect ratio 3.2.

Wing volume 0.817 cu ft.

Fuselage volume 1.208 cu ft.

Maximum frontal area 1.204 sq ft.

The model is mounted on the MAC at $0.30c$, and is on the tunnel centerline. The horizontal tail is on.

Measured lift 302.1 lb, measured drag 46.6 lb, measured pitching moment -63.6 ft-lb, $\alpha_u = 5.0$ degrees.

The effective tunnel area is $7 \times 10 - (0.5/12)(34) = 68.58$ sq ft.

From Fig. 6:16, τ_1 for $b/B = 0.73$ and $B/H = 1.43$ is 0.881, and the solid blocking for the wing is

$$\epsilon_{sbW} = \frac{(0.989)(0.881)(0.817)}{(68.58)^{1.5}}$$

$$= 0.00125$$

From Fig. 6:15, using $t/c = 0.146$ and the NACA 111 shape, $K_3 = 0.926$. From Fig. 6:16, using $b/B = 0$ and $B/H = 1.43$, $\tau_1 = 0.863$. The solid blocking for the body becomes

$$\epsilon_{sbB} = \frac{(0.926)(0.863)(1.208)}{(68.58)^{1.5}}$$

$$= 0.00170$$

The wake blocking is

$$\epsilon_{wb} = \tfrac{1}{4}(6.33/68.58)0.0720 \quad \text{(see p. 340 for } c_{Du})$$

$$= 0.00166$$

The total blocking is

$$\epsilon = 0.00125 + 0.00170 + 0.00166$$

$$= 0.00461$$

(Equation 6:35 yields $\epsilon = 0.0043$.)

As a matter of interest, Thom's short-form solid blocking is

$$\epsilon_{sb} = \frac{(0.90)(0.817)}{(68.58)^{3/2}} + \frac{(0.96)(1.208)}{(68.58)^{3/2}}$$

$$= 0.0033$$

The slightly higher solid blocking of Thom's method (0.0033 as compared to 0.0030) almost exactly compensates for neglecting the pressure gradient effects and essentially ends up with the same drag.

The uncorrected coefficients are

$$C_{Lu} = \frac{302.1}{(102.2)(6.33)} = 0.466$$

$$C_{Du} = \frac{46.6}{(102.2)(6.33)} = 0.0720$$

$$C_{mtr} = \frac{-63.6}{(102.2)(6.33)(1.152)} = -0.0852$$

The pressure gradient drag due to the wing is (eq. 6:32)

$$\Delta C_{DW} = \frac{(0.989)(0.881)(0.817)(0.0720)}{(68.58)^{1.5}}$$

$$= 0.000090$$

$$\Delta C_{DB} = \frac{(0.926)(0.863)(1.208)(0.0720)}{(68.58)^{1.5}}$$

$$= 0.000123$$

The corrected dynamic pressure becomes

$$q = (102.2)[1 + 2(0.00461)]$$

From Fig. 6:23 with $AR = 8.4$ and $\lambda_T = 0.5$, $b_v/b = 0.775$. By eq. 6:42, $b_e = 6.47$ ft, and from Fig. 6:30, using $k = 0.647$ and $\lambda = 0.7$, $\delta = 0.117$.[*]

Using a "tail length" of $MAC/4 = 0.224$ ft,[†] $l_t/B = 0.0224$, and $k = 0.647$, Fig. 6:54 yields $\tau_2 = 0.078$.

Hence the corrected lift coefficient is

$$C_L = 0.466[1 - 2(0.00461)] - (0.078)(0.117)\frac{6.33}{68.58}(0.466)(57.3)(0.088)$$

$$= 0.460$$

---

[*] The body effect of Ref. 6:21 increases δ by 10 per cent. Since it only produces a change in α of 0.06 degree at $C_L = 1.0$, and a change in drag of 0.0003 at $C_L =_, 1.0$, its inclusion is not worth the extra trouble.

[†] See p. 293.

The corrected angle of attack is then

$$\alpha = 5.0 + 0.117(6.33/68.58)(0.460)(57.3)(1 + 0.078)$$

$$= 5.34$$

The pitching moment coefficient corrected for blocking and wing streamline curvature is

$$C_{mtr} = -0.0852[1 - 2(0.00461)] + 0.25(0.00198)$$

$$= -0.0838$$

The corrected drag coefficient is

$$C_D = 0.0720[1 - 2(0.00461)] - 0.00009 - 0.00012 + 0.117\frac{6.33}{68.58}(0.460)^2$$

$$= 0.0734$$

From eq. 6:50 (using eq. 6:52 for a tail lift curve slope),

$$\Delta C_{mcgt} = \frac{(0.1)(3.2)}{3.2 + 2}(0.8)(57.3)\frac{2.16}{6.33}\frac{3.10}{0.897}\frac{6.33}{68.58}(0.117)(0.71)C_L$$

$$= 0.0254 C_{LW}$$

$$= 0.0117$$

and the corrected pitching moment coefficient becomes

$$C_{mcgt} = -0.0838 + 0.0117 = -0.0721$$

The above includes the fair assumption that all the lift is due to the wing.

6:31. Summary of Three-Dimensional Boundary Corrections, Open Test Section. There is little solid or wake blocking effect for open test sections since the stream is free to expand as need be. The previously reported wing corrections then reduce to

$$V = V_u \tag{6:70}$$

$$q = q_u \tag{6:71}$$

$$R = R_u \tag{6:72}$$

$$\alpha = \alpha_u + \delta(S/C)C_L(57.3)(1 + \tau_2) \tag{6:73}$$

$$C_L = C_{Lu} - \tau_2 \, \Delta\alpha \cdot a \tag{6:74}$$

$$C_{m\frac{1}{4}} = C_{m\frac{1}{4}u} + 0.25\tau_2 \, \Delta\alpha \cdot a \tag{6:75}$$

$$C_D = C_{Du} + \delta(S/C)C_L^2 \tag{6:76}$$

The sign of δ will be negative so that the downwash corrections will be subtractive. For the case of wing and body and wing-body and horizontal tail, Sects. 6:21 and 6:22 should be consulted.

6:32. Boundary Corrections for Control Surface Hinge Moments. Little information has been released on boundary corrections for control surface hinge moments. It is apparent that the small size of such surfaces on complete models makes hinge-moment corrections quite unnecessary. Larger models, such as are used for reflection plane tests, have their hinge moments increased by solid jet boundaries in a manner similar to the increase of pitching moment. The increase of hinge moment due to the walls is of the order of 8 per cent for a 30 per cent flap on a large reflection plane model.

PROBLEMS

6:1. Calculate the drag due to buoyancy for a three-dimensional Rankine ovoid, fineness ratio 4.0. The maximum thickness is 2 ft, and the slope of the static-pressure curve is -0.008 lb per sq ft per ft.

6:2. Same for a similar two-dimensional ovoid in the same tunnel.

6:3. Calculate the increase of velocity (solid blocking) for a 65,316 airfoil, 2-ft chord, if tested in a closed rectangular jet 8 ft wide and 4 ft high.

6:4. Calculate the effective twist due to the tunnel walls on a tapered wing of span 8 ft, $AR = 8$, tested in a round closed jet of 9-ft diameter at $C_L = 1.0$.

6:5. A wing has a 10-ft span. The root chord is 3 ft, and the tip chord is 1.5 ft. Using Schrenk's method, find the span load distribution.

6:6. The wing of problem 6:5 is to be tested in the following tunnels; find the value of δ for each. (*a*) 12 ft round, open jet. (*b*) 12 ft round, closed jet. (*c*) 12 ft elliptical closed jet, 2 to 1 breadth ratio. (*d*) 12 ft square closed jet. (*e*) 12 ft by 8 ft rectangular, closed jet.

6:7. A propeller of 4-ft diameter is to be tested in a round closed tunnel of 9-ft diameter. What tunnel speed is needed to simulate a free-air speed of 100 mph, if a thrust of 200 lb is developed at 1000 rpm?

REFERENCES

6:1. H. Julian Allen and Walter G. Vincenti, Wall Interference in a Two-Dimensional-Flow Wind Tunnel with Consideration of the Effect of Compressibility, *TR* 782, 1944.

6:2. H. Glauert, Wind Tunnel Interference on Wings, Bodies, and Airscrews, *R&M* 1566, 1933.

6:3. Ira H. Abbott, Albert E. Von Doenhoff, and Louis S. Stivers, Jr., Summary of Airfoil Data, *TR* 824, 1948.

6:4. A. Thom, Blockage Corrections in a High Speed Wind Tunnel, *R&M* 2033, 1943.

6:5. Robert S. Swanson and Thomas A. Toll, Jet Boundary Corrections for Reflection Plane Models in Rectangular Wind Tunnels, *TR* 770, 1943.

6:6. H. J. Stewart, The Effect of Wind-Tunnel-Wall Interference on the Stalling Characteristics of Wings, *JAS*, September, 1941.

6:7. J. R. Gavin and R. W. Hensel, Elliptic Tunnel Wall Corrections, *JAS*, December, 1942.

6:8. K. Kondo, The Wall Interference of Wind Tunnels with Boundaries of Circular Arcs, *ARI, TIU*, 126, 1935.

6:9. H. Glauert, The Interference of the Characteristics of an Airfoil in a Wind Tunnel of Circular Section, *R&M* 1453, 1931.

6:10. L. Rosenhead, Uniform and Elliptic Loading in Circular and Rectangular Tunnels, *PRS*, Series A. Vol. 129, 1930, p. 135.

6:11. A. Silverstein, Wind Tunnel Interference with Particular Reference to Off-Center Positions of the Wing and to the Downwash at the Tail, *TR* 547, 1935.

6:12. G. Van Schliestett, Experimental Verification of Theodorsen's Theoretical Jet-Boundary Correction Factors, *TN* 506, 1934.

6:13. T. Theodorsen, Interference on an Airfoil of Finite Span in an Open Rectangular Wind Tunnel, *TR* 461, 1931.

6:14. K. Terazawa, On the Interference of Wind Tunnel Walls on the Aerodynamic Characteristics of a Wing, *ARI, TIU*, 44, 1932.

6:15. H. Glauert, The Interference on the Characteristics of an Airfoil in a Wind Tunnel of Rectangular Section, *R&M* 1459, 1932.

6:16. M. Sanuki and I. Tani, The Wall Interference of a Wind Tunnel of Elliptic Cross-Section, *Proc. Physical Mathematical Soc. Japan*, Vol. 14, 1932.

6:17. L. Rosenhead, The Airfoil in a Wind Tunnel of Elliptic Cross-Section, *PRS*, Series A, Vol. 140, 1933, p. 579.

6:18. G. K. Batchelor, Interference in a Wind Tunnel of Octagonal Section, *ACA* 1, January, 1944.

6:19. Betty L. Gent, Interference in a Wind Tunnel of Regular Octagonal Section, *ACA* 2, January, 1944.

6:20. I. Lotz, Correction of Downwash in Wind Tunnels of Circular and Elliptic Sections, *TM* 801, 1936.

6:21. C. Branson Smith, Wind-Tunnel-Wall Corrections for Wing-Body Combination, *JAS*, April, 1949.

6:22. I. G. Recant, Wind Tunnel Investigation of Ground Effect, *TN* 705, 1939.

6:23. M. Biot, Correction for the Measured Rolling Moment of a Wing in a Circular Wind Tunnel, *ZFM*, August, 1933.

6:24. H. J. Stewart, A Correction to the Yawing Moment Due to Ailerons for Circular Wind Tunnels, *JAS*, June, 1939.

6:25. John G. Herriot, Blockage Corrections for Three Dimensional-Flow Closed-Throat Wind Tunnels with Consideration of the Effect of Compressibility, *TR* 995, 1950.

6:26. Robert S. Swanson, Jet-Boundary Corrections to a Yawed Model in a Closed Rectangular Wind Tunnel. *NACA ARR*, February, 1943 (Declassified).

6:27. Bertram J. Eisenstadt, Boundary-Induced Upwash for Yawed and Sweptback Wings in Closed Circular Wind Tunnels, *TN* 1265, 1947.

6:28. S. Katzoff and Margery E. Hannah, Calculation of Tunnel-Induced Upwash Velocities for Swept and Yawed Wings, *NACA TN* 1748, 1948.

6:29. Edward C. Polhamus, Jet-Boundary-Induced-Upwash Velocities for Swept Reflection-Plane Models Mounted Vertically in 7 by 10 Foot, Closed, Rectangular Wind Tunnels, *NACA TN* 1752, 1948.

6:30. James C. Sivells and Rachel M. Salmi, Jet Boundary Corrections for Complete and Semispan Swept Wings in Closed Circular Wind Tunnels, *TN* 2454, 1951.

6:31. Robert S. Swanson and Marvin J. Schuldenfrei, Jet-Boundary Corrections to the Downwash behind Powered Models in Rectangular Wind Tunnels with Numerical Values for 7 x 10 Foot Closed Wind Tunnels, *Wr-L-711*, 1942.

6:32. James C. Sivells and Owen J. Deters, Jet Boundary and Planform Corrections for Partial Span Models with Reflection Plane, End Plate, or No End Plate in a Closed Circular Wind Tunnel, *TR* 843, 1946.

6:33. Rudolph W. Hensel, Rectangular Wind Tunnel Blocking Corrections Using the Velocity Ratio Method, *TN* 2372, 1951.

6:34. G. I. Taylor, The Force Acting on a Body Placed in a Curved and Converging Stream of Fluid, *R&M* 1166, 1928.

6:35. B. Gothert, Wind Tunnel Corrections at High Subsonic Speeds Particularly for an Enclosed Circular Tunnel, *TM* 1300, 1952.

6:36. J. H. Preston and A. R. Manning: Calculations of the Interference on a Thin Symmetrical Aerofoil with Hinged Flap Spanning a Closed Wind Tunnel, *R&M* 2465, 1951.

6:37. J. M. Evans, Wind Tunnel Interference on Lateral Stability Derivatives, *ACA* 33, March, 1947.

6:38. W. J. Duncan, A Simple Approach to Wind Tunnel Constriction Effect, *Aircraft Engineering*, June, 1949.

6:39. Alan Pope, *Basic Wing and Airfoil Theory*, McGraw-Hill Book Company, New York, 1951.

6:40. Clarence L. Gillis, Edward C. Polhamus, and Joseph L. Gray, Jr., Charts for Determining Jet-Boundary Corrections for Complete Models in 7 x 10 Foot Closed Rectangular Wind Tunnels, *WR-L-123*, 1943.

6:41. E. B. Klunker and Keith C. Harder, On the Second-Order Tunnel Wall Constriction Correction in Two-Dimensional Compressible Flow, *TN* 2350, 1951.

6:42. F. Riegels, Correction Factors for Wind Tunnels of Elliptic Section with Partly Open and Partly Closed Test Section, *TM* 1310, 1951.

6:43. S. Katzoff, Clifford S. Gardner, Leo Diesendruck, and Bertram J. Eisenstadt, Linear Theory of Boundary Effects in Open Wind Tunnels with Finite Jet Lengths, *TR* 976, 1950.

6:44. James C. Sivells and Rachel M. Salmi, Jet-Boundary Corrections for Complete and Semispan Swept Wings in Closed Circular Wind Tunnels, *TN* 2454, 1951.

6:45. Abe Silverstein and S. Katzoff, Experimental Investigation of Wind-Tunnel Interference on the Downwash behind an Airfoil, *TR* 609, 1937.

Chapter 7

THE USE OF WIND-TUNNEL DATA

One of the top airplane designers in Great Britain has been credited with the statement that he "could go on designing airplanes all day long if he had not also to build them and make them fly," and his point is surely well taken. Data may *easily* "be taken all day long"—as long as they are not used to design airplanes.

Indeed, the very subject of extrapolating wind-tunnel data to full scale will probably bring many a grim smile to aeronautical engineers who see this page. The aerodynamicist disparages the wind-tunnel engineer; the wind-tunnel engineer thinks the aerodynamicist wants too much; and if any poor soul is assigned the combination of jobs, well, one is reminded of the classic experiment of crossing a hound dog and a rabbit wherein the offspring ran itself to death.

Probably the nearest approach to the truth lies in the fact that wind tunnels are very rarely called upon to test exact models of items that may be flown. Though this offers a magnificent "out" to the wind-tunnel engineer, it is not meant that way. Reynolds number effects on small items are too great even if they could be accurately constructed; hence the small excrescences are left off the models. In many cases the aerodynamicist who plans on adding these items selects the lowest possible drag values with the net result that he underestimates their interference and overestimates the performance of the airplane. The cure for this situation is to consolidate these items and minimize their effect. Room for improvement can surely exist when examples can be cited of airplanes that have no less than twenty-two separate air intakes and over thirty removable inspection panels. Of course, the effects of small protrusions can be tested in the full-scale tunnel on the actual airplane itself, provided the wingspan is not too great.

345

Unfortunately very little correlation between flight-test and wind-tunnel data is available. This lack is attributed to the dual reasons that after flight test there is rarely time to back up and correlate with the wind tunnel, and that, even when it is done, the success or failure of the methods used is generally a company secret. The literature reveals only a handful of papers on correlating wind tunnel and flight. Three sources available are Millikan (Ref. 7:1), Hockman and Eisiminger (Ref. 7:2), and Hills (Ref. 7:3). These papers should surely be consulted for serious work on this facet.

Any flight-test and wind-tunnel correlation always suffers from a great number of unknowns. The tunnel data suffer from inexact or unknown Reynolds number extrapolation; possible uncertainties in corrections to the data such as tare and interference and wall effects; errors in duplicating the power-on effects with fixed-pitch propellers; omission of manufacturing irregularities and small excrescences; and insufficient deflections of the model under load. The flight-test data suffer from pilot techniques, accelerations due to gusts, errors in average center of gravity locations, and unknowns of propeller efficiencies. Considering the impressive room for disagreements, the generally good agreement found is quite remarkable.

We will take up, in turn, each of the important aerodynamic quantities usually measured in the tunnel and say what we can about their use.* First, however, we need to consider the boundary layer, for the understanding of scale effects is essentially the understanding of the boundary layer.

7:1. The Boundary Layer. Owing to viscosity of the air, the air very near the wing is slowed gradually from freestream velocity far out to zero right at the wing. The region in which this velocity change takes place is called the *boundary layer*, and the velocity gradients in the boundary layer very largely determine whether the drag of a body is x, or $10x$. A boundary layer in which the velocities vary approximately linearly from the surface is called *laminar*; † one whose velocities vary approximately exponentially from the surface is called *turbulent*. Their drag

---

* A discussion of the use of high-speed data will be found in Chapter 11.

† Both laminar and turbulent flow may be demonstrated simply with a cigarette held very still in still air. The rising smoke column will be smooth (laminar) for about 10 in. and then will turn turbulent. Talking or any other tiny disturbance will also make the laminar flow become turbulent.

values based on *wetted area* (approximately double *wing area*) are given by

$$C_{D \text{ laminar}} = 2.656/\sqrt{RN} \qquad (7:1)$$

$$C_{D \text{ turbulent}} = 0.910/(\log_{10}RN)^{2.58} \qquad (7:2)$$

and plotted in Fig. 7:1 along with a drag curve of a 23012 airfoil.

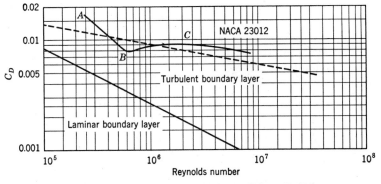

FIG. 7:1.   Plot of $C_{D0 \text{ min.}}$ vs. log RN (from TR 586).

The boundary-layer thickness, defined as the distance from the surface to the point where the velocity in the boundary layer is 0.99 times the velocity just outside the boundary layer, is given by

$$\delta_{\text{laminar}} = 5.2 \ \sqrt{l^2/RN} \qquad (7:3)$$

$$\delta_{\text{turbulent}} = 0.37l/(RN)^{\frac{1}{5}} \qquad (7:4)$$

where l = distance from body leading edge and RN = Reynolds number based on l and freestream velocity.

Several important phenomena are known about the boundary layer. First, both its drag and its thickness are related to the Reynolds number. Second, laminar flow, having far less drag, has less energy with which to surmount roughness or corners and it hence separates from a surface much more easily than does turbulent flow. Third, the maintenance of a laminar boundary layer becomes more difficult as the Reynolds number (its length) increases. Fourth, laminar flow is encouraged by a pressure gradient falling in the direction of flow, or by being thinned by artificial means such as suction through a porous surface or by cooling. In the light of these actions we may examine how a flow can change widely under conditions of changing Reynolds number.

Assume that the wing shown in Fig. 7:2 is in a stream of such turbulence that laminar flow will change to turbulent at a Reynolds number of 1,000,000, and further assume a model size and velocity such that the Reynolds number of the entire flow length shown in *A* is 1,000,000. We note two items: first, the laminar flow in is unable to negotiate the curve of the airfoil and

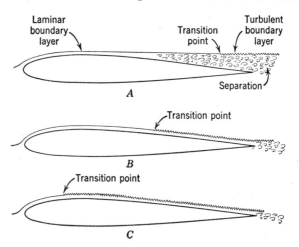

FIG. 7:2.   Effect of increasing Reynolds number on boundary-layer flow.

excessive separation is evident; * and, second, transition takes place *before* 1,000,000 since the flow downstream of the maximum thickness has a rising pressure gradient that discourages laminar boundary layer. Here then is a case where we have too much laminar flow, and the resultant drag is excessively high, corresponding to a point *A* in Fig. 7:1 and the way the boundary layer behaves on a 23012 airfoil at a Reynolds number of 300,000. (It is the dream of every model builder to trip the laminar boundary layer and reduce the separation. In almost every case the tripper costs as much as is saved; see Fig. 8:2.)

Returning to Fig. 7:2*B*, which corresponds to a higher Reynolds number, we see that the transition point has moved forward according to item 3, and now we have the maximum laminar flow and minimum drag. This corresponds to *B* in Fig. 7:1, and a 23012 airfoil at a Reynolds number of 650,000.

* Also see Fig. 1:9.

The still higher Reynolds number illustrated in Fig. 7:2C fails to show a decrease of drag, even though both laminar and turbulent drag decrease with increasing Reynolds number, since there has been a great increase in the region of turbulent flow. This is point C in Fig. 7:1. ($RN = 1,200,000$.)

Further increase in Reynolds number yields a reduction in drag coefficient although the transition has now reached the minimum pressure point and its further forward motion is resisted by the falling pressure gradient from the leading edge to that point.

Since the pressure pattern of every airfoil is unique, and since the same may be said of every airplane design, it is apparent that tests made in the Reynolds number range where laminar separation is developed will be exceedingly difficult to interpret for full scale. Unfortunately there is no simple Reynolds number that we can exceed and be sure of good correlation, and we shall have to take up various items separately to consider how they are affected. The above discussion may serve as a basis for understanding the difficulties.

First, however, it seems in order to discuss the methods of artificially making the boundary layer turbulent, if it should be so at higher flight Reynolds numbers. There are four ways to do this. One is to glue small wires or threads near the wing or body leading edge. These increase the drag coefficient of the model by both the drag of the wires and the resulting forward movement of the transition point. If several wires of different diameters are tested and if the drag increase is plotted against wire diameter, extrapolation of the curve to zero wire diameter will indicate the drag caused by the forward movement of the transition only. The drag of the model with the transition at the proper location can be used to extrapolate to higher Reynolds numbers.

A second method is to introduce turbulence into the airstream by screens just ahead of the model. It is difficult to figure the exact screen size and distance, and perhaps the trip-wire method is superior.

A third method is to mount a wire ahead of the leading edge of a wing and use its wake as a tripper. This is the only method that works in some cases, although it is in general applicable only to two-dimensional tests.

The fourth method is also a tripper strip method but uses salt or, better, fine (0.002 in.) Carborundum dust glued in a strip about 0.5 in. wide just aft of the wing or body leading edge. A thin swath of lacquer quickly dusted seems a good binder.

More important than how to trip the boundary layer is *when* to trip it, and here most unfortunately no exact answer is possible. A working rule is: If, after roughness has been added along the surface leading edges, a measurable change in data takes place

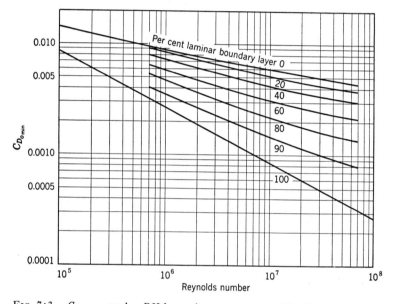

Fig. 7:3. $C_{D0\ min.}$ vs. log RN for various percentages of laminar flow. Zero form drag assumed.

run the program with the roughness on. It is almost a certainty that roughness should be used on the wing leading edges ahead of ailerons, and probably on the tail surface leading edges as well. Roughness is unnecessary in regions where turbulent flow has already been established.

Figure 7:3 shows the drag coefficients corresponding to different amounts of laminar and turbulent boundary layers at various Reynolds numbers. Zero form drag is assumed. In this chart are shown the theoretical minimum wing drag of 100 per cent laminar flow and the decrease in drag coefficient due to extension of the laminar layer. For example, extension of the laminar layer from 20 to 60 per cent at $RN = 2,000,000$ reduces the drag coefficient from 0.0073 to 0.0048.

In extrapolating drag coefficients, it is necessary to make due allowance if the Reynolds number of the tunnel data is the "effective" Reynolds number. This procedure is necessary because the part of the drag associated with skin friction decreases with increasing Reynolds number. Thus for a given effective Reynolds number the friction coefficients are larger than at a numerically equal test Reynolds number. The difference between measured drag and the actual drag at the equivalent free-air Reynolds number may be read from the turbulent drag curve of Fig. 7:1. An example is given.

Example 7:1

The drag of a wing is measured at a test Reynolds number of 3,000,000 and a turbulence factor of 2.0. The measured drag coefficient is 0.0082. Find the equivalent free-air drag coefficient.

1. As $RN_e = TF \times RN$

$$RN_e = 2.0 \times 3,000,000 = 6,000,000$$

2. From the turbulent drag curve of Fig. 7:1, $C_D = 0.0073$ at $RN = 3,000,000$ and 0.0066 at $RN = 6,000,000$.

$$\Delta C_D = 0.0073 - 0.0066 = 0.0007$$

3. The measured drag is therefore too high by 0.0007, and $C_D = 0.0082 - 0.0007 = 0.0075$.

7:2. Scale Effect on Drag. Although drag may well be the least important of the tunnel measurements needed to a high degree of accuracy (since it affects economy but not safety) it seems logical to follow up the discussion already pretty well along.

The first conclusion (from Fig. 7:1) is that, even though comparison tests between objects may be made with fair accuracy, a test Reynolds number of 1,500,000 to 2,500,000 would be needed if extrapolation is intended. This necessitates a $1\frac{1}{2}$- or $2\frac{1}{2}$-ft chord at 100 mph or equivalent. An ameliorating condition is that, if a low Reynolds number separation exists and is cured by some change, the probability that it will arise at a higher Reynolds number is extremely small.

If a terrific effort is made to maintain true profile on the full-scale airplane, tunnel wing drag extrapolated to the new Reynolds number (by the aid of Fig. 7:3) should be only slightly optimistic owing to the drag of the flap and aileron cut-outs, control surface inspection doors, and tank filler cap covers, etc., not represented on the model.

The effects on the minimum drag of the complete airplane are more difficult to handle. There are truly an immense number of small items on the full-scale ship that cannot be represented at model scale. Whether they under- or overcompensate for the drag reduction expected from higher Reynolds number is any man's guess. Frequently the tunnel engineer assumes that the two exactly compensate, but he would hate to guarantee better than ± 0.0020 in C_D.

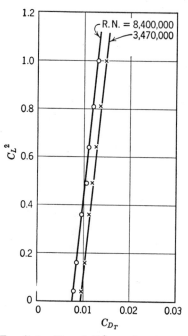

Similarly, the rate of change of drag with lift, usually considered as the change in span efficiency factor e, should not change for straight wings.* For instance (Fig. 7:4), it has been observed that, when C_L^2 for a given airplane is plotted against the total drag coefficient C_{DT}, the graph is nearly a straight line. Further, since we may write †

$$e = \frac{1}{\sqrt{(dC_D/dC_L^2)\pi A R}} \quad (7:5)$$

FIG. 7:4. Plot of C_L^2 vs. C_{DT} for an NACA 23012 at two Reynolds numbers.

it becomes apparent that the slope of the line dC_D/dC_L^2 may be used to find e. (See also Sect. 5:5.) Fortunately the slope of this line is practically independent of Reynolds number, and a wind-tunnel test may hence be used to determine full-scale e. A plot of the 23012 airfoil at two Reynolds numbers is given in Fig. 7:4.

As has been noted, the determination of the amount the C_L^2 vs. C_{DT} curve is moved over (i.e., the scale effect on $C_{D0\text{ min. (ship)}}$)

---

* e for swept wings is not as tractable as for straight wings. Sometimes the tip stall is reduced by higher Reynolds number in a manner that increases e, and other times e is reduced.

† Frequently e is defined as the square of e as given in eq. 7:5.

with increasing Reynolds number is not so simple; in fact, no direct rule is known. If similar tests have been completed in the past and flight tests made, perhaps the comparison may yield the ΔC_D necessary. For an entirely new ship, the minimum drag may be measured at several velocities, and a plot of $C_{D0\ min.}$ vs. log RN may be made. The straight line that usually results from such a plot may be extrapolated to find the approximate full-scale $C_{D0\ min.}$ (Fig. 7:5).

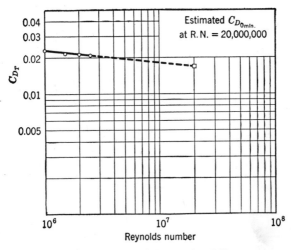

FIG. 7:5.   Plot of C_{DT} vs. log RN.

Another method of extrapolating total ship drag to full-scale Reynolds number is as follows:

1. Plot C_D vs. C_L, tunnel data.

2. Subtract $C_{Di} = C_L^2/\pi AR$ from the C_D plot to obtain $C_{D0\ (tunnel)}$.

3. Estimate $C_{L\ max.}$ (full scale) from Fig. 7:8, Ref. 7:4, or other sources, and extend C_{D0} until it is horizontal at $C_{L\ max.}$. The increased curvature of the C_{D0} curve should be moved to an increased C_L in a manner similar to that described in Sect. 7:3.

4. Decrease $C_{D0\ min.\ (tunnel)}$ by the C_D change in *wing* drag from tunnel Reynolds number to full scale. See Fig. 7:1. (This is the controversial step. Some engineers make no change to tunnel $C_{D0\ min.}$ as manufacturing irregularities on the actual ship may increase the drag as much as increased Reynolds number decreases it.)

5. Add C_{Di} back in to get the final extrapolated drag curve. In this step use values of C_L up to $C_{L\,max.}$ (full scale).

Special attention should be paid to the extrapolation of C_D at $C_{L\,max.}$ In many cases the tunnel engineer neglects the drag increase that accompanies the increase of $C_{L\,max.}$ with Reynolds number, and predicted glide angles near $C_{L\,max.}$ are then considerably above the attained values.

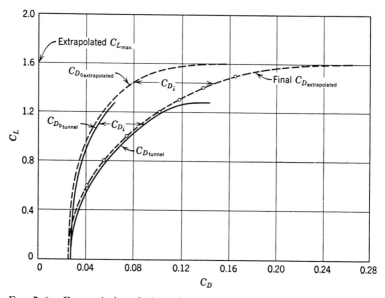

FIG. 7:6.   Extrapolating airplane drag curve to full-scale Reynolds number.

The methods outlined above for getting full-scale values from tunnel data are successful only when applied by experienced aerodynamicists.

In closing we may state that, though the low-drag "bucket" found in the tunnel may be a bit optimistic, the shape of the drag curve up until the $C_{L\,max.}$ effects predominate seems to follow closely the drag obtained in flight.

7:3. Scale Effects on the Lift Curve.   The effect of Reynolds number on the lift curve is indeed profound, and often quite unpredictable.   We will first discuss the work of Jacobs (Ref. 7:4) on the NACA forward thickness airfoils, and then treat the newer profiles.

1. *The forward thickness airfoils.*   In *TR* 586 (Ref. 7:4), Jacobs indicates that variations in lift curve slope caused by increasing

Reynolds number are very small, but in general the lift curve will be straightened up; the slope will increase slightly; * and the stall will become more abrupt. (See Fig. 7:7.) Lift curves already straight at the lower Reynolds numbers will be extended at higher ones. It follows that $C_{L \, max.}$ and the angle at which it occurs are

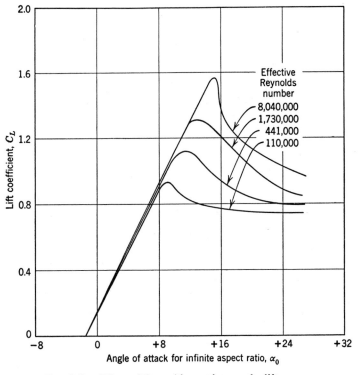

Fig. 7:7. Effect of Reynolds number on the lift curve.

increased. The amount of the increase of both angle and $C_{L \, max.}$ is of paramount value to the tunnel engineer.

The method outlined in Ref. 7:4 enables the $C_{L \, max.}$ at Reynolds numbers below 8,300,000 to be determined for a large group of airfoils and enables the engineer to estimate possible Reynolds number effects on new airfoils.

The method is to read the $C_{L \, max.}$ at $RN_e = 8,300,000$ and the stall type from Table 7:1. Then the increment (usually nega-

* At very low values of the Reynolds number, about 150,000, the lift curve again steepens, and $dC_L/d\alpha$ may then exceed 2π/radian.

TABLE 7:1

Airfoil NACA	Scale Effects on $C_{L \max.}$	Airfoil NACA	Scale Effects on $C_{L \max.}$
0006	A	23006	A
0009	B_0	23009	C_2
0012	C_0	23012	D_2
0015	D_0	23015	D_2
0018	E_0	23018	E_2
0021	E_1	23021	E_2
0025	E_2		
0030	..	43012	D_4
		43015	D_4
2212	C_3	43018	E_4
2409	B_2	63012	D_6
2412	C_2	63018	E_7
2415	D_2		
2418	E_2		
4406	A		
4409	B_4		
4412	C_4		
4415	D_4		
4418	E_4		
4421	E_5		

tive) is selected from Fig. 7:8 and added to the high Reynolds number $C_{L \max.}$ to get $C_{L \max.}$ at the desired Reynolds number. Unfortunately this seemingly simple method is of lessened value

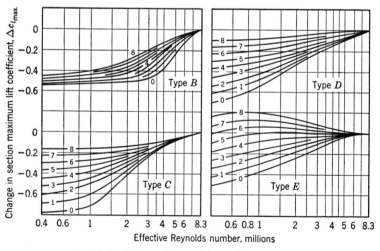

Fig. 7:8.   Effect of Reynolds number on $C_{L \max.}$.

in most practical cases for two reasons: first it concerns *section*
$c_{l\,max.}$ values when wing $C_{L\,max.}$ values are usually needed; and,
second, the tunnel engineer will probably not find the desired
airfoil in Table 7:1. Though a method considering local downwash and local Reynolds numbers exists (Ref. 7:6) that enables
the wing $C_{L\,max.}$ as well as the location of the first stalled area to
be determined, it is useless without full information as to the
effect of Reynolds number on the particular airfoil in question.

The way around the problem is largely empirical. Many
tunnel engineers have had sufficient experience correlating tunnel
data with flight tests so that they feel qualified to estimate
$\Delta C_{L\,max.}$ due to Reynolds number. Most of their estimations run
around $\Delta C_{L\,max.} = 0.15$ for the range from a tunnel test at
$RN_e = 1,500,000$ to full scale $RN = 6,000,000$. They then proceed as follows:

1. The straight part of the lift curve from tunnel data is extended with the same slope.

2. Through the value of $C_{L\,max.}$ (full scale) as estimated, a
horizontal line is drawn.

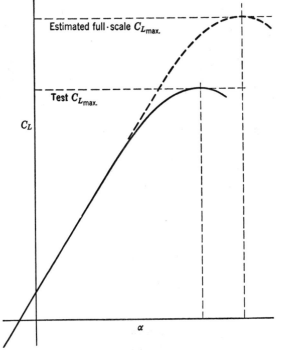

Fig. 7:9.

3. The curved portion of the test lift curve is then raised until it has the proper value of $C_{L\ max.}$ and shifted laterally until it joins the straight part of the constructed full-scale lift curve.

The net result is a full-scale lift curve having the proper value of zero lift, slope, and $C_{L\ max.}$, but probably having an angle of maximum lift that is too great and a stall that is too gentle. These two deficiencies are not serious, however, and the engineer has at least something with which he can work.

Since the speed of the airplane is reduced for landing, it is sometimes possible to obtain tests at landing Reynolds number in a tunnel of moderate capacity.

Maximum lift coefficients measured in different wind tunnels agree much better when based on "effective" Reynolds numbers (see Sect. 3:4) than when based on the test Reynolds numbers. Increased Reynolds numbers obtained by added turbulence are satisfactory for maximum lift measurements.

In Ref. 7:3, agreement on $C_{L\ max.}$ within ± 0.1 was found when data from 1,500,000 were extrapolated to 26,000,000 by Jacobs' method.

2. *Low-drag airfoils.* The effect of scale on the lift character-istics of low-drag airfoils has not been as systematically studied as for the other airfoils previously discussed. Fortunately for a large number of the low-drag types complete information up to $RN = 9,000,000$ is available in Ref. 6:3, but if an entirely new airfoil is under test, estimating the way it will behave at much greater Reynolds number may be a very difficult job. This applies particularly to airfoils whose lift curves show wide breaks in slope at low Reynolds numbers. For this type both the extra-polation to full scale and the effect of flaps at full scale are a matter of almost pure conjecture. As before, the angle of zero lift and the lift curve slope near zero lift are virtually unaffected by scale.

7:4. Scale Effects on Flap Characteristics. We are usually justified in expecting a little more from a flap full scale than is found in a tunnel at low Reynolds number, provided that the basic airfoil does not suffer extreme effects itself. In a number of fairly typical examples flight turned up about 0.2 more flap lift coefficient increment than did the tunnel. Figure 7:10 illus-trates a tunnel range in which the flap increment was unaffected by scale.

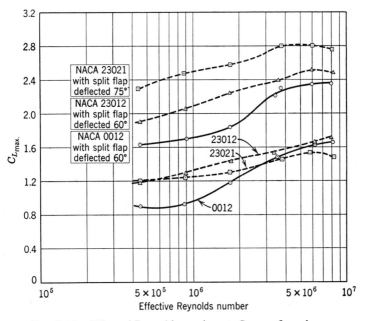

FIG. 7:10. Effect of Reynolds number on $C_{L\,max.}$, flaps down.

7:5. Scale Effects on the Pitching Moment Curve. The static longitudinal stability of airplanes having airfoils with forward thickness (such as the 23012, etc.) seems to change little from typical tunnel Reynolds numbers of around 1,000,000 up to flight values of around 20,000,000. Indeed, the power-on tests made at 500,000 in the tunnel seem to agree a little better than those made with power-off, perhaps because of the windmilling propeller present in the power-off flight measurements. Usually

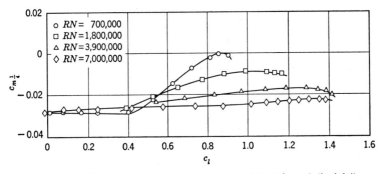

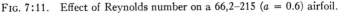

FIG. 7:11. Effect of Reynolds number on a 66,2–215 ($a = 0.6$) airfoil.

the tunnel-flight discrepancy is in the direction of slightly more stability of the airplane than was predicted in the tunnel.

But the extrapolation of pitching moments when the airfoil thickness is well rearward (such as in the 65 and 66 series airfoils) is far more difficult to handle. The pitching moment variation of the 66,2-215 ($a = 0.6$) airfoil is shown in Fig. 7:11 from tests made in the British compressed-air tunnel and reported in Ref. 7:3. Obviously, the extrapolation of even the data made at 1,800,000 would be a very difficult job. Nor were trippers of much value here, and satisfactory tests were accomplished only by going to high Reynolds numbers.

7:6. Effect of Scale on Longitudinal Stability and Control. In general the longitudinal characteristics will not be seriously different from those indicated by tunnel tests. Frequently one finds the model neutral point a little farther forward than full scale when power is off, and in pretty fair agreement with power on. The elevator needed to trim rarely varies more than 2 degrees from that indicated by the tunnel. Some other characteristics as determined by wind-tunnel and flight tests of a two-engined propeller-driven fighter bomber may be of interest, even though they cannot be taken as typical; they are given in Table 7:2.

TABLE 7:2

Parameter	Wind Tunnel	Flight Test
$dC_h/d\alpha$ ($\delta_E = 0°$)	-0.0014	-0.0011
$dC_h/d\delta$	-0.0044	-0.0044
$d\epsilon/d\alpha$	0.45	0.41

C_h = hinge moment coefficient, δ = control deflection.

7:7. Effect of Scale on Directional Stability and Control. The directional stability in flight in a number of instances has been seriously less than indicated in the wind tunnel, necessitating a redesign of the vertical tail. The reasons for this difference are not fully understood. In a number of airplanes the rudder was not powerful enough to yaw the ship into rudderlock on the model, but did so in flight. Catastrophies have been avoided only because rudderlock flight tests are always made quite gradually and with full expectancy of trouble. The comparative values in Table 7:3 are from wind-tunnel and flight tests of a two-engined fighter-bomber, propeller driven.

TABLE 7:3

Parameter	Wind Tunnel	Flight Test
$dC_n/d\delta_R$	-0.00126	-0.00085
$d\psi/d\delta_R$	-0.787	-1.39
$dC_h/d\psi$	-0.0010	-0.0005
$dC_h/d\delta_R$	-0.0037	-0.0027
$dC_n/d\psi$ (free)	-0.00125	-0.00045

7:8. Effect of Scale on Lateral Stability and Control. The agreement between flight and tunnel tests on the lateral parameters seems to be generally satisfactory. The disagreement between tunnel and flight for aileron power is expected from considerations of cable stretch and wing flexibility. The values listed in Table 7:4 are from wind-tunnel and flight tests of a two-engined fighter-bomber, propeller driven. Though they are normal values they cannot be taken as typical for all airplanes, of course.

TABLE 7:4

Slope	Wind Tunnel	Flight Test
$dC_l/d\delta_a$	0.00175	0.00144
$C_{l\ max.}/\delta_a$	$0.023/18°$	$0.022/20°$
$dC_l/d\psi$	0.00128	0.00076
dC_l/dC_n	-0.688	-1.69

REFERENCES

7:1. Clark B. Millikan, J. E. Smith, and R. W. Bell, High Speed Testing in the Southern California Cooperative Wind Tunnel, *JAS*, February, 1948.

7:2. Marion T. Hockman and Robert E. Eisiminger, The Correlation of Wind-Tunnel and Flight Test Stability and Control Data for an SB2C-1 Airplane, *JAS*, January, 1948.

7:3. R. Hills, Use of Wind Tunnel Model Data in Aerodynamic Design, *JRAS*, January, 1951.

7:4. Eastman N. Jacobs, The Variation of Airfoil Section Characteristics with Reynolds Number, *TR* 586, 1937.

7:5. F. B. Bradfield and D. L. Ellis, The Use of Model Data in Aeroplane Design, *JRAS*, August, 1939.

7:6. H. A. Pearson, Span Load Distribution for Tapered Wings with Partial Span Flaps, *TR* 585, 1937.

7:7. James M. Nissen, B. L. Gadeburg, and W. T. Hamilton, Correlation of the Drag Characteristics of a Typical Pursuit Airplane Obtained from High-Speed Wind-Tunnel Tests, *TR* 916, 1948.

Chapter 8

SMALL WIND TUNNELS

In order to avoid the impression that useful wind tunnels must have a large jet and a speed of 100 mph or more, it seems pertinent to discuss some uses of smaller tunnels. A 30-in. tunnel was used by Van Schliestett in the program presented in *TN* 506 (Ref. 6:12), and a still smaller tunnel was used by Merriam and Spaulding (Ref. 3:1) in their outstanding calibrations of pitot-static tubes. Other examples could be given of successful programs carried out with the most inexpensive equipment.

The fundamental advantage of a small wind tunnel is traceable to the economics of tunnel operation. Small tunnels cost less to build and less to run. Though economy in operation is frequently neglected in tunnel proposals, it should not be, especially when it is realized that the electricity cost alone of some tunnels exceeds $100 an hour!

A further advantage of a small tunnel is the small size of the models and the consequent savings in construction time. Small size may be a disadvantage, it is true; but those who have shaped a solid mahogany block 6 by 4 feet know well what is meant.

The most successful tests made in a small tunnel are, obviously: (1) those unaffected by Reynolds number and (2) those where any change due to Reynolds number is inconsequential.

8:1. Tests Unaffected by Reynolds Number. The tests most completely free from Reynolds number effects are those embracing pressure readings. Such experiments as static-pressure surveys and the aforementioned pitot-static calibration are in this group. The value of pressure distributions around airfoils is well known and has been given renewed attention by a greatly increased interest in boundary-layer flow and in airfoils in general. Individual companies have been tending to design their own airfoils. The small tunnel can play an important part in this work.

The many criteria (see Sect. 4:18) which are determinable from pressure surveys are within reach of nearly all wind tunnels.

Many experiments concerning wind-tunnel boundary corrections are suitable for the small tunnel. These, too, are unaffected by Reynolds number.

A further use of small tunnel is in the study of flow patterns. Such studies are accomplished by sketching the behavior of tufts which are emplaced all over the model. These drawings require both a skilled artist and a lot of tunnel time. So little is known of proper shaping for the best flow that it is not at all unusual for this type of test to be performed.

The progress of the stall over a wing is also essentially unchanged by Reynolds number, although the entire stall is usually delayed on the full-scale airplane.

Two tests for military airplanes that could be performed in a small tunnel include jettison tests of the drop-type external fuel tanks and tests of the flow from gasoline dump valves. Both these actions frequently develop unforseen complications.

It should be noted that the expression "unaffected by changes in Reynolds number" must not be taken too broadly. By this is customarily meant that *reasonable* changes in Reynolds number produce little effect, and in turn this implies that the range under consideration will be free from movement of the transition point, i.e., above $RN_e = 2,500,000$, or transition points artificially fixed (see Sect. 7:1). The absence of change in e and $\alpha_{Z.L.}$ is limited by these stipulations. Pressure distributions at low angle of attack and the slope of the lift curve seem almost unaffected on down to $RN = 200,000$. There are few accurate data below a Reynolds number of 200,000 on which to base further discussion.

8:2. When Reynolds Number May Be Ignored. Tests wherein any variations of results due to Reynolds number are inconsequential embrace both qualitative tests and tests wherein the taking of data is secondary, i.e., using tunnel testing for instruction purposes.

Qualitative tests are those that are expected to lead either to more testing or to abandonment of the project. They include the testing of radical ideas with a searching attitude for something promising.

8:3. The Small Wind Tunnel for Instruction. Almost no type of testing is performed in a large tunnel that cannot be duplicated in a small tunnel, the possible exception being tests of powered models. Hence a small tunnel is invaluable for instruction.

Many schools have a small wind tunnel, not unlike that shown in Fig. 8:1, for the use of undergraduates. The jet size is about 24 in. by 36 in., and the overall dimensions are such that a space

Courtesy Georgia Institute of Technology.

FIG. 8:1.   A small wind tunnel.

14 ft by 30 ft is sufficient for the tunnel and motor. Twenty to twenty-five horsepower will provide 100 mph in the test section.

Walls for the test section are designed so that they may be wholly or partially removed, thus enabling tests to be performed with open or closed jet and studies to be made of asymmetrical boundaries.

Many of these smaller tunnels do not use a six-component balance. The necessity for completing a test in the usual laboratory period of 3 to 4 hours precludes as complete a test as might be desired.

A list of experiments suitable for instruction is presented below. Each requires about 3 hours. Doubtless, as trends change, additional tests may be added, and many of those suggested below will become obsolescent.

Experiment 1. Jet Calibration

Tunnel condition: Open jet, balance out.

Apparatus: Pitot-static tube, yawhead, turbulence sphere, 2 micro-manometers, meter stick.

Tests: 1. Read dynamic pressure at 2-in. stations across jet. Plot per cent variation in dynamic pressure from centerline value against station.

2. Read angle of flow at 2-in. stations across jet. Plot flow inclination in degrees against station.

3. Determine the turbulence.

4. Read static pressure at tunnel centerline from plane of jet to exit cone at 3-in. intervals. Plot static pressure against station.

5. Read dynamic pressure at tunnel centerline for various pressures in the settling chamber. Plot dynamic pressure against settling·chamber pressure.

Experiment 2. Balance Alignment and Aspect Ratio

Tunnel condition: Open jet, balance in.

Apparatus: Two wings of similar profile and chord but different aspect ratio, 4 and 6.

Tests: 1. Install wing of $AR = 6$. Read L, D, M from below zero lift to stall.

2. Invert model and repeat.

3. Same for wing of $AR = 4$.

4. Plot all data, and make alignment and boundary corrections. (Final data include tare drag and interference, but with models of about 3-in. chord the evaluation of these effects is extremely difficult.) Note on plots $\alpha_{Z.L.}$, $dC_L/d\alpha$, $C_{L\,max.}$, $C_{d0\,min.}$, C_{m0}, ac.

Experiment 3. Tailsetting and Downwash

Tunnel condition: Open jet, balance in.

Apparatus: Model with horizontal tail having variable incidence.

Tests: 1. Read L, D, M from zero lift to stall with tail off.

2. Repeat with tail on, elevator zero, and tail incidence $-8°$ to $8°$.

3. Plot α vs. C_m, and downwash ϵ vs. α. Determine α_{tail} and tail incidence for $C_L = 0.2$.

Experiment 4. Static Longitudinal Stability

Tunnel condition: Open jet, balance in.

Apparatus: Model with removable tail and movable elevators.

Tests: 1. Run model from zero lift to stall reading L, D, M. Tail off.

2. Repeat with tail on and elevators 0, $-5°$, $-10°$, $-15°$.

3. Plot C_m vs. C_L for each elevator setting and C_m vs. δ_e. State $\dfrac{dC_m}{dC_L}$.

Also plot C_L vs. α.

Experiment 5. Profile Drag by Momentum Theory

Tunnel condition: Closed tunnel, balance out.

Apparatus: 12-in. chord airfoil, wake survey rake, meter stick, multiple manometer.

Tests: 1. Read wake $0.7c$ behind airfoil trailing edge with wake survey rake from $\alpha = -3°$ to $6°$. Plot C_{d0} vs. α.

2. Read wake at $\alpha = 0$ at 40, 50, 60, 70, 80, 90 mph (indicated). Plot C_{d0} vs. Reynolds number.

Experiment 6. Pressure Distribution

Tunnel condition: Closed jet, balance out.

Apparatus: Pressure wing; multiple manometer.

Tests: 1. With tunnel set at 60 mph read the pressure distribution for eight angles of attack including zero lift, maximum lift, and after the stall. Calculate and plot the normal and chordwise pressure distributions to get C_N, C_C, and CP, and plot these quantities against α.

Experiment 7. Dynamic Stability

Tunnel condition: Open jet, balance out.

Apparatus: Flying wing model, dynamic stability rig.

Tests: At 40, 60, 80 mph disturb model and time oscillations. Plot period vs. velocity.

Experiment 8. The Boundary Layer

Tunnel condition: Open jet, balance out.

Apparatus: 15-in. chord NACA 0015 wing, mounting rig, boundary-layer mouse, manometer.

Tests: Place mouse at 5, 10, 15, 20, 25, 30, and 35 per cent chord, and read dynamic pressures at 0.03, 0.06, 0.09, 0.12 in. from surface. Determine transition region by plotting velocity profiles and velocity at constant height.

8:4. Flow at Very Low Reynolds Numbers. The small tunnels operate at low Reynolds numbers, and it is fitting to have a good understanding of flow at these values in order to avoid the pitfalls into which many engineers have fallen. Indeed, a remarkable correlation exists between the state of the wind tunnels available and the type of airfoils used on then current wings: At Reynolds numbers of around 50,000 a thin wing with 4 to 6 per cent camber appears best, and was used in early aircraft such as the Breguet, and many World War I fighters. At Reynolds numbers around 150,000 the Clark Y performs properly, as do other sections with perhaps 4 per cent camber and 12 per cent

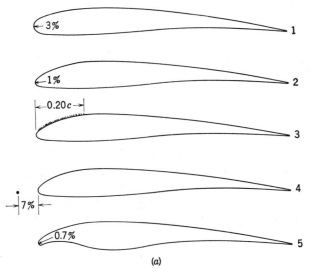

(a)

Fɪɢ. 8:2a.

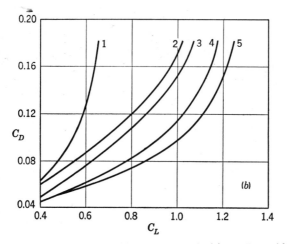

Fɪɢ. 8:2b.   Performance of the five profiles shown in (a) at a Reynolds number of 30–45,000; $AR = 6.0$.   (From an unpublished paper by Seredensky.)

thickness. They in turn were used on the *Spirit of St. Louis* and many other airplanes of the 1925–1935 era. At 4,000,000 to 8,000,000 the symmetrical sections of slightly higher thickness show up well, and we find those on many aircraft of the 1935–1940 era. Later, of course, the tunnels with lower turbulence became available, and they in turn influenced design greatly from 1940–1950 until high subsonic effects began to crowd out other problems.

The point of the above discussion is to draw attention to the fact that most "modern" airfoils will yield embarrassingly poor results at low Reynolds numbers, and teachers trying either 0015 or 65 series wings at $RN = 150,000$ will find themselves with extremely wiggly lift curves, and drag curves for symmetrical wings showing less drag at 5-degree angle of attack than at zero— an "impossible" state of affairs.

The explanation is fairly simple; a 0015, for instance, has separation on both upper and lower surfaces at zero angle of attack at low Reynolds numbers. As soon as sufficient angle is reached, the lower surface has smooth flow, and the increased detachment on the upper surface is not enough to overcome the great drag reduction on the lower surface.

The unexpected and important effect of proper transition is shown in Fig. 8:2, where the proper boundary-layer conditions result in one-third of the drag of a conventional profile.

In summary, then, models for small tunnels should, in order to avoid hopelessly confusing the student and giving him a false impression of the ultility of tunnels in general, be designed for the Reynolds numbers at which they will be run, 12 per cent Clark Y wings, or the similar NACA 4412 sections being suitable in the range 150,000–200,000.

Model builders will need a more thorough discussion of low-Reynolds-number aerodynamics, and they may consult Ref. 8:1 and seek information from the Low Speed Aerodynamic Research Association in England.

REFERENCE

8:1. Alexander M. Lippisch; Wing Sections for Model Planes, *Air Trails*, April and May, 1950.

Chapter 9

NON-AERONAUTICAL USE OF THE
WIND TUNNEL

A large and fertile field of research, almost totally neglected by the wind-tunnel engineer, is that covering industrial or non-aeronautical experiments. The relatively little work the author has done in this realm has exposed an almost appalling lack of aerodynamic considerations in a lot of places that sorely need them: smoke losses have occurred; signs and buildings have been blown down; even boats have been turned over. Had tunnel studies been made, those losses could have been avoided. Several such problems will be outlined in the pages to follow, and tunnel engineers everywhere whose tunnels have idle time should do a little looking into these and other problems.

9:1. Boats. Boats have come into the wind tunnel in all categories: raceboats, ocean liners, sailboats. Raceboats are seriously affected by drag and turnover angle. For drag a ground-board should be employed to simulate the water (it is not a very good representation), and care should be taken that tare and interference are properly evaluated. Fast boats will overturn if they pitch to large angles of attack, and the speed and angles allowable for safe operation should be made known to the driver. Camber over the forward portion of the boat will increase its aerodynamic stability. In tests of this sort it is also advisable to simulate the exhaust from the engines either by tufts or smoke and to ascertain the probable carbon monoxide conditions in the cockpit.

Figure 9:1 shows Sir Malcolm Campbell and his DeHaviland Goblin powered raceboat in the Fairey wind tunnel. The two orifices are the twin intakes for the jet engine. Figure 9:2 shows the author and a model of a very fast raceboat built by the Ventnor Boat Company. Closures around the mounting struts at the ground plane had not then been installed.

Wilford and Klemin in Ref. 9:1 reported some of the very few tests of sails in a wind tunnel. They mounted the sailboat on the floor of the tunnel, using a flush endplate to simulate the ground and a distribution of screens to simulate the varying wind velocity close to the water. The model was mounted on a spindle at the center of buoyancy in the hull, and heel moments were measured about that axis. Their report brought forth a long list

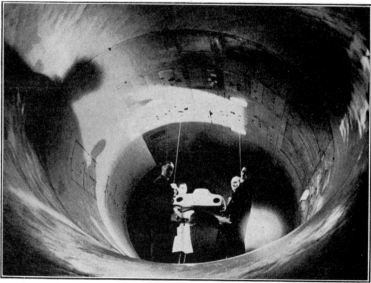

Courtesy Fairey Aircraft Corp.

FIG. 9:1.   One-third-scale model of Sir Malcolm Campbell's new jet-engined speedboat in the Fairey wind tunnel.   Sir Malcolm is at the left.

of possible paths for the improvement of sails, many of which have been followed up with increased efficiency.

Unreported wind-tunnel tests of smoke nuisance on several of the latest ocean liners indicate that much valuable knowledge has been gained by the tests. In a number of vessels the modern "decorations" on the stacks are the direct result of the tunnel tests. The effects of lateral wind can be nicely determined for boats of this caliber using the same mounting described above (a spindle at the center of buoyancy), and, in view of the bulk of the larger boats. a certain amount of attention to drag is also in order.

9:2. Automobiles. As road speeds have increased, more and more attention has been given to streamlining of automobiles, although in truth their short length and the fact that they are not always operated aligned with the relative wind makes the problem nearly insoluble.

In problems of this type, and elsewhere, the author begs the tunnel engineer not to prove homself guilty of single-track

Courtesy Georgia Institute of Technology.

Fig. 9:2.   The author adjusting a speedboat model before installing ground-plane seals around mounting struts.

thinking but to consider more than his end of the problem. The sloping windshield in autos is a good example of unilateral approach; they are moderately streamlined but let in so much sun that a visor is frequently needed, and thus the streamlining is lost. In this occasion, too, the tunnel engineer must make sure of his set-up so that he truly represents the actual conditions as nearly as possible. The client always seeks the largest model possible, and normal aerodynamic limitations apply here as well as elsewhere.

Race cars, particularly those designed for attempts at the world speed record, must of necessity pay much attention to wind-tunnel tests. For instance it was indicated in the wind tunnel that Sir John Cobb's racer (that subsequently set the record of 394.196 mph) had only an allowable nose rise of 12 in. This in turn necessitated running the tests on the extraordinary level salt flats, where the sand waves are believed to be less than 2 in. per 1000 ft. It is tragically possible that many of the unfortunate accidents on the Daytona "track" could have been eliminated by preliminary tunnel work.

9:3. Buildings, Bridges, and Signs. It is probably not too severe to say that the building trade in general has failed to take advantage of the benefits they could obtain from wind-tunnel work. It is not too much to say that any structure demolished by wind could have been built in a redesigned manner at little change in cost so that it would have remained intact. The author knows of a large factory which has for the past 5 years averaged a yearly roofing loss of over $4000. From an aerodynamic standpoint the roof is nearly perfect for developing local low pressures, as dramatically illustrated when the wind blows. As another example, thirty apartment houses suffered roof removal from winds of less than hurricane force. In both cases tripper strips or minor redesign could have averted expensive repairs. It will amaze aerodynamicists to learn that many building codes require stressing to the dynamic pressure only, no attention being paid to local distribution whatsoever.

Dramatic exceptions to the lack of wind-tunnel work are those reported by Dryden and Hill (Ref. 9:2) on the Empire State Building, and by Klemin, Schaefer, and Beerer (Ref. 9:3) on the Perisphere and Trylon. The last-mentioned tests are of considerable interest to the aerodynamicist since the sphere close to the ground is a case easily approached by theory.

Probably the structure most often seen vanquished by the wind is the ordinary signboard. Built to design specifications that usually make no special allowance for local velocities, it is not unexpected that they should succumb in ordinary windstorms. Signs located on high buildings add enough load to the building so that city codes usually limit their size, although strange to say the possibility of drag-decreasing slots that would permit a larger sign for a given load has not been investigated—a whole business realm awaiting opening by the aerodynamicists.

Tests of shingle attachment strength and general high-velocity resistance are illustrated in Fig. 9:3.

The spectacular failure of the long and beautiful Tacoma bridge illustrates still another field needing the attention of the wind tunnel. This remarkable structure, apparently engineered in a satisfactory manner according to previous design criteria, had an unusually narrow width for its length, and was in addition located in a natural cut where high wind velocity was frequent.

Courtesy University of Wichita.

FIG. 9:3. Wind-tunnel tests of a shingle installation.

The jumping action of the bridge before failure showed the need for wind-tunnel analysis, and such was actually under way when the final failure occurred. Later tests in a specially built wind tunnel having a very long and narrow test section reproduced the catastrophic motion that ended with the total destruction of the multimillion dollar structure.

9:4. Smoke Nuisance and Exhaust Fumes. Locomotives and trucks have come in for wind-tunnel revisions of the exhaust systems mentioned in the section on boats above (Ref. 9:4). Indeed, the omission of the lowerable rear window on automobiles is the direct result of tunnel tests that showed a large fraction of the exhaust gases flowing into such open windows.

Figure 9:4 shows the original configurations of the Canadian National Railways Model 6400 as tested in the John's Street

Courtesy Canadian National Research Council.

F1G. 9:4.   Locomotive model and its "image" in the open-throat wind tunnel of the Canadian National Research Council.   This type of test has been almost entirely replaced by the groundboard arrangement.

tunnel of the Canadian National Research Council in Ottawa. As shown, excessive smoke came back into the engineer's face, a trouble completely overcome by fairing the various bumps shown in the picture.   The image test is now almost completely replaced by a groundboard rather than a real mirror image to simulate the ground.

9·5. Topography.   Figure 9:5 shows a model of the Rock of Gibraltar in a wind tunnel, where studies were being made to find smooth approach paths for the local airport.   Doubtless many similar tests could be performed for some of the more mountainous airfields in this country.   The Japanese have made models of cities that suffered from smoke nuisance, and indeed there is no telling how many American cities could be helped as regards fog, smoke, or general climatic troubles.   A parallel type of investigation being run in several wind tunnels is that of smoke dispersal from a smokestack.

9:6. Miscellaneous.   A vast field also exists for commendable tunnel work on air-conditioning outlets, rain-shielded inlets,

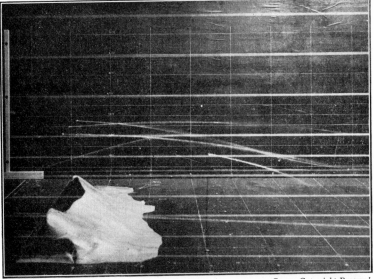

Crown Copyright Reserved.

FIG. 9:5.   Wind-tunnel tests of the Rock of Gibraltar, made to determine the safest approach paths to the landing field in its lee.

automobile manifolds, drying set-ups, anemometer calibrations, wind-driven power plants, and a host of other air-flow devices. It remains for the tunnel engineer to bring before the public the utility of his device and to make the value of tunnel tests more widely known.

REFERENCES

9:1. E. Burke Wilford and Alexander Klemin, *Yacht Sails in the Wind Tunnel*, New York University Publication 9, 1937.

9:2. H. L. Dryden and G. C. Hill, Wind Pressure on a Model of the Empire State Building, *Journal of Research, National Bureau of Standards*, April, 1933.

9:3. Alexander Klemin, Everett B. Schaefer, and J. G. Beerer, Aerodynamics of the Perisphere and Trylon at World's Fair, *Proceedings of the American Society of Civil Engineers*, May, 1938.

9:4. J. J. Green, The Wind-Tunnel Development of a Proposed External Form for Steam Locomotives, *Canadian Journal of Research*, 1933.

9:5. O. Flachsbart, Wind Pressures on Solid Walled and Framed Structures (in German), *International Association for Bridge and Structural Engineering Publications*, Vol. 1, 1932.

9:6. R. A. Frazer, The Severn Bridge Aerodynamic Research, *Nature*, Jan. 1, 1949.

Chapter 10

ROTOR TESTING

The greatly increased importance of the helicopter justifies a fairly lengthy consideration of the problems involved in rotor testing, although the state of the art is currently very fluid, and, particularly in the field of wall corrections, much still remains to be done. Hence this chapter must be confined to discussing some of the methods currently used rather than methods widely agreed upon as satisfactory.

10:1. General Discussion. As an introduction to the problem of rotor testing, consider the many flight paths of a helicopter: it may fly straight up; climb at a number of angles; fly level; and descend both with and without power. In encompassing this range the rotor varies in acting like a propeller, like a yawed propeller, and finally somewhat like a porous disk. Yet throughout the entire range the rotor disk is essentially horizontal. Thus to truly simulate both the aerodynamic and gravitational forces on a rotor in flight we would require a model that remained fixed while the wind tunnel revolved about it. Only the Rhode St. Genese tunnel (Sect. 1:17) is capable of such a maneuver. Fortunately, however, the exact simulation of the rotor is not required for good testing results since the gravity forces are normally small compared with the centrifugal ones. We may therefore in general use a typical wind tunnel for rotor testing, in the great preponderance of the programs one with an open throat. But holding the rotor horizontal for starting may be necessary, especially if the rotor has lag hinges which let the blades tumble as they come over the top until the centrifugal forces build up.

The two set-ups found most often in rotor testing use either pitching or yawing the rotor to simulate the desired flight path angle (see Figs. 10:1 and 10:2), the pitching set-up being preferred.

10:2. The Rotor Model. The design of a model rotor presents some difficulties not encountered with the usual wind-tunnel model of an airplane. To begin with, the hub and hinge design and construction can usually be worked out in a satisfactory

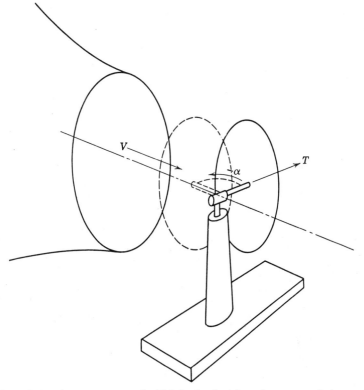

FIG. 10:1. A rotor test stand which is simply adapted to most wind-tunnel set-ups but keeps the rotor in a vertical plane.

manner, but some inherent difficulties arise with the rotor blade representation. For one thing, it is common practice in rotor design to have the blade statically balanced about its quarter-chord line. Such a balance rules out the homogeneous blade and requires either a built-up blade or a solid wood one with a metal leading edge. For most model sizes the built-up blade is not practical, both because of the small size of the skin, ribs, etc., and because of the exaggerated effect of the skin wrinkles due to the scale of the model. The wood blade works well, however, and the metal leading edge is convenient to use as a tie-in to the metal hub. Mass balances for achieving static balance may be built into each blade tip, with, of course, a secure locking device.

The model should be equipped with adequate flat surfaces for leveling and angle measurements, some type of hinge lock to be used during balancing, and an ample supply of spare parts. Blade angles should be measured with their slack taken out in the

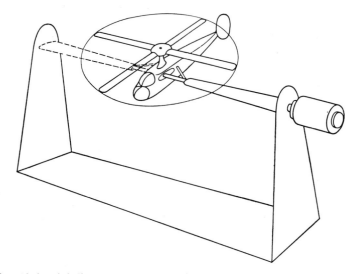

FIG. 10:2. A helicopter test set-up which has the rotor horizontal for starting and part of the operating range.

direction of low pitch, since they will be so held during operation by the centrifugal torque that develops (see Ref. 10:1).

It would be gratifying to include also matching the dynamic characteristics of the full-scale blades when the model is designed, but this is rarely possible since the extremely light construction necessitated thereby is not practical.

10:3. Preparations for Testing. In addition to the customary dimension checking of the rotor model, two additional checks are required before running tests. The first of these is the evaluation of the torsional constants so that the torsional deflections that arise when any similarly shaped body is rotated may be computed. This "dynamic twist" varies with the blade angle as well as with the rpm and cannot be eliminated. The only alternative is to evaluate it and make allowance for it when presenting the data. Even a solid metal blade suffers from this effect and would, as previously mentioned, complicate the set-up by destroying the balance about the blade quarter chord.

The second "extra" check is a run to determine whether the blades are sufficiently similar to "track": follow in the same path as the preceding one. A simple procedure for determining tracking is to rub a little colored chalk on each blade tip, a different color for each blade, and allow the tips to strike a piece of paper when they are rotating. A spread of $\frac{3}{16}$ in. is reasonable for a 5-ft rotor.

There is more possibility that a rotor will fail during testing than that airplane models will fail, and owing to the large centrifugal force on the blades special precautions should be taken to minimize the danger of flying parts, some of which may have the same energy as a "forty-five" pistol bullet. Yet, at the same time, the shielding must not turn the open test section into a closed one.

Possibly the best solution for shielding is $\frac{1}{2}$-in. hardware cloth so placed that all equipment is shielded, and bullet-proof glass shields for the personnel. It is in order to note that it is not adequate to shield only the plane of rotation since the progress of a failure may easily twist the rotor through 90 degrees before the final failure occurs. The customary safety net should be adequate for the protection of the wind-tunnel fan.

10:4. Special Rotor Instrumentation. For a rotor test, the usual measurements are: lift or thrust, drag or H-force, torque, roll, pitch, instantaneous flapping angle, instantaneous lag angle, rpm, and the various vibration frequencies. The loads are rarely large, and the needed degree of accuracy * and sensitivity probably will not be met by the tunnel external balances. Auxiliary strain-gage measuring equipment may then become in order for lift and drag, or, better, thrust and H-force, since the latter make the data more useful to the helicopter aerodynamicist.

Torque may be measured in a number of ways, and again the tunnel balance will in all probability not have enough accuracy. Indeed, considerable work-up of the data would be required even if the accuracy was sufficient. In some cases the characteristics of the drive motor are such that it may be calibrated before the test and a plot of input kilowatts against torque constructed.

* About ± 0.05 lb in thrust and ± 0.003 ft-lb in torque is needed in a typical 10-ft tunnel set-up.

Sometimes the motor may be floated and torque measured with a strain gage on a torque arm. All the methods mentioned so far would make the data include any changes in friction in the drive system and not yield pure rotor torque. The best procedure,

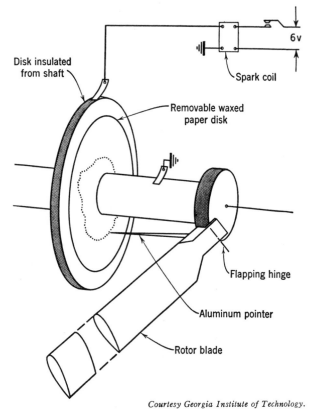

Courtesy Georgia Institute of Technology.

FIG. 10:3. An apparatus for measuring the flapping angles of a rotor.

when it is practical, is to use a floating gear torque nose similar to the devices for measuring the torque of an airplane propeller. An oil spray lubrication should be used to avoid the wide temperature-change effects inherent in grease.

The instantaneous measurement of the flapping angle may be accomplished with good accuracy by means of the apparatus shown in Fig. 10:3. Basically it is as follows: a commercially available wax-covered paper disk, upon which lines are marked showing the number of degrees from a reference line, is clamped to an insulated disk which is fixed. A pointer on the blade hub is made large enough to clear the disk by about $\frac{1}{16}$ in. When desired conditions are reached, a high-tension circuit is closed, and the sparks made from the pointer to the insulated disk punch holes in the waxed paper. After adding the effects of a tare run to account for the centrifugal loads on the pointer, this system yields accuracies of flapping angle to within ±0.1 degree. A plot for one type of rotor is shown in Fig. 10:4.

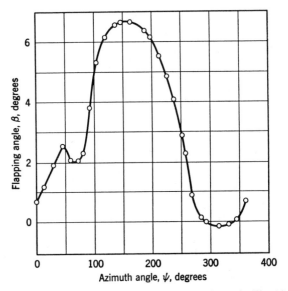

Fig. 10:4. A record taken by the apparatus shown in Fig. 10:3.

Measuring the rpm of a rotor (if a synchronous drive motor is not employed) requires special equipment since the usual tachometers cannot yield the accuracy of ±1 rpm frequently needed. Special tachometers of this accuracy can be purchased, but most of them are quite expensive. If the test can be arranged to use certain particular rpm's, an exceedingly accurate tachometer can be constructed from materials usually found in any laboratory. Such a tachometer is shown in Fig. 10:5. Its principle is as follows: A contact (A) is arranged on the rotor shaft so that a neon light (B) flashes each time the circuit is closed, that is, once a revolution. In front of the neon light, and illuminated by it, is a marked disk (C) rotated at a fixed speed by a synchronous motor (D). To one side is an ordinary tachometer. If the flashing of the light is synchronized with the rpm of the disk, marks on the disk will appear to stand still.

Consider the case when the synchronous motor turns 900 rpm, and there is a single mark on the disk. If the neon light makes the mark appear to stand still, and the tachometer reads (as close as can be determined) 900 rpm, the rotor speed is quite exactly 900. If, however, the light flashes more rapidly, so that the single

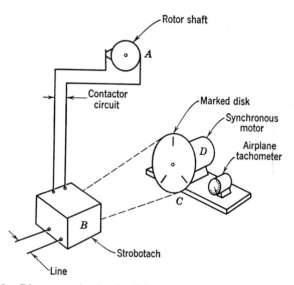

FIG. 10:5. Diagrammatic sketch of the strobotachometer developed at the Georgia Institute of Technology.

mark appears twice, then the speed is exactly 1800 rpm. By making several annular rows, each of a different number of equally spaced marks, almost any rpm can be measured. In actual practice, numbers instead of marks are used, and a list of numbers that will appear to stand still and the rpm they then represent is employed in the operation procedure. The tachometer is needed to get close to the speed since, in the example above, the appearance of one mark could mean 225, 450, or 900 rpm. A little thought will reveal that four annular rings on the synchronous motor disk having 4, 5, 6, and 7 marks each will yield a "stopped" ring nearly every 25 rpm from 900 to 1600 if the synchronous motor turns at the rate of 900 rpm.

The accuracy of this strobotachometer is linked directly to the accuracy with which the line frequency is maintained. In most cities this is not a source of appreciable error.

It should be mentioned that the usual tuft studies may be made on rotor blades, but in all probability it will be more desirable to photograph them than to approach them close enough for vis-

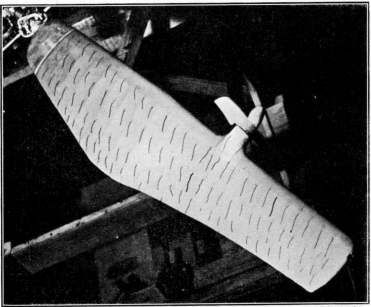

Courtesy Georgia Institute of Technology.

FIG. 10:6. Tuft study of a propeller-driven rotor in the static thrust condition. The turbulence caused by the propeller is clearly visible. The tufts were easy to see in the original negative but have been darkened by hand for reproduction.

ual observation under stroboscopic light. For this type of photography, instantaneously flashing apparatus is commercially available. The centrifugal force on very light streamers does not appear to be serious enough to affect the value of these tests if the model is run at the customary rpm's (Fig. 10:6).

Another technique, developed by the NACA, employs balsa dust to make the flow visible. With this set-up balsa dust is introduced into the airstream with a strong light illuminating the field through a slit. Figure 10:7 shows the success of the method.

10:5. Testing Procedure. One of the most critical periods in rotor testing is the initial run-up to full rpm. During that time

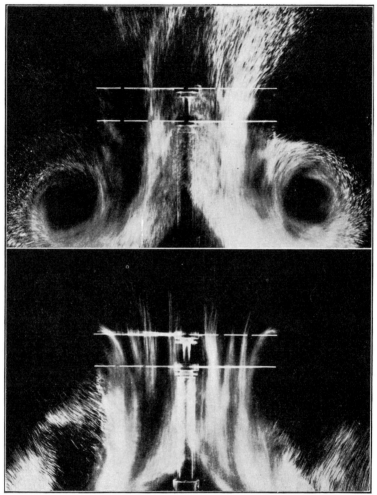

Official Photograph, National Advisory Committee for Aeronautics.

FIG. 10:7.   Observation of the flow through a coaxial helicopter rotor using the balsa-dust method. *Top photograph*: rapid thrust increase. *Bottom*: steady hovering flight.

the blade motions of the rotor are usually at a maximum since enough centrifugal force has not yet arisen to hold the blades to small deflections. It would be desirable to have the hinges locked by remote control until the full rpm is reached.

Usually it is good practice to bring the rotor up to speed before the tunnel is turned on, and to leave it running at the end of a run until the tunnel airstream has died down. This procedure cannot, of course, be followed when very high blade angles are being run to simulate high forward speeds because rotor drive power may be inadequate or rotor strength considerations may make static thrust an impossible state. A solution here is to bring the tunnel wind up gradually and add the rotor power after the windmilling has commenced.

A basic parameter of rotor operation is

$$\mu = \frac{V \cos \alpha}{\Omega R} \qquad (10:1)$$

where V = freestream velocity, ft per sec; α = angle of attack; Ω = angular velocity of the rotor, radians per sec; R = rotor tip radius, ft.

A succession of μ values may be obtained, obviously, by varying the rotor rpm, the tunnel speed, or both, but it may be advantageous to employ a synchronous rotor drive motor and vary only the tunnel speed. This procedure eliminates the need for measuring one variable, and is protective in the sense that the sudden feathering of the blades will not result in overspeeding. It also tends to approach the manner in which a rotor is actually run.

10:6. Tare, Interference, and Alignment. The tare, interference, and alignment are not as easily evaluated in a rotor test as they are in an airplane or wing-alone program. Ordinarily no attempt is made to determine the tare of the rotor supports other than by themselves. This procedure neglects the effect of the active rotor on the support. Customarily it is convenient to remove the rotor and, with the wind on, read the various components, including torque, and use these data for the tares.

The interference of the rotor drive windshield may be evaluated by means of a dummy shield as shown in Fig. 10:8. In the particular set-up shown, no measurable effect of the windshield on the free-air rotor flow was detected. Although this single program

is by no means conclusive, it is probably not in error to assume
that the effect of a support stand of 0.1 rotor diameter located
0.2 rotor diameter from the plane of rotation will be small. In
Figs. 10:2 and 10:8 are shown methods wherein second supports

FIG. 10:8. A set-up for determination of the windshield interference on a
rotor's performance.

may be added. As is customary with such set-ups, the assumption is made that the second support has the same effect on the
data as the first: i.e., they have no effect on each other.

The mean alignment of the tunnel airstream for a particular
rotor probably may best be determined from tests of a wing with
equal span. Runs that would parallel the wing normal and inverted runs do not seem to have much promise since blade
settings of sufficient accuracy do not seem possible.

10:7. Boundary Corrections for Rotor Testing. We have seen how the vortex pattern of a wing and its thickness distribution is simulated by an appropriate distribution of sources, sinks, and vortices, and contained within the free or closed jet by the proper added systems. The same procedure would be in order for the determination of the boundary corrections for a rotor. Unfortunately the vortex pattern varies widely with the rotor flight condition and in addition is quite difficult to express mathematically. The net result is that no special boundary corrections have been worked up for rotors, and the only cases where they are known are when the rotor is acting like a propeller or bluff body. It seems in order to consider each of the major flight conditions separately to see the current status of the corrections:

1. *Hovering flight.* No boundary corrections are needed for hovering flight. There should be, however, no obstruction such as balance or walls closer than 1.5 rotor diameters "above" and "below" the rotor. Ground effect when desired may be deliberately simulated by a groundboard of 2.5 rotor diameters or more (Fig. 10:9).

2. *Horizontal flight.* Many tunnel engineers use the ordinary wing downwash corrections for a rotor in horizontal flight, although there is a wide difference between wing and rotor vortex patterns and the assumption of similarity may not be justified.

3. *Inclined climbing flight.* The boundary corrections for the condition of climbing flight are not known. The condition of model power and size such that some air is entrained from outside the tunnel stream does not represent any real condition and should not be tested.

4. *Vertical ascent.* Vertical ascent is the same as the case of a thrusting propeller, and the boundary corrections are then properly zero in an open jet. The corrections for propeller data as given in Sect. 6:28 should be used if the test is run in a closed jet.

5. *Vertical descent.* A rotor in vertical power-off descent in a tunnel stream develops a flow similar to a porous disk perpendicular to the stream, and the boundary corrections are then properly zero. The three-dimensional wake-blocking corrections would be used if the test is made in a closed jet.

6. *Vortex ring stage.* The gap between the thrusting flow pattern of vertical ascent and the drag pattern of vertical descent is covered by a mixed flow known as the vortex ring stage. It too should need no corrections if run in an open jet.

It is interesting to note that slow power-on vertical descent may be simulated in the tunnel, but so far on account of power requirements it remains outside of the ability of actual helicopters.

Courtesy Georgia Institute of Technology.

FIG. 10:9.   Testing a rotor for ground effect.

10:8. Presentation of the Data.   Testing a rotor model for a particular helicopter parallels powered-model testing for an airplane.   That is, in order to save taking a mass of useless data, each value of the thrust must be aligned with the particular flight condition, consideration being paid to the power available from the engine.   Usually the test program is carefully worked out

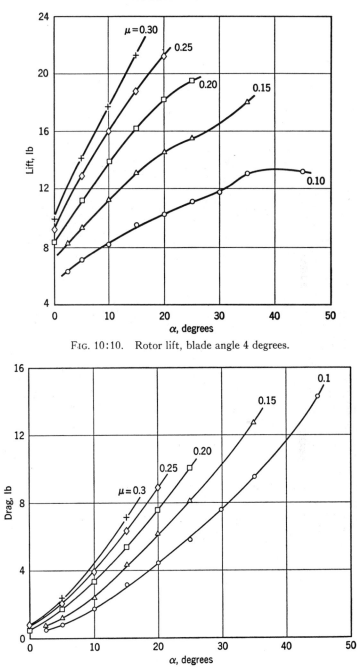

FIG. 10:10.   Rotor lift, blade angle 4 degrees.

FIG. 10:11.   Rotor drag, blade angle 4 degrees.

beforehand, and several points are taken near a desired one in order that final exact data may be obtained by crossplotting.

Fundamental rotor research need not follow such a program. In general, blade angles can be varied in selected steps, and the lift, drag, and torque (or thrust, H-force, and torque) can then be

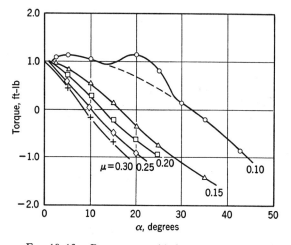

FIG. 10:12.   Rotor torque, blade angle 4 degrees.

read through a range of α. High blade angles correspond to the ascent conditions and need only be tested in the negative α range; low blade angles are needed only in the high α range. Some sample plots of rotor data are presented in Figs. 10:10, 10:11, and 10:12.

REFERENCE

10:1. Wilbur C. Nelson, Airplane Propeller Principles. John Wiley & Sons, New York, 1944, p. 60.

Chapter 11

NEARSONIC AND TRANSONIC TESTING

Although supersonic wind-tunnel testing was a limited though practical reality before 1930, there was ample evidence as late as 1940 that the range from just below the speed of sound to slightly above it would be forever denied to wind-tunnel engineers. Yet, in one of the great triumphs of modern aerodynamics, the gap has now been completely closed: conventional tunnels are useful to a Mach number of about 0.96; "bump" testing bridges from well below Mach 1.0 to about Mach 1.15 for small models; and special though undescribed throats allow surprisingly large models to be tested right through the difficult Mach 1.0 range.

It will be seen that there is a tremendous difference between a wind tunnel useful up to Mach = 0.96 and one capable of testing right through Mach = 1.0 and on into the low-supersonic range. The former may be more properly called a *nearsonic* tunnel; the latter is truly *transonic*. Frequently this important distinction is not made, the word *transonic* being interpreted to refer to transonic velocities on a model at below sonic freestream speeds.

We will first deal with the design and use of a nearsonic tunnel. Later on in the chapter a method of transonic testing will be described. First, however, before considering the conditions in a wind tunnel, it seems in order to review briefly the transonic flow problems in free air.

In order for air to pass over a body it must go faster than the freestream velocity. This effect produces nothing untoward as long as the maximum velocity reached anywhere in the flow is not above the speed of sound; subsonic flow decelerates smoothly and with a minimum of loss.

If the flow anywhere exceeds the velocity of sound by more than a very small amount, it may only decelerate through shock waves. As it passes through these waves a sudden rise of pressure ensues which is responsible for the troubles of transonic flight. The rise, occurring on the surface of an airplane, causes a detachment of the boundary layer not unlike that occurring at a low-speed stall; the drag greatly increases, the airflow buffets the surfaces, and, worst of all, the changing flow pattern can result in loss of the airplane through changes in trim too large for the controls to overcome. If the shock waves and the wake of an airplane flying at transonic speeds could be seen they would look like Fig. 11:1.

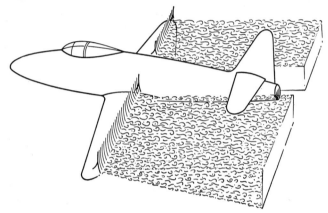

Fig. 11:1.   Sketch of wing shock at about $M = 0.8$.

In other words, a small shock, nearly normal to the freestream, appears on the surface of a body somewhere around Mach = 0.7. The shock moves towards the rear of the body, and grows in strength and extent as the Mach number increases. At Mach = 1.0 it reaches the trailing edge of the body, and a second shock appears well ahead of the body. With increasing Mach number above 1.0 the forward shock approaches the body until it becomes attached (a function of the leading edge angle of the body) and both front and rear shocks incline rearward with an angle slightly greater than the Mach angle, whose sine is $1/M$. The Mach number at which the forward shock becomes attached to the airplane is assumed to be the end of the transonic regime for the particular shape and normally occurs around Mach = 1.4.

The freestream difficulties described above are uniquely complicated when the airplane in question is held immobile in a duct while the air streams by it. The shock waves then reflect from the jet boundaries and can restrike the airplane as they never could in free air, and in addition a new phenomenon arises that severely limits model size when the test section has solid walls. This effect is discussed in the next section.

11:1. Choking and Wave Reflection. As the speed of sound is approached in a wind tunnel, the testing conditions change greatly from those encountered at low subsonic speeds, and special procedures must be followed in order to make valid tests. The new difficulties are of two types, the first arising from the manner in which duct area and Mach number are related, and the second from the reflection of shock waves from the tunnel walls.

In order to understand the phenomenon called "choking" we have to backtrack a little and consider a subsonic-type wind tunnel such as shown in Fig. 1:3. To make the air in that tunnel go faster we need only increase the fan blade angle or rpm. But, placing a pitot-static tube in the test section and properly interpreting its readings, we find that, no matter how much power we apply, the speed in the test section never exceeds $M = 1.0$. In fact we find that (silly though it sounds—and certainly against every rule of subsonic streamlining) the only way the test section can be brought up to *supersonic* speed is to put a bump at its front. Here is how this comes about: At low subsonic speeds where constant density is a very reasonable assumption, the flow conditions closely follow the simple rule

$$A_1 V_1 = A_2 V_2 \qquad (11:1)$$

where A and V are duct areas and velocities, respectively. At higher speeds large changes in air density occur, and the use of eq. 11:1 is no longer justified. Many other equations relating the different flow quantities may then be written, the most pertinent of which (eq. 2:6 of Ref. 11:1) is

$$(1/A)(dA/dx) = (M^2 - 1)(1/V)(dV/dx) \qquad (11:2)$$

where V = velocity in the duct; A = duct area; x = distance along the duct from some reference; and M = Mach number.

Among other things eq. 11:2 tells us that $M = 1.0$ can occur only where dA/dx is zero. This corresponds, it develops, to a minimum section. Common sense tells us that flow cannot be supersonic until it has been sonic, and hence the bump or minimum mentioned above is necessary.

It is in order to ask where the extra power went that we put into the subsonic tunnel when its speed failed to increase. In that case the test section was the minimum or sonic section, and as the flow entered the *diffuser* it became supersonic, finally "shocking down" somewhere in the diffuser. The more power applied, the longer the region of supersonic flow, and the greater the power loss (which increases with the Mach number ahead of the shock). This will be more fully covered in the next chapter. The point we need to remember now is simply that sonic speed will always occur first at the minimum area section in a wind tunnel, and, once it does occur, the Mach number at the point will never increase no matter how much power is applied. The tunnel is then *choked*.

It was noted before that the test section is the zone of minimum area in a subsonic type wind tunnel. Once a model is placed in it, however, the section of minimum tunnel area is then a plane taken through the maximum thickness of the model perpendicular to the jet axis. Sonic speed will now first occur at the model, but testing with $M = 1.0$ on the model is not feasible; the shock that formed on the body at some earlier Mach number has become strong enough by the time $M = 0.95$ is reached to extend to the tunnel ceiling and reflect back, confusing the flow pattern. Clearly there is then little comparison to free flight.

Of great interest to the engineer is the determination of the limits for satisfactory testing, and for this we go to eq. 2:3 of Ref. 11:1 as follows (γ = ratio of specific heat of air at constant pressure to that at constant volume; γ is very nearly 1.4 below $M = 3.0$):

$$\frac{A_2}{A_1} = \frac{M_1}{M_2} \left[\frac{1 + \dfrac{\gamma - 1}{2} M_1{}^2}{1 + \dfrac{\gamma - 1}{2} M_2{}^2} \right]^{-\frac{\gamma+1}{2(\gamma-1)}} \tag{11:3}$$

Equation 11:3 relates the Mach number and area at stations 1 and 2 in a duct. It is plotted in Fig. 11:2 for a wide range of Mach numbers, and in a slightly different form in Fig. 11:3. From Fig. 11:3 can be determined whether a given model put in a given high subsonic stream will cause to it choke, or, conversely, the approximate uncorrected Mach number at which a given tunnel-model combination should experience choking. The *corrected* Mach number (see Sects. 11:15 and 11:16) will be more than the above value, owing to wall blockage effect.

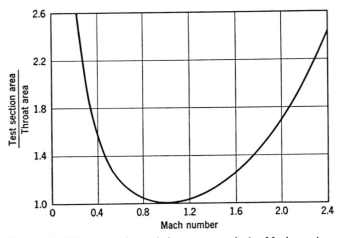

FIG. 11:2.   The area ratio needed to get a particular Mach number.

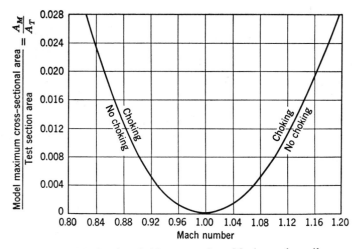

FIG. 11:3.   Model size for choking at various Mach numbers (from area-Mach-number relation).

Some additional discussion is needed regarding choking since the ideal case is considerably altered when a model is included. First of all, there are three "definitions" of choking: (1) when the speed of sound is first reached on a wall; (2) when the mass flow is a maximum (this is evidenced by the failure of the reference *

_____

* Reference Mach number is the clear jet Mach number obtained during calibration and indicated by some upstream total and static pressure orifices.

Mach number to increase); (3) when an increase of power fails to produce an increase of model forces.

The above choking conditions give identical values for a clear jet with a uniform velocity distribution but differ when a model produces widely varying Mach numbers across the test section. Under this condition Mach = 1.0 occurs at the wall ("wall choke") very near the choking reference Mach number. An increase of power will still produce an increase of reference Mach number and an increase of force on the model. Shortly thereafter, the reference Mach number fails to increase with tunnel power ("mass choke"), but model forces still increase. The force increase here is not fully understood but may be associated with the changes that take place in the tunnel boundary-layer thickness and consequently in the tunnel calibration. Finally, an increase of tunnel power produces change of neither reference Mach number nor model forces ("full choke").

When sufficient power exists it is standard procedure to run a little beyond wall choke. After working up the wall pressures, the exact wall-choke Mach number is indicated on the plotted curves. Some engineers prefer to use data only up to 0.02 below wall choking (Fig. 11:28), but others have successfully used lift and moment data as high as 0.01 above M_{choke}. It is suggested that the 0.02 delta be kept for drag data.

One can readily see from Fig. 11:3 that, as Mach = 1.0 is approached, the permissible size of the model rapidly drops to extremely small values, until at Mach 1.0 the theoretical size is zero. A reasonable compromise is to pick a model size such that the Reynolds number, which unfortunately exerts a profound effect, is as large as possible while the Mach number still is satisfactory.

Example 11:1

Calculate the choking Mach number and the allowable maximum test Mach number for the model of example 6:5.

1. The frontal area of the model is 1.204 sq ft, and the cross-sectional area of the tunnel less boundary-layer displacement thickness is 68.58 sq ft.

2. $A_m/A_t = 1.204/68.58 = 0.0175$.

3. From Fig. 11:3, $M_{choke} = 0.86$. According to general practice, testing should be kept below $M = 0.84$ in a tunnel with a solid wall test section.

Before leaving the phenomenon of choking, it should be noted that frequently the model support and not the model furnishes the maximum cross-sectional area and hence the location of M_{choke} A simple device to remove this trouble is a tunnel "liner" (Fig. 11:4), which decreases the clear jet area at all stations except that of the model support, making the model station truly the smallest in the entire tunnel. In designing such a liner, the effective area at the vertical strut should be reduced to allow for

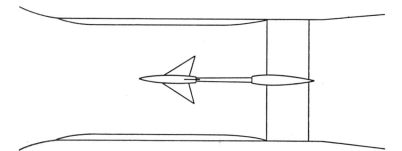

Fig. 11:4. Liner installed in test section of nearsonic wind tunnel. The shape of the liner near the vertical strut determines how close the model may be to the vertical strut. As shown, the model is mounted for a yaw test.

the sting pod and for the presence of a large model wake. Engineers failing to make the above allowances have found their liners too small and choking still occurring at the strut. In this connection, it is advisable to continue the row of wall pressure orifices from which choking is to be determined as far back as the vertical strut.

11:2. Discussion of Nearsonic Tunnel Design. For a tunnel to operate up to about Mach 0.96 no changes from the normal subsonic design are mandatory, but several are usually made. The large power requirements call for careful attention to the basic design in order to get a high energy ratio; some provision will have to be made for cooling; and usually a dust screen is provided to reduce sand blasting.

The basic design for high efficiency embraces a long diffuser before the first corner in order to reduce the losses in the two high-speed turns. For the low-power tunnel discussed on p. 68 over 75 per cent of the total power is used between the end of the entrance cone and the end of the second corner. For more efficient designs this percentage increases and the total power required drops. Thus the diffuser becomes the most important single part of the high-speed wind tunnel from a power standpoint.

A diagrammatic sketch of a nearsonic tunnel is shown in Fig. 11:5. It seems in order to work our way gradually around it, noting differences between it and the subsonic tunnel, but treating these differences qualitatively instead of quantitatively.

First of all the methods of calculating the losses in a wind tunnel as discussed in Chapter 2 may be used to get an indication of the losses in the nearsonic tunnel. In the nearsonic tunnel,

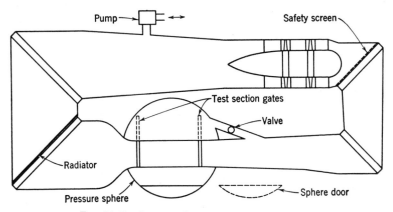

Fig. 11:5.   Layout of nearsonic-pressure tunnel.

however, changes in density tend to reduce the losses in the diffusers a very small amount while increasing the losses in the entrance cone, also a small amount. For the purposes of preliminary calculations the isentropic laws can be used to find the density along the tunnel, and the losses as they occur can be applied to find the local temperature. Our tools for this work are the equation of state, the continuity equation, and the isentropic law. We may start by assuming a temperature and pressure at any point in the tunnel, calculate the losses as they arise, and at each section add in the heat rise due to the work expended on the section. It will normally be necessary to repeat the calculation if estimates of total power needed are in error.

We need make no changes in the test section of a tunnel to use it for nearsonic work—special mountings and bumps excluded, but since our rental costs will be high, more attention should be paid to (and money allowed for) gadgets that make for more rapid model and jet changes. Compressed-air lines, built-in photo lighting, built-in tool boxes, microphone, and speaker systems, and so forth, are generally in order. A new difficulty will be to get the boundary-layer divergence exactly right; customarily some sort of adjustment is provided.

We have previously discussed the diffuser to the effect that a long one will probably be required. Since the power loss here can be very serious, careful surveys of the diffuser flow both with and without a model in the test section should be made to determine that the diffuser does not stall. If it does, vanes or boundary-layer control devices should be employed to re-form good flow. It has been found that flow in the breather can make serious diffuser troubles. The high power cost of a safety screen makes its employment quite a debatable question.

Similarly, attention to the corner vanes will pay off. Normally, the first set of vanes is not used for cooling. One reason is that they do not have sufficient heat-transfer area, and further the tunnel temperature is highest in the settling chamber and cooling is hence easiest to do there. A secondary reason is that the first set of vanes is likely to be damaged if a model failure occurs. With such an accident, there will be enough trouble without adding in a tunnel half full of water.

Internal coolers are briefly discussed in Sect. 2:12. A neat trick for finding leaks (not mentioned therein) is to add a little fluorescein to the water and inspect the coolers with ultraviolet light.

In general it may be said that an air-exchange tunnel is about 25 per cent more efficient than a comparable internally cooled tunnel, and considerably cheaper to build. Of course air-exchange tunnels do not have the control over Reynolds number that pressure tunnels have, nor for the same power can they reach as high Mach numbers. As a matter of interest, the exchange of air is necessary for other than cooling if internal-combustion engines are run in the tunnel; the exchange (sometimes as much as 33 per cent) limits the variation in γ due to the contamination of the products of combustion.*

The required pressure rise for a nearsonic tunnel is rarely obtainable with a single row of fan blades. In the various tunnels are to be found counterrotating fans, those with prerotating

* The 10 per cent contaminated air employed by the Saab tunnel (Fig 1:13) is probably not enough to affect γ measurably.

vanes (sometimes adjustable), and multistage arrangements of nearly every type imaginable. One decisive feature has emerged: the tunnel speed is most easily controlled by adjustable fan pitch rather than adjustable fan rpm, even though the latter is better theoretically. An added advantage of the constant rpm operation is that is permits the economies of the constant-speed electric motor. Against these advantages must be weighed the increased cost of the pitch-changing mechanism, and the difficulties of bringing a constant-speed motor up to speed.

Both wood and aluminum blades are found in these large installations, the aluminum appearing quite a bit better for withstanding flying model parts and for changing damaged blades. Typical inspection procedure is to change two metal blades (out of, say, thirty) every week. The curing, shaping, and finishing of a large wood propeller can take a year.

Downstream of the fans there is normally a dust screen, sometimes nylon cheesecloth or a bronze screen of about 30 mesh. Its purpose is to collect as much dust as possible so that the model is spared excessive sand blasting. Every month or so the screen is cleaned. Placed in the settling chamber, the dust screen may double as a turbulence reducer.

The entrance cone must be more carefully laid out for the nearsonic tunnel than for a low-speed one since it is desired that the velocity always increase from settling chamber to test section, where it will be close to sonic. (An early sonic velocity will result in poor test-section flow.)

Surprisingly, the variation in Mach number that one might expect as the result of lateral temperature gradients is greatly reduced as the air flows into the test section. According to Corrsin (Ref. 11:8), Mach number variations in the settling chamber are reduced by the contraction according to

$$m_2/M_2 = (M_1/M_2)^2(m_1/M_1) \qquad (11:4)$$

where m is the Mach number variation and stations 1 and 2 are settling chamber and test section, respectively. According to eq. 11:4 the large variation in Mach number that might be caused by a side-entry air exchanger letting cool (70° F) air into the sides of the return passage while the center stream is at high (130° F) temperature would be reduced to a Mach number variation of only 0.0005 in the test section for a reasonable value of $M_2/M_1 = 10$.

It has already been noted that the power required for a wind tunnel goes up roughly as the cube of the speed. For convenience in rough figuring, tunnel engineers frequently remember that there is approximately 7 horsepower in a square foot of standard air at 100 mph (from $HP = qAV/550$), and thus, using the cube law and estimated values of the tunnel energy ratio, power requirements can be mentally figured. For instance, a tunnel having a 100 sq ft test section and an energy ratio of 8 will need $7 \times 100/8$ or 90 hp at 100 mph. The same tunnel at $M = 0.66$ (500 mph) will need 125×90 or 11,000 hp. The only remaining design changes we can make to save some of this enormous power requirement is to reduce the density, which directly reduces the power, or to use a gas (Freon-12, for instance) that has a lower speed of sound than air. Part of this density reduction will normally come about through a drop in static pressure from settling chamber to test section, but in any event power requirements remain very large. A number of nearsonic and transonic wind tunnels are presented in Table 11:1.

11:3. Calibration of the Test Section. The calibration of the test section of a nearsonic or transonic wind tunnel is easier than for a typical low-speed tunnel for two reasons. The first is that the distribution of Mach number is the most important factor by such a wide margin that other flow qualities are almost ignored; and the second is that the large contraction ratios that result from efficient designs normally give such excellently smooth flow that, once a good distribution of Mach number is achieved, the other qualities may be neglected with a reasonable degree of confidence. Indeed, in most high-speed tunnels the turbulence and angularity have never been measured.

Essential calibration then consists of mounting a static pipe (having flush orifices every 6 in.) along the axis of the tunnel and reading the local static pressure for particular settings of the total-head and static-pressure tubes placed at the front of the test section.

This seems a good place to introduce a few new terms that come up in connection with nearsonic wind-tunnel testing and perhaps to review the true meaning of some of the low-speed terms.

TABLE 11:1. NEARSONIC AND TRANSONIC WIND TUNNELS

All are of the single-return type except the RAE 7 by 10, which has an annular return.

Tunnel	Location	Cooling	Mach Number Range	Jet Shape	Jet Length	HP	Remarks
AEDC PWT Transonic	Tullahoma, Tenn.	Internal	0.8–1.6	16 ft, square	.....	100,000	Under construction, 1952
Boeing 8 x 12	Seattle, Wash.	Air exchange	0–1.2	8 x 12 ft, rectangular	1.16B	54,000	Under renovation, 1952
CARI 3.3 ft	Sweden		0–0.85	3.3 ft, round	.....	1,300	*Saabsonics*, January, 1950
Cornell Aero Lab 3 x 4 ft Transonic Insert	Buffalo, N. Y.	Internal	0–1.25	3 x 4 ft, rectangular	2.26B	12,000	
Cornell Aero Lab 8½ x 12 ft	Buffalo, N. Y.	Internal	0–0.96 and 1.2	8½ x 12 ft, rectangular	1.25B	14,000	0.25 to 2.0 atmospheres
DTMB 7 x 10	Carderock, Md.		0–1.20	7 x 10 ft, rectangular		27,000	Under construction, 1954
NACA 7 x 10 #2	Langley Field, Va.	Air exchange	0–0.95	7 x 10 ft, rectangular	1.5B	10,000	
NACA 8 ft Transonic	Langley Field, Va.	Air exchange	0–1.2	8 ft, polygon	1.50D	16,000	
NACA 8 ft Transonic Pressure	Langley Field, Va.	Internal	0–1.3	8 ft, square	.....	25,000	
NACA 12 ft	Moffett Field, Cal.	Internal	0–0.97	12 ft, round	.....	11,000	⅙ to 6 atmospheres
NACA 16 ft	Langley Field, Va.	Air exchange	0–1.1	16 ft, round	1.5D	60,000	

NACA 11 ft	Moffett Field, Cal.	Internal	0–1.5	11 ft, square	.....	200,000	Ready August, 1955
NACA 16 ft	Moffett Field, Cal.	Air exchange	0–0.95	16 ft, round	.....	27,000	
NAMTC	Point Mugu, Cal.	Continuous blowdown	0–1.2	16 x 16 in.	.....	15,400	
NPL 8 x 20 in.	Teddington, England		0–0.90	8 x 20 in., rectangular	0.83B	Intermittent	
University of Minnesota	Rosemount	Continuous induction	0–1.4	12 x 16 in.	......	......	
ONERA "Paul Dumanois"	Modane Avrieux, France	Air exchange	0–0.97	26.2 ft, round	46 ft	110,000	Atomes, July, 1951
Saab Transonic	Linkoping, Sweden	Open circuit	0–1.4	2.3 x 3.3 ft	......	Four DH Goblins	Aircraft Engineering, December, 1952
RAE 7 x 10	Farnborough, England	Internal	0–0.90	7 x 10 ft, rectangular	15 ft	4,000	Flight, Jan. 5, 1948
Southern California Co-op	Pasadena, Cal.	Internal	0–0.96 and 1.2	8½ x 12 ft, rectangular	1.5B	12,000 (45,000 in 1955)	0.2 to 4.0 atmospheres
United Aircraft 8 ft	East Hartford, Conn.	Air exchange	0–0.95 or 210 mph	8 or 18 ft, octagonal	2.0D	7,000	
Vickers-Armstrong	Weybridge, Surrey, England	Air exchange	0–0.90	3 x 2 ft, rectangular	1.67B	1,700	
WADC 10 ft	Dayton, Ohio	Internal	0–1.22	10 ft, round	2.0D	40,000	0.12 to 2.0 atmospheres
WADC 6 in. Transonic	Dayton, Ohio	Air exchange	0–1.24	6 in., circular	......	350	....

It is only a low-speed approximation to say that the total head is equal to the sum of dynamic and static heads. Actually, the total head (which is another term for the stagnation pressure) is found exactly from

$$p_s = p\left(1 + \frac{\gamma - 1}{2} M^2\right)^{\gamma/(\gamma-1)} \tag{11:5}$$

where p_s = stagnation pressure; p = static pressure; γ = ratio of specific heats of air = 1.4; and M = the Mach number.

Expansion of the term in the parentheses according to the binomial theorem, and substitution from the dynamic-pressure equality

$$(\rho/2)V^2 = (\gamma/2)pM^2 \tag{11:6}$$

(see p. 19 of Ref. 11:1) results in the approximate relation

$$p_s = p + q(MF) \tag{11:7}$$

where $MF = 1 + (M^2/4) + (M^4/40)$ and $q(MF) = q_c = $ "impact pressure." * The assumption of negligibly small Mach number results in the familiar low-speed relation

$$p_s = p + q \tag{11:8}$$

Now, then, the original concept of the dynamic pressure sprang from the low-speed validity of eq. 11:8 and from the fact that the various coefficients in general change very little with Mach and Reynolds numbers at low speed so that the use of q in reducing data leads to presumably constant coefficients and great ease in calculations. Linear supersonic theory also indicates that q is a suitable parameter in that range. Thus we use the dynamic pressure as out reference for force data reduction in the transonic range, even though the wide variation of the coefficients with Mach number reduces its utility. But one must bear in mind that in the high-subsonic range the pitot-static tube yields the impact pressure rather than the dynamic pressure as it did at low speed. If the dynamic pressure is needed, we must read the stagnation and static pressures separately, use eq. 11:5 to find the Mach number, and then eq. 11:7 to find q.

---

* q_c is also known by the regrettable name of "compressible q," regrettable because it implies that there is a compressible dynamic pressure when dynamic pressure is neither compressible nor incompressible, but simply $(\rho/2)V^2$ or $(\gamma/2) pM^2$.

Conveniently, the pitot-static tube for subsonic work remains quite useful in the transonic range. According to Pearcy in Ref. 11:4 the stagnation pressure as read with a pitot-static tube having a hemispherical nose and an orifice whose diameter is one-quarter of the tube diameter will be accurate to at least $\pm 0.002 q_c$ (essentially the accuracy of measurement) up to Mach = 1.0. (The case for flows above Mach 1.0 is covered in the next chapter.) The above error rises gradually to about $-0.003 q_c$ at 5 degrees of yaw or pitch.

Kiel tubes are satisfactory until shocks off the lips have serious loss, say $M = 1.05$ at least; and they can be designed to hold their yaw performance through ± 50 degrees.

The static pressure as determined by a static-pressure tube suffers from the same type of tip and stem errors found at low speeds, but a little more severely. In general the static-pressure error increases positively above $M = 0.9$. Design features of a number of static-pressure tubes are given by Lock, Knowler, and Pearcy in Ref. 11:5 for the range up to $M = 0.9$. However, since it is never possible to make tip and stem errors continue to balance out for the transonic range, it is probably the best practice to use a static tube that has neither type of error. Such a tube may be made by placing the static orifices 20 diameters ahead of the stem and 8 diameters behind a 10-degree included angle conical tip. This tip should have a base a few thousandths of an inch larger than the tube diameter in order to assure a tripped boundary layer.

Thus, in essence, a longer pitot-static tube is called for in the nearsonic regime; the turbulence sphere will be useless, and flow direction may be measured with a normal subsonic yawhead or a wedge. For best results any probe should be calibrated.

The major flow calibration, Mach number distribution, is shown for one tunnel in Fig. 11:6. We see from the figure the apparent impossibility of designing a test-section expansion that will correct for the boundary layer throughout the Mach and Reynolds number range. For the tunnel shown the correction is practically perfect through $M = 0.88$, but the expansion of the test-section walls should be a little greater for the higher Mach numbers. Note the short supersonic region in the diffuser when the test section is at Mach $M = 1.0$. In some tunnels this zone has actually been used for supersonic tests on an emergency basis.

The subsonic criterion of constant indicated airspeed for a particular run also "goes by the boards" for the nearsonic case where Mach number is the primary parameter. Since the Mach number is defined by the ratio of static to total pressure according to the relation

$$M = \sqrt{[2/(\gamma - 1)][(p_s/p)^{(\gamma - 1)/\gamma} - 1]} \qquad (11:9)$$

(from eq. 1:35 of Ref. 11:1) we need only know (and hold constant for a particular Mach number) the ratio of the static pres-

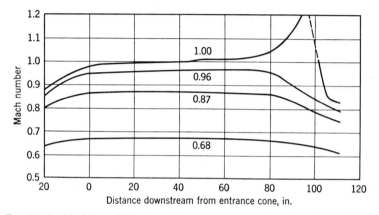

FIG. 11:6. Variation of Mach number along a nearsonic test section. Numbers are nominal Mach numbers.

sure to the total head in the test section. We may obtain these values by a total-head tube located either in the settling chamber or well out of the boundary layer in the forward part of the test section, and a piezometer ring also located at the forward end of the test section.

It is, by the way, important that the small piezometer ring be *in* the test section (but outside of the influence of the model). The reason for this is that a piezometer ring in the entrance cone will determine the static pressure and hence the Mach number there, but the area-Mach number equation (eq. 11:3) becomes very sensitive near $M = 1.0$, and small changes in the Reynolds number which produce small changes in the boundary layer may cause wide changes in test-section Mach number. Ingenious static-pressure gadgets have been utilized in some tunnels which increase in sensitivity near Mach = 1.0 and enable a nozzle piezometer to operate satisfactorily. The test-section static-pressure piezometer ring is also useful as a reference for the multiple manometers.

The type of micromanometer found of greatest value in transonic and supersonic work is shown in Fig. 11:7. Basically, it consists of a null-type mercury manometer referenced to vacuum. Special additions include a ground leadscrew and counter for direct reading, an overflow can at the top, and a light source which projects an image of the top of the mercury column on a ground glass to aid in making accurate settings. With such a manometer, readings to 0.001 cm are possible, although repeat pressure settings usually run 3 to 5 times that. Very high accuracy is needed since small errors in Mach number amount to large errors in dynamic pressure. A variation of not over 0.002 in Mach number in the high subsonic range is considered adequate.

Another type of manometer, not shown, floats a knife edge instead of projecting the miniscus, and has a stretchable scale to allow for density changes of the fluid. If a manometer is not a null type it must have some allowance for the change of reservoir level.

11:4. Model Support Systems. The discussion in Sect. 11:1 shows clearly that the normal three-point model support system using windshields would be entirely impractical for nearsonic work from a choking standpoint since their large frontal area

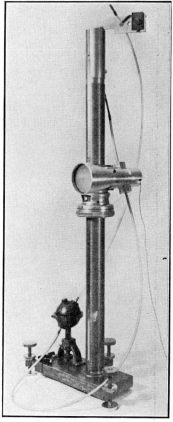

Courtesy Cooperative Wind Tunnel.

Fig. 11:7. Absolute-pressure mercury manometer. For normal operation vacuum is applied to the low-pressure side of the manometer, but the same arrangement (i.e., illuminated eyepiece, vernier scales) is quite workable with other fluids without the vacuum reference.

would in an average installation cause choking in the low-Mach-number range. To get around this, the frontal area of the struts may be reduced by removing the windshields and replacing the customary blunt load members by streamlined ones, or by tying the model in with tension wires. Both these artifices have been tried but in general have been superseded by single or triple

Courtesy Boeing Airplane Co.

FIG. 11:8.   B-47 model mounted on a single swept strut.

swept struts or by sting mounts from a vertical strut. In any case, since powered tests are seldom made at nearsonic speeds, the struts do not need provisions for power and cooling leads.

Considering the swept struts first, like their low-speed counter-parts they may be used singly or in combination. Generally, however, when they are used singly a strain-gage balance is incorporated in the model, and the model is pitched through a pitch strut carried internally by the swept strut (Fig. 11:8). When three swept struts are used (Fig. 11:9), they are ordinarily tied into the external wind-tunnel balance, and the model is pitched in the customary way by the exposed pitch strut. Neither the

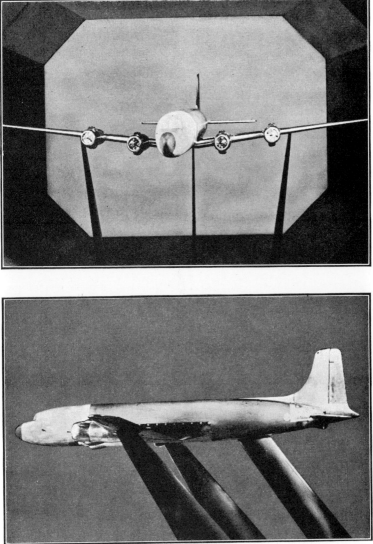

Courtesy Douglas Aircraft Corp.

FIG. 11:9. Front and side views of the Douglas DC-6 on triple swept strut mounting system in the Southern California Cooperative Wind Tunnel. The closure seen at the back of the top picture is the test-section pressure gate. (Note that the struts do *not* attach at the nacelle.)

single strut not the three struts allow for yawing the model; when yawing is mandatory, the model is mounted on a sting with its wings vertical, and the angle of attack becomes yaw.

Swept struts utilize a number of phenomena which add to their performance. First, by having most of their volume well behind the model, the frontal area at the model station is reduced, and through their sweep and thin circular-arc profiles the Mach number at which the drag starts to rise is high.

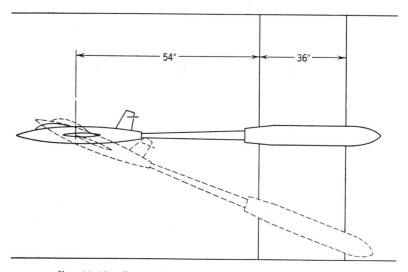

Fig. 11:10.   Reasonable vertical strut and sting installation.

A second and by far the most popular mounting for transonic work is the vertical strut and sting combination shown in Figs. 11:10 and 11:11. This mounting is more rigid than the swept strut and has a wider angle-of-attack range, and, through a double worm drive, the model remains on the tunnel centerline as its angle of attack is changed. The vertical strut is costly powerwise, however, needing around 500 hp at $M = 0.95$ in a 0.5 atmosphere 8-ft-high installation.

Current practice is to design a vertical strut for the above tunnel to handle a lift load of 2000 to 3000 lb and 500 to 700 lb of side force, depending on the length of sting employed, and it goes without saying that an internal strain-gage balance is always employed.

The sting length is governed by the angle-of-attack range and flow quality desired. In general the model must be a chord * and a half ahead of the vertical strut for good flow, but little is gained by going farther ahead than that. The forward posi-

Courtesy Cornell Aeronautical Laboratory.

FIG. 11:11.   B-29 model mounted to simulate yaw and pitch, using sting and vertical strut arrangement.

tions have the smaller angle-of-attack range, usually about ±20 degrees, while the short sting position may yield ±30 degrees. If more than the customary angle range is required, bent stings may be used to change the above ranges to 0 to 40 degrees or 0 to 60 degrees.

Yaw tests are handled with a sting mount by rotating the model until its wings are vertical, and the strut pitch mechanism then

* Of the vertical strut.

simulates yaw. Stings bent 1, 2, or 3 degrees are then used to
yield an angle of attack during yaw. (See Fig. 11:4.)

A liner (Fig. 11:4) is almost always used with the vertical
strut. The sting mount used in combination with a swept strut
is shown in Fig. 11:12.

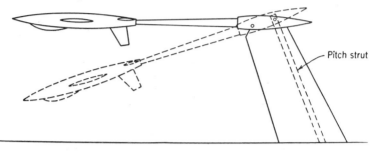

Pitch strut

Fig. 11:12.   Typical swept strut and sting installation.   The usual angle of
attack range is from +4 to −20 degrees.

Still another type of model support is the thin plate mounting
shown in Fig. 11:13. This mounting enables the external balance
to be used without the choking effect of a three-strut system or
alterations of the model afterbody to permit the use of a sting and

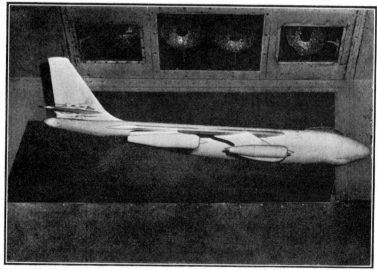

Courtesy Boeing Airplane Co.

Fig. 11:13.   B-47 model on plate mounting. . Plate windshield occupies lower
portion of picture.

internal balance. The thin plate support is about 0.25 in. thick and about as long as the model to be tested. It extends from the model through a windshield and on into the external balance. Such a mounting is most useful in the Mach number range from 0.8 to 0.9 where some additional cross-sectional area can be tolerated, or with tunnels whose special arrangements have eliminated choking. The plate mounting has almost zero interference.

11:5. Tare and Interference Evaluation. The evaluation of the strut tare and interference is even more important at transonic speeds than at lower speeds, since it is in many cases relatively larger on account of a smaller model size. Unfortunately the evaluation process is much more difficult, for reasons to be brought out.

It will be recalled that the attaching bayonets are simulated in subsonic tare and interference runs by dummies which merely run up inside the image windshields which are mounted from the test-section ceiling, and that a total of four runs is needed to evaluate tare, interference, and alignment. Since the swept struts are exposed in their entirety, they must be imaged as before, but, because of their size and the loads upon them, an attachment at the model with swept struts cantilevered to the ceiling is not possible. Accordingly the lengthy procedure of the type given in eqs. 4:10, 4:12, 4:13, and 4:14 must be used, necessitating in the transonic case six runs. This procedure is so rare and complicated * and has been given in such detail by Millikan in Ref. 11:2 that it will not be repeated here. Some idea of the complexity of the set-up may be obtained from Fig. 11:14.

The effect of a sting behind a body is to reduce its drag by furnishing a shape for the wake to stabilize upon. Obviously the sting effect increases with increasing ratio of sting to base diameter. It is secondarily a function of the body shape ahead of the base cut-off. Obviously also the effect is smallest when the sting is smallest. The reduction of drag caused by an $0.6D$ sting is shown in Fig. 11:15.

The evaluation of the sting effect is approached in three ways. The first is to try several different size stings, seeking to find the way the sting interference is varying, and hence extrapolate it to

* The wide change of blocking with small changes of strut area makes the determination of true Mach number quite difficult.

Courtesy McDonnell Aircraft Corp.

Fig. 11:14. Two of the six configurations needed for the evaluation of tare and interference using triple swept struts. *Top*, wing and body normal; *bottom*, wing and body inverted. The image system is installed in both configurations.

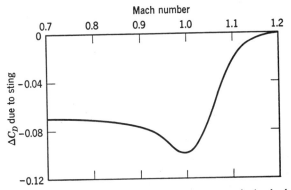

FIG. 11:15.   The effect of a 0.6D sting on one particular body.

zero sting. The second is to measure the model base drag and subtract it from the total drag.   The engineer using the data is then
expected to add in whatever base drag he feels will be developed
in flight.   The third is to mount the model on a yoke (Fig. 11:16)
and make runs with and without the
sting.   This procedure would be satisfactory if the yoke did not have a
profound effect on the model flow.
One may in general conclude that
more progress needs to be made before
a completely satisfactory tare and interference evaluation is possible with
the sting mount.

The single swept strut suffers severely from interference effects which
may make its use inadvisable.   This is
particularly true for aileron tests with
a swept-wing model.   Here the combination of swept wing and swept
strut makes the strut into sort of a
reflection plane, and the rolling moment produced, say, by left aileron
down is almost completely erased by
the image right aileron which is down
also.   Aileron tests at least must be
run with a sting rather than a swept
strut.   Sometimes runs made with the
model on swept struts and with the

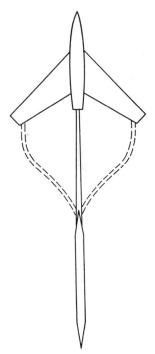

FIG. 11:16.   Yoke method of
evaluating sting interference.

model sting mounted can be used to evaluate the tare and interference.

11:6. Model Design. Wind-tunnel models for use at nearsonic and transonic speeds may still be of wood, but the great majority of them will need a steel beam and steel control surfaces. In many the wing has the wood (mahogany) glued to the steel beams, but with the grain parallel to the line of flight rather than perpendicular to it as is usually done when no beam is provided. See Fig. 5:2. This orientation provides greater strength for the wing trailing edge. A number of commercial bonding agents are satisfactory for the wood-steel joint.

The control surfaces may become rather small, and great ingenuity is required to enable angle settings to be made without cumbersome hinges. One excellent arrangement is to provide a long hinge pin, drilled for each deflection angle desired (Fig. 11:17). This will provide for a number of discrete settings with

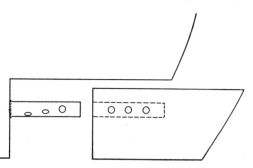

FIG. 11:17.   Method of providing for positive angle settings when space is at a premium.   (Only one hinge is shown.)

negligible control cut-out and no exposed hinge. The holes must be carefully drilled and pins well fitted as very little play represents a large angle error.

Metal models are obviously difficult to make, purely from a physical filing standpoint, and, happily, steps have been taken to reduce this labor. Either a profilometer can be used to follow a wood model, or direct castings can be made. New methods which are a trade secret (but commercially available) result in castings requiring only a mild buffing before use. Still another approach is to cast a low-strength alloy on to a steel beam.

In order to avoid model failures rather stringent safety factors are employed, models being designed to an ultimate factor of safety of 5.0, or a yield factor of safety of 3.0. These limits lead to the anomaly that a part satisfying all requirements for flight may not be "strong enough" to be tested in a wind tunnel!

Possibly a little greater accuracy is desirable for a high-speed model than for a low-speed one, at least in physical dimensions, since the scale is smaller.

There is a wide difference of opinion about the usefulness of brace wires in the nearsonic range. At one tunnel streamline wires buzzed to the extent that they were useless; at another they worked well. Round wires normal to the stream buzzed at some tunnels, but worked well when swept; at other tunnels they worked either way. One may reasonably suspect that the frequency and amplitude of the test-section wall vibrations entered into each of the above situations.

There is also a difference of opinion as to whether a simulated jet engine should be faired over or left hollow. Whenever possible, the author prefers the hollow duct as best simulating the actual flow.

Acceptable model design standards have been well summarized in Southern California Cooperative Wind Tunnel Report P-3 as follows:

1. Sharp fillets and other stress raisers should be avoided wherever possible.

2. Non-structural parts such as tanks and fillets, where strength is not a factor, should be made of light-weight material.

3. If wood is used, the materials and methods of fabrication should correspond to the best aircraft practice. All attachments to the wood should have adequate bearing area to resist loads applied. Wood screws are not considered an acceptable method of attachment.

4. The attachment screws, etc., of models or model component parts such as slats, brakes, spoilers, and surfaces that will be run at stall or that will be subject to vibratory loading should be secured with an acceptable safety device (elastic stop nuts, nylon inserts, shakeproof washers, wiring). In rotating-propeller models, all attachment screws must be secured with an acceptable safety device.

5. All highly stressed model support stings, struts, brackets, etc., must be magnaflux inspected, and any structural castings must be X-ray inspected.

6. Careful attention should be given to the proper fits to stings, sting balances, balance-to-model retention pins, strut-to-model trunnion pins, etc.

7. Rotating-propeller models, owing to oscillating loads and fatigue conditions, dictate additional model requirements:

(*a*) Each propeller shaft is to be equipped with a tachometer for continuous rpm monitoring.

(*b*) Before each test period, all propeller blades are to be zyglo inspected and shafts are to be magnaflux inspected. The inspection report should be included in the stress report together with a statement of the time-stress history of any previous testing.

(*c*) Propeller blade clamping is to be avoided in high-stress regions.

(*d*) High fatigue limit stresses and low notch sensitivity are important criteria in choosing a blade material; from experience, 14ST6 appears to be the most satisfactory blade material.

(*e*) Blade surface roughness should not exceed 200 microinches rms, and wherever possible the direction of finish marks should be parallel to maximum tension stress.

(*f*) The propeller assembly is to be statically and dynamically balanced on the model shaft and bearing assembly.

(*g*) The fundamental natural frequency of the propeller shaft should be at least 1.5 times the maximum rpm. At any operating speed,

$$(0.8fn/N) > S > (1.2fn/N)$$

where fn = shaft natural frequency; S = shaft rpm; and N = total number of blades on either single or counterrotating propeller.

(*h*) Snap rings and other large stress raisers should be avoided on propeller shafts.

(*i*) Propeller pullers should be provided on all sting-supported models to avoid possible damage to the balance.

11:7. Strain-Gage Balances. Most of the magnificent wind-tunnel balances with which the nearsonic wind tunnels were originally equipped now lie idle under a layer of dust; testing conditions having strayed so far from the concepts prevailing when the tunnels and balances were built. Now that models for multimillion-dollar wind tunnels are so small a child could easily carry them, the original balances designed for loads ranging in the tens of thousands of pounds are hopelessly inaccurate. Indeed, even had the balances sufficient accuracy, the conventional three-point support could not be used owing to the choking it would incur.

The problems of smaller loads and mountings of less interference have been met by electric strain-gage balances placed internally in the models. Such balances frequently require tailoring to fit the individual model, both for size and loads, and, though they include the not small interference of the support on the model in their readings, they must be used since they offer the only mountings for testing complete models near the speed of sound. Since they move with the model, they read not lift and drag, but normal and chord force. As a matter of interest the usual cost for the balance alone, not including the reading equipment, is around $10,000.

Although there are many different electric strain-gage balances, no particularly superior design or superior hook-up has evolved. Some engineers use the beam flexure shown in Fig. 4:22; others, an eccentric column. Some prefer electric addition of components, others prefer external addition. Some use direct-current gage excitation. On one point, however, there is general agreement: when room is available, each flexure should have a completely doubled circuit so that failure of a gage (which used to be a great deal more prevalent that it is now) requires only switching to a second circuit. Customarily, the better of the two is determined during calibration and used for normal running, the second remaining in reserve.

The three-component balance shown in Fig. 11:18 is definitely not shown as a particularly superior design (although it has

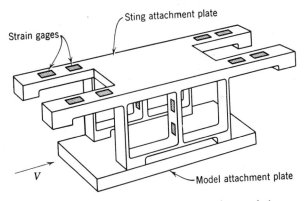

FIG. 11:18.   Three-component electric strain-gage balance.

worked well in a number of cases) but serves merely to illustrate one type of three-component balance. It has electrical addition. Separate power sources for each circuit instead of a common lead are used by some, and variable amplification in the potentiometer circuit is convenient to change the calibration slopes and spread the estimated load over the meter range for greatest accuracy. Drift may become excessive if too much amplification is used.

Load ranges of a typical balance are as follows:

Normal force	500 lb	Pitching moment	180 ft-lb
Chord force	100 lb	Rolling moment	40 ft-lb
Side force	75 lb	Yawing moment	40 ft-lb

The linkage of an internal balance is so well concealed by its case that photographs of balance exteriors would explain practically nothing. We may, however, note that internal balances have been built from 0.5-in. diameter to about 3-in. diameter. Normally the angular deflection under load is kept below 15 minutes.

A transformation of body-axes data (such as that taken with an internal balance) to the more frequently used wind axes may be accomplished by the following relations:

$$L_W = -C \sin \alpha + N \cos \alpha$$
$$D_W = C \cos \alpha \cos \psi + S \sin \psi + N \sin \alpha \cos \psi$$
$$Y_W = -C \cos \alpha \sin \psi + S \cos \psi - N \sin \alpha \sin \psi$$
$$RM_W = RM \cos \alpha \cos \psi - PM \sin \psi + YM \sin \alpha \cos \psi$$
$$PM_W = PM \cos \psi + RM \cos \alpha \sin \psi + YM \sin \alpha \sin \psi$$
$$YM_W = YM \cos \alpha - RM \sin \alpha$$

In the above relations, N, C, and S are body normal, chord, and side forces positive up, back, and to the right wing; and RM, PM, and YM are the rolling, pitching, and yawing moments about body axes positive when the moment tends to put the right wing down, nose up, or nose right.

11:8. Calibration of the Internal Strain-Gage Balance. The calibration of an internal strain-gage balance is similar to that of the large external balance in that the various loads are applied singly and in combination and the calibration slopes for each component determined. However, the calibration of an internal balance is greatly simplified by the acceptance of interactions, and their subsequent inclusion in the work-up of the data, instead of an interminable effort to get them out. On the other hand, deflections and heat effects are more important than with the external balance and must receive special care.

The first step in the internal balance calibration is to place the model and balance on the sting which will actually support it in the tunnel, and if possible on the strut to be used as well (Fig. 11:19). Loading then proceeds through the design loads both positive and negative while all components are read to determine the interactions. During the loading the sting and balance will of course deflect, and the pitch-changing mechanism of the strut should be operated as the loads change to keep the model always level.* The major deflections are due to normal and pitch loads, and their effects may be combined into an angle-of-attack corrections chart such as that shown in Fig. 11:20 for use during actual running.† Normally the various slopes, deflections, and interactions may be determined in a few days. However, there are other items which must be investigated.

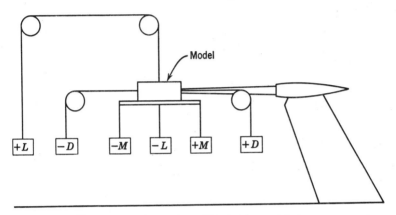

Fig. 11:19.   Set-up for calibrating internal balances.

For instance, wide temperature changes occur in most high-speed tunnels, and, although as previously explained the strain-gage circuit itself is heat-compensated, thermal deflections in the balance rig may well cause serious change in the readings. Accordingly, after the balance has been found satisfactory from a load and deflection standpoint it should be subjected to a heat range of 40 to 140° F (or higher) and the amount of creep determined. It is not possible to correlate thermal creep with tunnel temperature owing to various lags. Hence, if creep is excessive, it should be eliminated by redesign of the balance, by heater strips in the balance that always keep it at the same high temperature, or by an insulation arrangement which decreases the rate at which heat can reach the balance. Intermit-

---

* Another method is to read the deflections and include their effects when computing the balance constants.

† At some tunnels the angle of attack is read by a remote-reading plumb bob in the model.

tent tunnels have an advantage as regards the temperature problem since one then has a "zero" reading both before and after each point.

Balance stability (constant reading) with time is also important. To satisfy the usual stability needs there should be no noticeable reading shift when one-half the maximum loads are applied to the balance simultaneously and held for 2 hours. If a time shift is evident, the cause is probably a poor gage bond, or overloaded gages.

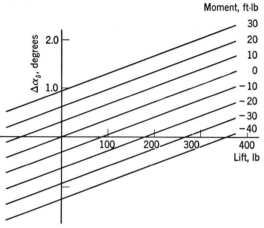

Fig. 11:20.   Angle-of-attack correction grid for use with an internal strain-gage balance.

Sensitivity, or minimum load response, is obtained by applying progressively smaller loads until the minimum that will produce a response is obtained. *Hysteresis* is the degree to which a balance will return to a repeated load or no-load reading; *linearity* is the variation (usually less than 0.5 per cent) of the reading-load curve from a straight line. The necessary acceptance limits for sensitivity, hysteresis, and linearity depend on the particular test at hand.

11:9. Treatment of Balance Interactions.* The determination of the balance interactions has been covered in the previous section. It now remains to see how they are treated in the work-up of the data.

---

* Also see "Generalized Equations and Standard Nomenclature for the Data Reduction Connected with Sting Balances of the Type Used by the Cornell Aeronautical Laboratory" by H. F. Kelsey, *Cornell Aeronautical Laboratory Paper* WTO-016, June, 1952.

The true normal force, chord force, and pitching-moment readings may be determined from the following relations:

$$NF = K_{NF}(NF)_a - K_{CFNF}(CF) - K_{PMNF}(PM) \quad (11{:}10)$$

$$CF = K_{CF}(CF)_a - K_{NFCF}(NF) - K_{PMCF}(PM) \quad (11{:}11)$$

$$PM = K_{PM}(PM)_a - K_{NFPM}(NF) - K_{CFPM}(CF) \quad (11{:}12)$$

where K_{NF}, K_{CF}, K_{PM} = slopes of the normal force, chord force, and pitching-moment calibration curves.

$(NF)_a, (CF)_a, (PM)_a$ = aerodynamic loads, i.e., balance readings minus wind-off readings for the particular angle of attack under consideration.

K_{CFNF} = slope of the effect of chord force on normal force, etc.

$(NF), (CF), (PM)$ = total normal force, chord force, and pitching-moment readings (i.e., without subtracting the wind-off reading).

The solution of the complete interaction equations is very tedious, and it is far better to make $K_{NFCF} = 0$ by finding a balance normal axis along which no normal force appears in the chord force. Use of this axis also makes $K_{CFNF} = 0$. We may also solve for a balance effective center about which normal force and chord force do not affect pitching moment. The interaction equations then reduce to

$$NF = K_{NF}(NF)_a - K_{PMNF}(PM) \quad (11{:}13)$$

$$CF = K_{CF}(CF)_a - K_{PMCF}(PM) \quad (11{:}14)$$

$$PM_{bc} = K_{PM}(PM)_a \quad (11{:}15)$$

These equations are much easier to use than the full relations. Normally, the balance axis is less than 0.25 degree from the geometrical axis.

We have now noted the main difference between the low- and high-speed wind tunnels, and we have discussed model design, mounting, and load measuring. Let us see next how the nearsonic tunnel is operated.

11:10. Nearsonic Tunnel Operation. Our starting point assumes that the procedure outlined in Sect. 5:2 regarding tunnel procurement has been followed, and the tunnel is now ready for a test. Estimates of tunnel time requirements may be based on 1 minute per reading, 2.5 minutes to change Mach numbers, 5 minutes at the end of each run to check balance drifts, plus 10 minutes access time for air-exchange tunnels and 30 minutes for pressurized tunnels. If additional time is required for pumping,

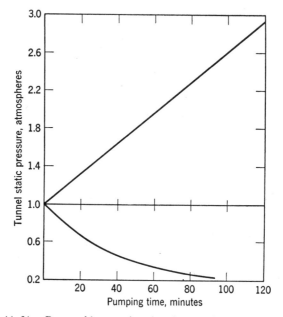

FIG. 11:21.   Reasonable pumping time for a 10-ft transonic tunnel.

it may be estimated from the tunnel pumping time chart. Installation of the model should be combined with pumping the tunnel up or down (see Fig. 11:21), using the gate seals to permit the test section to remain at atmospheric pressure. At the end of the model installation, the test section is vacuum cleaned and then sealed off. If the run is to be made above atmospheric pressure the tunnel proper is pumped a little above the desired running pressure and the extra air is bled into the test section for most rapid equalization. If the run is at lowered pressure, the test section is sucked down until its pressure equals the rest of the tunnel, at which time the gates are opened and the run begun. (The difference in procedure is prompted by a desire not to bleed *from* the test-section housing, which often stands open and collects dust, into the tunnel.)   The tunnel with pressure adjusted is now ready to run.

The pressure gates can also be used to reduce the shut-down time for model changes.   To accomplish this, the tunnel fan is feathered and left at synchronous rpm.   The gates are closed, making the test section available for model changes without a

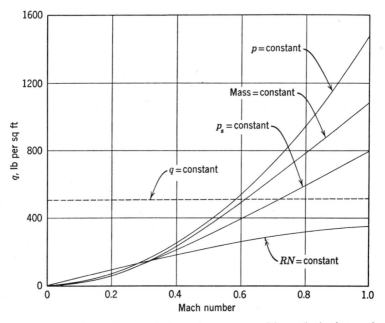

FIG. 11:22.   The variation of dynamic pressure with method of tunnel operation.

draft of air or the noise of the drive.   As soon as the model change is completed, the test section may be brought to the proper pressure, the gates lowered, and the fan unfeathered into driving pitch.   Not only does this procedure save several minutes during the coming-up-to-rpm procedure, but in the tandem type of drive (d-c plus a-c motors) it saves the shock of throwing the a-c motor on the line and its subsequent pull into phase.

There are three standard ways in which a pressure tunnel is run, and two for the operation of an air-exchange tunnel.   The pressure tunnel may be run constant mass, constant dynamic pressure, or constant Reynolds number.   Air-exchange tunnels are always run constant total head, and may in addition be run constant temperature. The advantages and disadvantages of each method of the methods is described below, along with details of the operational procedure followed. For comparison, the manner in which the dynamic pressure and Reynolds number vary with each method are shown in Figs. 11:22 and 11:23. The

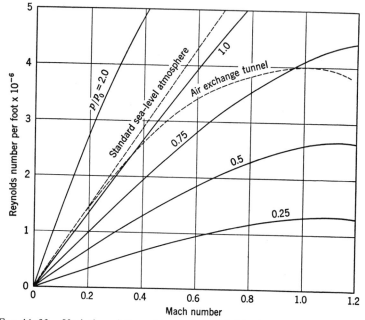

FIG. 11:23. Variation of Reynolds number with Mach number in a pressure tunnel using constant mass operation. Stagnation temperature = 100° F. p/p_0 = static pressure in standard atmospheres.

Reynolds number may be found from Fig. 11:24. We will first consider the operation of a pressure tunnel.

Constant-mass operation is the most rapid method of obtaining data. Using this arrangement a tunnel pressure ratio is selected from the tunnel performance chart (Fig. 11:25) which will either give a desired Reynolds number range or, more often, will deliver the highest Reynolds number at the choking Mach number. A chart is then prepared (Fig. 11:26) which tells the tunnel operator what wind-off static pressure he must maintain for the expected temperature range.* This static pressure (which is of course constant throughout the whole tunnel when the wind is off) falls

* Some engineers merely set the desired pressure without regard to temperature effect.

off in the test section as the speed builds up, but under constant-mass operation no corrective pumping is done. For example, a still test-section static pressure of 0.5 atmosphere reduces to a little over 0.3 atmosphere at Mach = 1.0. Corrective pumping

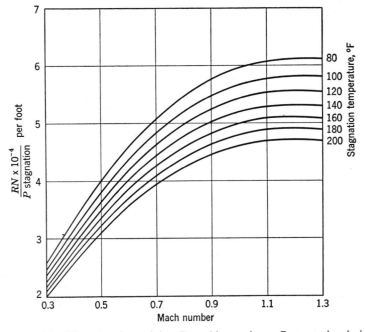

FIG. 11:24. Chart for determining Reynolds number. *P* stagnation is in centimeters of mercury.

will be done, between runs, however, if the leakage makes the resulting density change exceed some preselected value, say 1 per cent.

Constant-mass operation is, as stated previously, the fastest method of getting data at varying Mach numbers. On the other hand it results in wide variations of the dynamic pressure so that a balance strong enough to hold the high-speed loads may not be accurate for the low-speed ones. It is also a far cry from constant Reynolds number, and so the data may suffer from the change of more than one variable.

A second and very desirable method of running a transonic-pressure tunnel is the so-called "constant *q*" method. Under this system the tunnel pressure is varied with each Mach number so

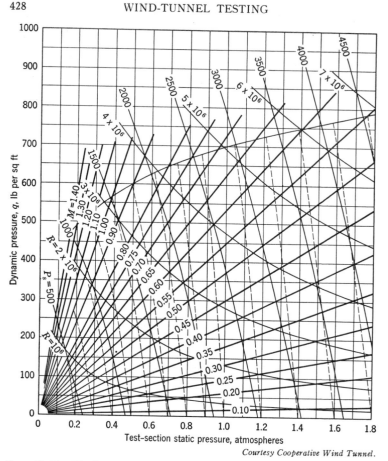

Courtesy Cooperative Wind Tunnel.

Fig. 11:25. Typical transonic-pressure tunnel performance chart. R = Reynolds number per foot, P_s = absolute stagnation pressure, lb per sq ft. A tunnel run at constant mass operates approximately on the dashed lines. This chart was constructed assuming a stagnation temperature of 95° F and $\gamma = 1.4$. The line joining the ends of the dashed lines is a tunnel power limitation.

that the dynamic pressure remains essentially constant. Thus the load range remains nearly constant and balance accuracy is the same for each speed. Surprisingly, constant q does not yield a more constant Reynolds number than constant mass.

To accomplish a "constant q" run * a chart is first prepared

* In this paragraph the Mach number setting is exact, while q is nearly constant. The low-speed operational procedure using the two piezometer rings for exactly constant q but allowing small variations in Mach number is of course possible also.

of $p_s - p$ vs. p (Fig. 11:27) for a constant Mach number, where p_s is the stagnation pressure and p the static pressure. As the model angle of attack is changed at the selected Mach number the resulting changes in p are compensated for by adjusting the

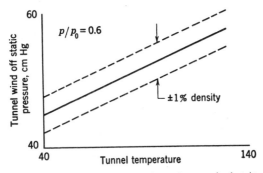

FIG. 11:26. Operator's tunnel density chart for nominal $p/p_0 = 0.6$ run.

propeller pitch so that a new value of $p_s - p$ is obtained which keeps the operation on the constant Mach number line. The resulting q is slightly different from its predecessor but not seriously so. The exact value of q as obtained from p and the Mach number is of course used for the data reduction of the particular point.

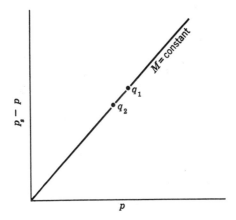

FIG. 11:27. Tunnel operator's chart for nominal constant q run.

The above procedure has been found necessary since direct change of the tunnel static pressure by pumping or bleeding is neither exact nor quick. When a series of Mach numbers are to be run, it is most rapid to pump the tunnel to the lowest static pressure and take the first points at the highest Mach number. Air is subsequently bled in to raise the static pressure as the Mach number is dropped.

Constant Reynolds number is attained by adjusting the tunnel static pressure according to the Reynolds number being held. Usually the heat-storing capacity of the cooling system makes it impractical to attempt holding a particular temperature as well.

The air-exchanger tunnels, having their settling chambers vented to the atmosphere, operate at nominally constant head, the only change being that of the atmosphere. This is ordinarily such a slow variation that it need only be read every several hours. The dynamic pressure remains very nearly the same for a particular Mach number from day to day but changes widely with Mach number (though not as much as for constant mass). The availability of rapid changes in the amount of air exchanged makes it possible to run at constant temperature, tolerating perhaps 1° F variation. Constant temperature and a constant Mach number assure a constant velocity. This is important in making propeller tests. In addition, constant temperature helps keep balance drift to a minimum, and Reynolds number constant. A high temperature must be selected or perhaps a winter Reynolds number cannot be repeated in summer.

Runs in the nearsonic tunnel are ordinarily similar to those in the subsonic-type tunnel: changes of angle of attack at constant Mach number. Then, normally, the Mach number will be changed and the angle-of-attack range covered for the new setting. The process is repeated until the wall pressure orifices read $0.528 p_{stagnation}$ (wall-choke) or whatever limit has been selected. Choking will, of course, vary with the angle of attack of the model, and it is possible to prepare a chart such as shown in Fig. 11:28 to aid the tunnel crew in avoiding choking conditions.

In view of the high-frequency vibrations that occur some engineers prefer to record electric strain-gage readings on an oscillograph instead of trusting a meter to yield an average value. With this system the oscillograph records are faired by eye.

Paralleling the gage output into an oscilloscope is also handy to help monitor the buffeting that may take place. With such a set-up it is usually possible to skirt serious buffet troubles instead of waiting for them to build up to tunnel cut-off proportions.

Deflection compensating charts are not practical for tests employing pressure readings only, since the loads are not immediately known. For this special case a sighting device is used.

Most models buffet during part of their Mach number range. When the buffeting matches the natural frequency of the sting mounting, the amplitude of model displacement can rise to catastrophic values in a fraction of a second. Thus it is vital that the model be watched intensely during running at high speeds, and

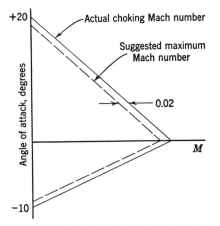

FIG. 11:28. Typical choking boundary chart.

that the watcher be equipped with both an angle-of-attack override and a tunnel emergency shut-off. Normally reduction of the angle of attack will stop the oscillations more rapidly than a tunnel cut-off and be less time-consuming to reorganize. In extreme situations the cut-off may be required.

The previously mentioned oscilloscopes on the strain beams do not entirely replace observation since it is necessary to tell when fog has dissipated or the model has lost a part.

Wind-off gravity runs will be needed for each configuration since the change from zero angle of attack puts a weight component into chord and normal force.* In the interests of economy, these gravity runs should be made outside the tunnel. Some engineers replace gravity tares by simple component calculations. As a matter of interest (and emergency procedure), if the drag (chord force) runs off the scale at high angles of attack, it may be

* This is with the wings horizontal. With the wings vertical for yaw tests the gravity tares will appear in chord force, side force, and yawing moments.

readable at low angles (with the model inverted) since the weight component than subtracts from the drag.

It is desirable to operate a nearsonic wind tunnel at the highest temperature possible to minimize the condensation of moisture in the air and its resulting ragged conditions across the test section. In some cases the air-exchange or cooling towers are adjusted to permit tunnel stagnation temperatures to exceed 180° F, but normally a maximum of around 120° F is tolerated. Above that figure the metal parts of the model become too hot to handle without gloves, working conditions for the tunnel crew become unreasonable, and many of the often-used model and tunnel fan finishes start peeling and bubbling. Still another reason for moderate temperatures is the zero shift often developed by strain-gage balances with wide temperature changes.

The modeling clay used in low-temperature work for fillets and general hole-plugging becomes much too flaccid at the higher temperatures and is in general replaced by high-temperature waxes, kept at around 120° F in electric pots. The waxes are a little harder to smooth than modeling clay but they have more strength and greater heat resistance. Plastic knives are useful for wax work since they will not scratch metal parts. Special care should be taken with holes plugged by wax in order to assure that they do not bulge out under the wide pressure changes found in the nearsonic work, and perhaps cause serious flow disturbances.

Deep holes plugged with wax should first be filled nearly to the top with cotton. The author well and sadly remembers taking an hour of tunnel time ($600) to dig out some holes not so prepared. Even better are tapped holes with screw inserts.

11:11. Choked Operation. There is still another way to operate a nearsonic wind tunnel, suitable for either an air-exchange or a pressurized type. This method is "choked operation."

In many (perhaps *all*) wind tunnels, pulsations from the fan and diffuser travel upstream into the test section and induce early and excessive model buffet. A way around this difficulty is to choke the diffuser just downstream of the test section. The short region of supersonic flow caused by the choke makes it impossible for pulsations to reach the test section, and in many cases choking has produced remarkable improvements in flow conditions.

A choke is just an artificial minimum area (see Fig. 11:29) provided downstream of the test section. It is usually made adjustable, and through eq. 11:3 controls the test-section Mach number, holding it constant for each setting. The operational procedure is to bring the tunnel up to full power and adjust the choke until the desired test-section Mach number is achieved. An angle traverse of the model is then made, and then another Mach number may be set. Actually this choked procedure is a time-saver since the Mach number is locked in by the choke, and

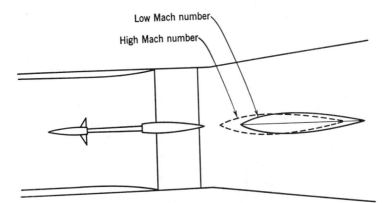

Low Mach number

High Mach number

FIG. 11:29.   Adjustable choke.

small changes of speed which normally occur with changes of angle of attack (and require constant readjusting) do not occur.

11:12. Transonic Testing.   There are no transonic tunnels unclassified at the present time, and hence descriptions and operating procedures are not available. However, the principles upon which a transonic tunnel could be based are broadly known, and bearing in mind that there are two problems to solve (choking and wave reflection) we may state the following:

1. Since blocking is positive in a closed throat and negative in an open one, it would seem that some sort of ventilated throat might eliminate blocking, which, in the final analysis, results in choking.

2. Wave reflection from the boundaries may be eliminated by either drastically changing the normal reflection angle so that the model is not struck by the rebound or by some sort of wave-absorption method. The normal reflection angle may be increased by surrounding the testing area by a jet of higher-velocity

air so that the main shock wave would be bent farther back before full reflection. This procedure seems fraught with difficulties.

There are at least two possible procedures for attaining wave absorption:

(*a*) A solid boundary reflects a shock wave as a shock; a free boundary reflects a shock as a rarefaction. It would seem that a combined free and solid boundary (perforated, for instance) would result in wave cancellation. Perhaps a different amount of free boundary would be needed for waves of various strengths.

(*b*) Some surfaces of high sound-absorption qualities—cotton batting, lamb's wool, chambered fiberboard, etc.—may prove adequate to absorb shock waves. (It is amusing to consider closing down a tunnel to send the test section out for dry-cleaning.)

Wave reflection should be most serious in round test sections where the reflection is focused by the equal distances of all wall

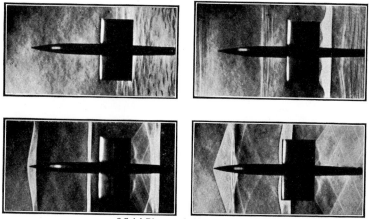

Official Photograph, National Advisory Committee for Aeronautics.

Fig. 11:30. Schlieren photographs taken through the sonic range at Mach numbers of 0.98, 1.02, 1.06, and 1.09.

points from the model. From this standpoint a square section would be better, and rectangular section best.

In addition to the above items, the area ratio formula (eq. 11:3) may be satisfied in a closed jet of constant area by letting some of the air out so that the remainder may expand to a higher Mach number.

Figure 11:30 shows some of the first photographs taken from a test in a wind tunnel through $M = 1.0$. Calibration of transonic tunnels is no different from the procedure for the nearsonic type as described earlier in this chapter, consisting mainly of static pipe readings.

11:13. Transonic Bumps. Weaver in Ref. 11:3 has presented a method of creating and using a small regions of high local velocities which enable the test speeds to go right through the speed of sound. It consists of placing a "bump" (sometimes a circular arc with a small flat on top) on the tunnel floor and utilizing a small reflection plane model in the zone that has the highest speed.

The set-up is shown in Figs. 11:31, 11:32, and 11:33. The bump usually has a height of around one-eithth that of the test

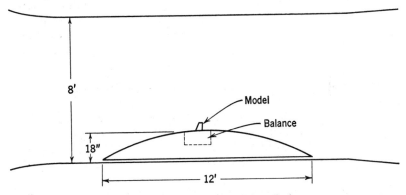

Fig. 11:31.   Typical "bump" installation.

section and a chord of about a tunnel width. Increased height increases the obtainable Mach number but increases the velocity gradients along a normal to the surface so that a smaller area is useful for testing, a reasonable allowable variation being 0.03 in Mach number across the model span. (See Fig. 11:34.) A weighted average (Sect. 3:13) is used for computing q.

The reflection plane model is placed on a small strain-gage balance located at the center of the nearly constant Mach number zone, and readings are taken for a range of angles of attack. If sufficient tunnel power exists, Mach numbers continuously variable through Mach = 1.0 and up to around 1.2 may be obtained, the upper limit being reached when the tunnel chokes, the normal shock then being a foot or so behind the model but in no way affecting it.

Bump tests are the only unclassified method for true transonic testing, and as such their invention is a remarkably important

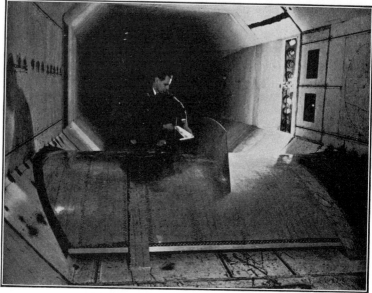

Courtesy Lockheed Aircraft Corp.

FIG. 11:32.   Bump with calibration plate installed in the Cooperative Wind
Tunnel.   View is looking downstream.

Courtesy Lockheed Aircraft Corp.

FIG. 11:33.   Close-up of typical bump model.   Note added body thickness
for boundary-layer allowance and method of simulating horizontal tail
mounting.

addition to the art. They do suffer from requiring such small models that the test Reynolds number is very low (around 1,000,000), and from the usual difficulty, found in all reflection plane testing but particularly severe for these small models, of exactly defining the boundary layer.

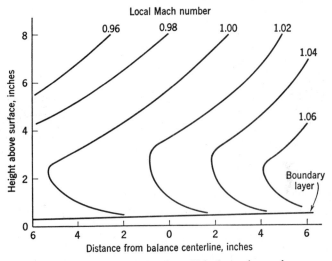

FIG. 11:34.   Typical distribution of Mach number on bump.

The free jet speed setting arrangement is not sufficiently accurate for bump speed settings since the local Mach number on the bump is near 1.0 and very sensitive to small changes. Accordingly a total-head tube is employed on the bump and used in conjunction with a pair of "teed" static holes on the top of the bump. This gives a good speed setting device, although often it is barely enough since unsteady flow in the tunnel caused by the separated flow downstream of the bump frequently makes the whole tunnel surge.

The low Reynolds number and the poor Mach number distribution makes interpretation of bump data quite difficult, and there is a trend away from the use of the bump for these reasons. For a long time, however, its use has been inescapable in bridging the transonic range. A second difficulty is the determination of the tare; our approach here is to let the tare be the difference between a bump value and a three-dimensional test value. Essentially this amounts to using the bump data to define the drag rise curve.

Bump models are so small relative to the rest of the tunnel that either blocking nor boundary corrections are large enough to be applied. Buoyancy corrections may be needed.

The results of bump tests are generally used without Reynolds number corrections of any type, and the correlation between tunnel test and flight test has been fairly good for drag rise, drag increments, and elevator needed to trim. The good elevator agreement is extremely important because it can assure safe flight.

11:14. Apparatus for Flow Visualization. It is indeed very instructive to see the flow about models at nearsonic speeds, perhaps even more so than at the lower speeds. And because density gradients are now stronger and more pronounced, optical devices can be used to see the flow pattern in addition to the usual tuft observations. Smoke, however, has so far not been successful in the high-speed regime.

More care must be taken with tufts at high speeds simply because of the larger loads they must bear. The cellophane tuft strips placed parallel to the stream normally will stay on as long as needed, and in particular cases may be further strengthened by a second layer of tape on top of the first, or by using a tape with cotton or nylon fibers built into it (Fig. 11:35). Besides flow di-

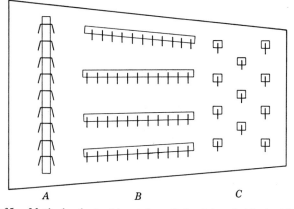

Fig. 11:35. Methods of attaching tufts. Only *A* is suitable for high-speed work.

rection and low-speed stall, tufts can indicate transonic shock stall and buffeting. Several strands of nylon A thread make a good high-speed tuft.

Several flow-visualization methods based on the more rapid evaporation which takes place when the boundary layer is turbulent have been advanced (Refs. 3:16, 11:10, 11:11, and 11:12). Some of these methods allow the turbulent area to evaporate completely so that dusting the model with talcum powder will emphasize the proper zones. Others emphasize the difference in appearance of wet and dry surfaces, and one of the newest (Ref. 11:12) uses a lacquer that fluoresces under ultraviolet light when dry. The above references should be consulted for the actual working methods.

Three optical devices are in common use for studying the flow through the effect of the density gradients: the shadowgraph, schlieren, and interferometer. The shadowgraph is more widely used than the others in nearsonic work, and it will be briefly discussed here. The others will be mentioned in the next chapter.

The shadowgraph is an important and frequently used device for making shock waves visible. Basically it consists of a spark-gap point light source which makes the density gradients appear shadowwise, allowing their position and angles to be studied. The density gradients in the wake are also usually strong enough to be visible.

A shadowgraph is a much cheaper device than a schlieren, but, even more important, it requires much less room at a time when space is at a premium. The physical set-up as used in a nearsonic wind tunnel is shown in Fig. 11:36.

The shadowgraph operates as follows: A high-intensity spark gap is placed abreast of the model so that it will cast a shadow of the model (and its flow) on the far wall. A camera position near the spark gap is selected such that the model will not blanket its own image, and triggering the camera is synchronized with the operation of the spark gap. At a number of angles of attack spark photographs are taken of the model and its flow. Besides the waves, the boundary layer and its transition and the wake are thus recorded for study. Shadowgraphs are also useful in determining whether reflected shocks are striking the model.

The various circuits of the shadowgraph are beyond the scope of this textbook, but a few practical comments may prove helpful. The tunnel wall surface, particularly in the oily pressure tunnels, works much better if it is spray-painted white with the paint gun held "too far away" to give a rough dull surface. The film employed in the camera should be relatively insensitive to yellow light. It is doubtful that any light source other than a spark gap would give the intensity needed for good pictures in a large tunnel.

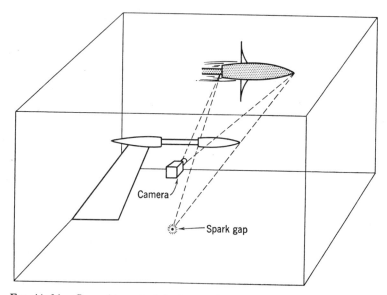

Fig. 11:36.   General layout of shadowgraph set-up in transonic wind tunnel.

11:15. Wall Corrections for Two-Dimensional Nearsonic Testing. The philosophy used in transforming the incompressible-flow wall corrections so that they may be used with compressible flow is quite difficult to master, and, indeed, some of the best minds in the field have stumbled over the process. Several factors must be considered simultaneously. First there is the general conception that a model in compressible flow behaves as would a longer model in incompressible flow. Then there is the change of Mach number as the stream temperature changes during expansion, and the many other changes that take place when the density and pressure change. Without further development, one may state the two-dimensional wall corrections including solid and wake blocking, streamline curvature, and the nearsonic Mach effects as follows * (the subscript u refers to the completely uncorrected data):

* These are adapted from Ref. 6:1. Buoyancy is the same for both compressible and incompressible flow.

$$V = V_u \left(1 + \frac{\epsilon_{sb}}{\beta^3} + \frac{\beta_4}{\beta^2} \epsilon_{wb} \right) \qquad (11:16)$$

$$q = q_u \left(1 + \frac{\beta_3}{\beta^3} \epsilon_{sb} + \frac{\beta_3 \beta_4}{\beta^2} \epsilon_{wb} \right) \qquad (11:17)$$

$$R = R_u \left(1 + \frac{\beta_7}{\beta^3} \epsilon_{sb} + \frac{\beta_7 \beta_4}{\beta^2} \epsilon_{wb} \right) \qquad (11:18)$$

$$M = M_u \left(1 + \frac{\beta_2}{\beta^3} \epsilon_{sb} + \frac{\beta_2 \beta_4}{\beta^2} \epsilon_{wb} \right) \qquad (11:19)$$

$$\alpha = \alpha_u + \frac{57.3\sigma}{2\pi\beta} (c_{lu} + 4c_{m\frac14 u}) \qquad (11:20)$$

$$c_l = c_{lu} \left(1 - \frac{\sigma}{\beta^2} - \frac{\beta_3}{\beta^3} \epsilon_{sb} - \frac{\beta_3 \beta_4}{\beta^2} \epsilon_{wb} \right) \qquad (11:21)$$

$$c_{m\frac14} = c_{m\frac14 u} \left(1 - \frac{\beta_3}{\beta^3} \epsilon_{sb} - \frac{\beta_3 \beta_4}{\beta^2} \epsilon_{wb} \right) + \frac{\sigma}{4\beta^2} c_{lu} \qquad (11:22)$$

$$c_{d0} = c_{d0u} \left(1 - \frac{\beta_6}{\beta^3} \epsilon_{sb} - \frac{\beta_3 \beta_4}{\beta^2} \epsilon_{wb} \right) \qquad (11:23)$$

In the above equations

$$\beta^2 = 1 - M_u^2 \qquad\qquad \beta_2 = 1 + 0.2 M_u^2$$
$$\beta_3 = 2 - M_u^2 \qquad\qquad \beta_4 = 1 + 0.4 M_u^2 \qquad (11:24)$$
$$\beta_6 = 3 - 0.6 M_u^2 \qquad\qquad \beta_7 = 1 - 0.7 M_u^2$$

These are plotted in Figs. 11:37 and 11:38. The constants have evolved from assuming that the ratio of specific heat at constant pressure to that at constant volume is 1.4. For tunnels using Freon gas instead of air, the original references should be consulted and appropriate changes made.

As before,

$$\sigma = (\pi^2/48)(c/h)^2$$

where c = model chord and h = test-section height. Λ is from Sect. 6:3.

See Sect. 11:16 for the simplest method of applying the above corrections.

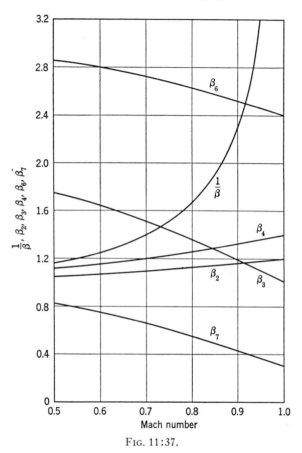

Fɪɢ. 11:37.

11:16. Wall Corrections for Three-Dimensional Nearsonic Testing. The low-speed solid blocking corrections may be extended to the nearsonic range by multiplying them by $1/\beta^3$. Thus

$$\epsilon_{sb(c)} = (1/\beta^3)\epsilon_{sb} \qquad (11:25)$$

where (c) refers to compressible flow. The low-speed wake blocking may be similarly extended by multiplying it by $1/\beta^2$

$$\epsilon_{wb(c)} = (1/\beta^2)\epsilon_{wb} \qquad (11:26)$$

The total nearsonic blocking corrections are then, as before, the sum of the wake and solid blocking

$$\epsilon_c = \epsilon_{sb(c)} + \epsilon_{wb(c)} \qquad (11:27)$$

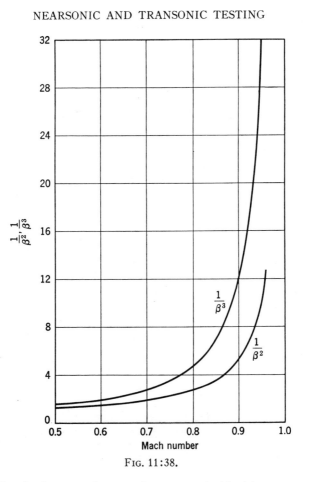

$$\frac{1}{\beta^2}, \frac{1}{\beta^3}$$

Mach number

FIG. 11:38.

As in the low-speed case, the nearsonic blocking corrections are quite complicated if the variation of the drag coefficient is left in the wake blocking term. In particular, this affects, among other things, the corrected Mach number, and it becomes impossible to make runs at a constant corrected Mach number. Fortunately, as in the low-speed case, we may frequently accept an increase of error at the higher angles, and use a low angle drag coefficient throughout. This procedure is helped by the fact that high angles of attack are rarely used at high Mach number in actual flight.

A second difficulty is that the wake blocking correction varies with $1/\beta^2$ whereas the solid blocking varies with $1/\beta^3$. A solution to this problem is to assume that the low-speed drag coefficient will vary with Mach number according to $1/\beta$. Then the near-sonic velocity increment may be found from

$$\epsilon_c = \epsilon/\beta^3 \qquad (11:28)$$

The streamline curvature corrections are the same as at low speed (Sect. 6:12) except that the quarter-chord length increased by $1/\beta$ is used to find τ_2. The additive corrections become

$$\Delta\alpha_{sc} = \tau_{2(c)}\delta(S/C)C_L(57.3)$$

$$\Delta C_{Lsc} = -\Delta\alpha_{sc}\cdot a = -\tau_{2(c)}\Delta\alpha\cdot a$$

$$\Delta C_{m(c/4)sc} = 0.25\tau_{2(c)}\Delta\alpha\cdot a$$

where a = slope of the lift curve per degree and the subscript c is used with τ_2 to denote that the lengthened quarter chord was used in this determination.

The complete corrections for nearsonic tests of a wing alone or wing and body (no horizontal tail) and zero longitudinal static pressure gradient * become:

$$V = V_u(1 + \epsilon_c) \qquad (11:29)$$

$$q = q_u(1 + \beta_3\epsilon_c) \qquad (11:30)$$

$$R = R_u(1 + \beta_7\epsilon_c) \qquad (11:31)$$

$$M = M_u(1 + \beta_2\epsilon_c) \qquad (11:32)$$

$$\alpha = \alpha_u(1 + \tau_{2(c)})\delta(S/C)C_L(57.3) \qquad (11:33)$$

$$C_L = C_{Lu}(1 - \beta_3\epsilon_c - \tau_{2(c)}\Delta\alpha\cdot a) \qquad (11:34)$$

$$C_{m\frac{1}{4}} = C_{m\frac{1}{4}u}(1 - \beta_3\epsilon_c + 0.25\tau_{2(c)}\Delta\alpha\cdot a) \qquad (11:35)$$

$$C_D\dagger = C_{Du}(1 - \beta_3\epsilon_c) - (\beta_4/\beta^3)\Delta C_{D\text{ wing}} - (\beta_4/\beta^3)\Delta C_{D\text{ body}}$$
$$+ \delta(S/C)C_L{}^2 \qquad (11:36)$$

The corrected dynamic pressure may also be found by using eq. 11:6 with corrected Mach number from eq. 11:32 and corrected static pressure from eq. 12:2.

The tail-on corrections are the same as above except for the moment correction, which should be treated as in Sect. 6:21 but using a tail length increased by $1/\beta$.

---

* As in the two-dimensional case, buoyancy corrections are the same for both incompressible and compressible flow.

† See eq. 6:69.

Normally the induced upwash angle is small enough that it may be neglected, making the final corrected angle only the geometric angle plus the sting and balance deflections and flow inclination angle. Even when the model is displaced off the centerline the wall corrections remain so small that off-the-centerline corrections are unnecessary. Similarly, corrections for streamline curvature are also normally negligible. Treatment of the tunnel static pressure for pressure measurements is the same as at low speed (Sect. 6:30) except that ϵ_c is used instead of ϵ.

Since there are few nearsonic open-throat wind tunnels, wall corrections for this type are not presented.

The above corrections (and those of the previous section) may be most easily applied by running the tunnel at a blocked Mach number. That is, when data are desired at Mach number A, the tunnel is run at Mach number B slightly below A, and the data treated as though they were taken at A. This is done as follows:

1. For a number of values of uncorrected Mach number M_u calculate ϵ_c and β_2 and find M from eq. 11:32.

2. Plot M vs. M_u.

3. For each desired Mach number pick off the corresponding values of M_u and operate the tunnel at M_u.

4. The resulting loads may be reduced to coefficient form by using the dynamic pressure based on M and the empty jet static pressure corrected from M_u to M by eq. 12:2.

Example 11:2

Calculate the boundary corrections for the fighter described below when it is tested in an 8 by 12 ft rectangular-throat wind tunnel with solid walls at Mach = 0.90. Neglect allowing for the boundary layer on the tunnel walls.

Model description: Straight-wing transonic fighter; span 3.0 ft; aspect ratio 3.0; wing area 3.00 sq ft; MAC = 1.038 ft; wing profile NACA 64-006; taper 2:1; fuselage 5-in. diameter, 36-in. length. Horizontal tail off.

From eq. 6:28 the wing solid blocking is

$$\epsilon_{sbW} = \frac{K_1 \tau_1 \text{ (Wing volume)}}{C^{3/2}}$$

$$= \frac{(0.963)(0.878)(0.126)}{(96)^{3/2}}$$

$$= 0.00011$$

K_1 was found in Fig. 6:15 for a 64 series airfoil 6 per cent thick; τ_1 is from Fig. 6:16 using $b/B = 0.25$ and $B/H = 1.5$. The wing volume was approximated as $0.7 \times$ thickness $\times$ span $\times$ chord.

From eq. 6:29 the body solid blocking is

$$\epsilon_{sbB} = \frac{K_3 \tau_1 \text{ (Body volume)}}{C^{3/2}}$$

$$= \frac{(0.924)(0.878)(0.234)}{(96)^{3/2}}$$

$$= 0.00020$$

K_3 was found from Fig. 6:15 for $d/l = 0.14$; τ_1 was found in Fig. 6:16 using $b/B = 0.0$ and $B/H = 1.5$. The body volume was approximated as $0.45ld^2$.

The wake blocking from eq. 6:31 is

$$\epsilon_{wb} = \tfrac{1}{4}(S/C)C_{Du}$$

$$= \tfrac{1}{4} \cdot \tfrac{3}{96} C_{Du}$$

$$= 0.0078 C_{Du} \quad \text{(or } 0.000093 \text{ using an estimated drag coefficient of } 0.0120)$$

The model frontal area is 0.292 sq ft, so that $A_{\text{model}}/A_{\text{test section}} = 0.00304$. From Fig. 11:3, M_{choke} will be 0.94, so that the specified Mach number is within the suggested limit of staying at least 0.02 below choking.

The drag increments due to the pressure gradient (eqs. 6:32 and 6:33) are negligible.

The total blocking increment is then

$$\epsilon = 0.00011 + 0.00020 + 0.000093$$

$$= 0.00040$$

From eq. 11:28 and $M = 0.90$

$$\epsilon_c = (12.1)(0.00040) = 0.00484$$

$$M = M_u(1 + \beta_2 \epsilon_c)$$

$$= 0.90[1 + (1.162)(0.00484)]$$

$$= 0.905$$

$$C_L' = (1 - \beta_3 \epsilon_c)C_{Lu}$$

$$= 0.9943 C_{Lu}$$

The vortex span from Fig. 6:23 is $0.77 \times 3.0 = 2.31$ ft, and from eq. 6:42 the effective span is 2.65 ft. From Fig. 6:30, δ is then 0.12. From Fig. 6:54, using a "tail length" increased by $1/\beta$ of 0.594, $\tau_{2(c)} = 0.18$.

The angle correction is then (eq. 11:33)

$$\Delta\alpha = (1 + \tau_{2(c)})\delta(S/C)C_L'(57.3)$$

$$= (1.18)(0.12)\tfrac{3}{96}C_L'(57.3)$$

$$= 0.254C_L'$$

of which $0.039C_L'$ is contributed by the streamline curvature correction.

The corrected lift coefficient is then (eq. 11:34 and Fig. 5:7 extrapolated to read 0.062 at an aspect ratio of 3.0 and thickness of 6 per cent)

$$C_L = C_L'[1 - (0.039)(0.062)]$$

$$= 0.9976C_L'$$

The induced drag correction becomes (eq. 6:41)

$$\Delta C_D = 0.12\tfrac{3}{96}C_L^2$$

$$= 0.00375C_L^2$$

From eq. 11:36 the corrected drag coefficient is

$$C_D = C_{Du}(1 - \beta_3\epsilon_c) + \delta(S/C)C_L^2$$

$$= 0.9943C_{Du} + 0.00375C_L^2$$

From eq. 11:35 the corrected moment coefficient is

$$C_{m\frac{1}{4}} = C_{m\frac{1}{4}u}(1 - \beta_3\epsilon_c) + 0.25\Delta\alpha_{sc}\cdot a$$

$$= C_{m\frac{1}{4}u}[1 - (1.19)(0.00484)] + (0.25)(0.039)(0.062)C_L$$

$$= 0.9943C_{m\frac{1}{4}u} + 0.0006C_L$$

The streamline curvature contributions to the above corrections are admittedly small, but their inclusion seems worth while in a general example.

11:17. Corrections for Nearsonic Propeller Tests. The problems of correcting propeller data taken at nearsonic speeds has been studied by Young (Ref. 11:7). His conclusions, based on the assumptions that the departures from stream velocity are small, that extensive shock waves are not present, and that the propeller thrust coefficients are not large, are that the correction to the tunnel velocity corresponding to the same thrust and rate of rotation is the same as that in incompressible flow corresponding to the same thrust coefficient increased in the amount $1/\beta^2$.

11:18. Testing for Transonic Buffeting. Nearly all high-speed airplanes exhibit buffeting to some degree in the range of $M = 0.80$ to 0.95, and the aerodynamicist is interested in determining the exact range for his particular airplane, raising it to a higher Mach number and/or reducing its severity. If the buffet is found in the wind tunnel in an early stage of the airplane's development, it is entirely possible that a design change can be made that will delay the buffeting to a higher Mach number and save much flight test and change time.

The buffeting may be explored in a number of ways: by measuring the pulsations in the wake and their severity, by measuring the variations in the wing root bending, by measuring the variations in the loads measured by an internal balance, and by visual observation of tuft or oil behavior.

Arbitrarily, engineers have set a variation in $\Delta h/q = \pm 0.05$ or a 5 per cent variation in wing root bending as the nominal buffet boundary when such methods are being used.

The internal balances may be used by connecting them into oscilloscopes and noting the Mach number when the normal "hash" increases in magnitude. This tunnel buffet Mach number in many cases agrees with the flight buffet Mach number but in others it does not. It is hoped that added research will increase the reliability of the test. Normally a chart like Fig. 11:39 is prepared to show the buffet limit of the particular airplane.

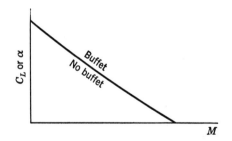

Fig. 11:39. Typical buffet zone variation with Mach number and angle of attack.

Another type of buffet is due to external bombs, fuel tanks, rockets, etc., mounted either flush or on short pylons under wings and fuselage. Usually these bodies are so shaped that their afterbodies form diffusers with the adjacent airplane surfaces, and buffeting takes place earlier than with the airplane alone.

Sometimes tuft observations can reveal the presence of buffeting in particular zones. If it is desired to investigate the phenomena further, flush buffet plates perhaps 1 in. by 1 in. may be mounted on strain gages circuited through an oscilloscope. The

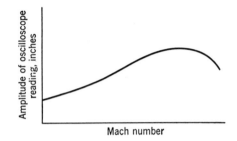

FIG. 11:40. Variation of buffet amplitude with Mach number for one case.

buffet plates may be calibrated by noting the deflection on the scope caused by a given load (1 in. per 0.5 lb per sq in. is reasonable), and hence readings of buffet Mach number, frequency, and intensity may be made. It is helpful if the strain-gage circuit is selected to be insensitive to higher frequencies (above 500 cps) such as are caused by noise.

Small buffet "pots" * as shown in Fig. 11:41 may also be made. They consist of small metal cells, threaded on the outside

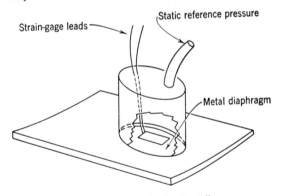

FIG. 11:41. A buffet "pot."

to screw into tapped holes in the model skin. A small strain gage is glued to the diaphragm of each and used with an oscilloscope

* Devices such as this that report pressures in terms of an electric current are called *transducers*.

to determine buffet as with the buffet plates. In some installations the buffet pots are rubber mounted rather than screwed in so that skin strains are not read as pressures. Details of buffet pot construction and use may be found in Ref. 11:9.

Serious buffeting may be reduced by moving the store away from the surface on a lone pylon, or by moving it fore and aft. If neither of these is effective, the diffuser action may be eliminated by a redesign of the store.

The frequency of the buffeting will be increased according to the model scale; the Mach number at which it occurs should be the same as full scale; and buffet is said to be undesirable if it occurs with a store at a lower Mach number than on the airplane by itself.

Another "new" problem not found in the tunnel is structure slippage. Thus, in flight a trimmed airplane may change its trim after a maneuver as the structure slips at its many joints and actually assumes a new configuration.

Allowance for the deflection of the fuselage in computing the airplane static stability is also now required for large, fast airplanes.

11:19. The Use of Transonic-Tunnel Data. The success or failure of the nearsonic tunnel hinges upon the results obtained from its data, of course. It has already been mentioned that bump tests, in spite of the tremendous variation between test and flight Reynolds number, have been used successfully to predict the critical Mach number (defined as the Mach number when $dC_D/dM = 0.1$), the shape of the drag rise curve, and the elevator needed to trim. Data from sting-mounted models have similarly been accurate. And, again, it is frequently assumed that the difference in model and production airplane smoothness is compensatory, and no change in drag due to Reynolds number is applied. The slope of the lift curve is also employed directly. No check points on $C_{L\,max.}$ are available.

The tunnel will also predict the shape of the moment curve, which characteristically shows a hook or climbing tendency near the stall when sweep is employed. This loss of stability is due to two factors: a loss of lift near the wingtips which are behind the airplane center of gravity, and an increase of downwash over the tail since the lift must now come mostly from the inboard wing area. Moment curves in the tunnel normally show the hook, but they start a little earlier than in flight. The tunnel engineer looks for elimination of the hook by relocation of the tail or boundary-layer control devices on the wings.

Sweep may also cause a lack of flap and aileron effectiveness. Indeed, sweep accompanied by thin wing profiles makes a vexacious problem. At low speed one-third less aileron effectiveness can be expected in flight than with the rigid tunnel model, and at high speed almost no aileron power at all. Boundary-layer fences in some cases give better results in the tunnel than in flight, and tunnel drags, varying widely with the way the base pressures are treated, may be either high or low.

PROBLEMS

11:1. An airplane model having a frontal area of 0.603 sq ft is to be tested in a 7 by 10 ft nearsonic tunnel. Find the choking Mach number.

11:2. Calculate the total head at $M = 0.93$ in standard air by eqs. 11:5, 11:7, and 11:8. Compare and discuss. Which is right?

11:3. What wind-off pressure level would you select to give the model of problem 11:1 the maximum Reynolds number in the tunnel described by Fig. 11:25?

11:4. If a model has a low-speed value of $\epsilon = 0.00031$, what clear-tunnel Mach number should be set to yield a freestream Mach number of 0.90?

11:5. Explain why the test-section static pressure falls off with increasing Mach number during a constant-mass run.

REFERENCES

11:1. Alan Pope, *The Aerodynamics of Supersonic Flight*, Pitman Publishing Corporation, New York, 1951.

11:2. C. B. Millikan, J. E. Smith, and R. W. Bell, High-Speed Testing in the Southern California Cooperative Wind Tunnel, *JAS*, February, 1948.

11:3. John H. Weaver, A Method of Wind Tunnel Testing through the Transonic Range, *JAS*, January, 1948.

11:4. H. H. Pearcy, The Effect of Condensation of Atmospheric Water Vapour on Total Head and Other Measurements in the NPL High Speed Tunnel, *R&M* 2249, 1944.

11:5. C. N. H. Lock, A. E. Knowler, and H. H. Pearcy, The Effect of Compressibility on Static Heads, *R&M* 2386, 1945.

11:6. Hans-Wolfgang Liepmann and Harry Ashkenas, Shock-Wave Oscillations in Wind Tunnels, *JAS*, May, 1947.

11:7. A. D. Young, Note on the Application of the Linear Perturbation Theory to Determine the Effect of Compressibility on the Wind-Tunnel Constraint on a Propeller, *R&M* 2113, 1944.

11:8. Stanley Corrsin, Effect of Wind Tunnel Nozzle on Steady Flow Non-Uniformities, *JAS*, February, 1952.

11:9. Taft Wrathall, Miniature Pressure Cells, ISA Conference Paper, September, 1952.

11:10. D. W. Holder, Transition Indication in the National Physical Laboratory 20 by 8 In. High-Speed Tunnel, *R&M* 2079, 1945.

11:11. E. J. Richards and F. H. Burstall, The China Clay Method of Indicating Transition, *R&M* 2126, 1945.

11:12. Jackson R. Stalder and Ellis G. Slack, The Use of a Luminescent Lacquer for the Visual Indication of Boundary-Layer Transition, *TN* 2263, 1951.

Chapter 12

SUPERSONIC-WIND-TUNNEL TESTING

The supersonic wind tunnel differs widely from the subsonic, nearsonic, and transonic types in that it is capable of only one Mach number without physical change. This characteristic, plus the need of greater power and of drying the tunnel air, results in a very complicated set-up.

Official Photograph, National Advisory Committee for Aeronautics.

Fig. 12:1.   The 6 by 6 ft supersonic tunnel at Ames Aeronautical Laboratory.

12:1. Summary of Supersonic Theory.   It seems in order to start the discussion of supersonic tunnels by briefly reviewing supersonic theory.   In addition, the most frequently used formulas will be listed, although other references must normally be consulted.

First of all, supersonic flow differs basically from subsonic flow in that the pressure impulses caused by a body cannot flow upstream and "warn" the air ahead to make way for the body yet to come.   The net effect of this new condition is a wave formation, the energy of which constitutes an additional type of drag. Skin friction exists in both subsonic and supersonic flow, but form drag becomes "wave drag due to thickness" and induced drag becomes "wave drag due to lift" in supersonic flow. In comparison to the subsonic case, skin friction may be reduced in supersonic flow since conditions for a laminar boundary layer (proper pressure gradients and cooling) seem more easily attained; drag due to the thickness may be many times the usual form drag; and drag due to lift is at least several times as great as the subsonic induced drag would be. Interestingly, aspect ratio almost disappears from the supersonic "induced" drag formula, so that we normally go to a wing of short span in order to make a certain square footage of wing have the minimum thickness ratio. Still further improvements are possible under certain conditions through the use of sweep or a Busemann biplane.* But even with the application of the best of known supersonic design principles, the supersonic airplane shows little promise of being as efficient as the subsonic type. For example, a very clean 1953 fighter with a lift-drag ratio of 10 at low speed develops an L/D of only 1.0 at Mach = 1.4. Thus, supersonic flight apparently has most promise in the military field, where it will be employed for high-speed run-in and for missiles.

But to return to the theoretical side, air expands easily and a flow may progress to a higher Mach number without loss according to the following formulas:

$$\frac{T_1}{T_2} = \frac{1 + [(\gamma - 1)/2]M_2{}^2}{1 + [(\gamma - 1)/2]M_1{}^2} \tag{12:1}$$

$$\frac{p_1}{p_2} = \left[\frac{1 + [(\gamma - 1)/2]M_2{}^2}{1 + [(\gamma - 1)/2]M_1{}^2}\right]^{\gamma/(\gamma-1)} \tag{12:2}$$

$$\frac{\rho_1}{\rho_2} = \left[\frac{1 + [(\gamma - 1)/2]M_2{}^2}{1 + [(\gamma - 1)/2]M_1{}^2}\right]^{1/(\gamma-1)} \tag{12:3}$$

Above Mach = 1.0 air cannot be slowed except by means of shock waves, with an accompanying loss of total head. For the slowing process there are few simple formulas. The temperature equation (12:1) still holds, and, since (it develops) the loss due

* See Ref. 12:1.

to the shock waves is a fraction of the total pressure, the equation

$$p_{\text{stagnation}} = p_f\{1 + [(\gamma - 1)/2]\,M^2\}^{\gamma/(\gamma-1)} \qquad (12:4)$$

where f = freestream, is of great interest.

The formula for the speed of sound a is

$$a = 33.42\sqrt{°F_{\text{abs.}}} \qquad \text{mph} \qquad (12:5)$$

It should be noted that the speed of sound depends only on the temperature. The ratio of the specific heat of air at constant

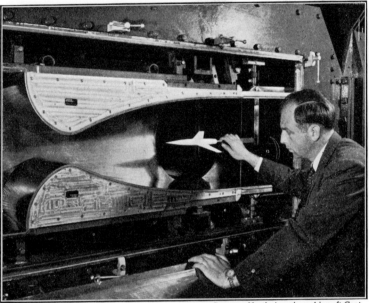

Courtesy North American Aircraft Corp.

FIG. 12:2. Close-up of model in supersonic test section. Note that in this installation it was not found necessary to streamline the sting support strut.

pressure to that at constant volume may be taken as 1.4 for most work below Mach = 3.0.

In most problems of supersonic flight it is enlightening to imagine that the airplane or missile in question is motionless while the stream is moving, and that the stream itself was created by some great fictitious reservoir blowing down to the freestream static pressure. This reservoir (which is at stream stagnation conditions) furnishes a location where stagnation pressure and temperature could have been, and thus supplies a reference for total-head losses. The stagnation pressure in a supersonic stream cannot be measured directly since there is always a loss through the shock wave that forms on any body—a great change from the subsonic case, where it is easy to measure the stagnation pressure.

It is also convenient to consider pressures over a body traveling at supersonic speed as being purely a function of the local surface angle relative to the flight path. Those outer surfaces visible from the front of the body (with intervening body parts cut away) will be at pressures above atmospheric; those exterior surfaces invisible (i.e., turned away) from the flight path will be at pressures below atmospheric. In both cases the approximate surface pressure coefficients are given by

$$C_p = \frac{p - p_f}{q_f} = \frac{2\eta}{\sqrt{M_f{}^2 - 1}} \quad (57.3)$$

where η = angle between a surface and the freestream, f.

Some additional useful formulas are given in Sect. 12:9.

The vast difference in the distribution of the lift in subsonic and supersonic flow is illustrated in Fig. 12:3. The subsonic pressure distribution for an NACA 65A-010 at an angle of attack of 0.93 degree and a lift coefficient of 0.1 is shown in Fig. 12:3a. Figure 12:3b shows the pressure distribution over a biconvex circular-arc airfoil, also 10 per cent thick, at a Mach number of 2.13 and an angle of attack of 4.0 degrees. It then develops a lift coefficient of 0.13. Dashed lines in Fig. 12:3b illustrate the pressure distribution as determined from the shock-expansion theory (Chapter 4 of Ref. 12:1), and the agreement between theory and experiment is good except on the upper surface near the trailing edge where the pressure rise due to the upper surface shock wave has worked its way upstream. Variations between theoretical and experimental subsonic pressure distributions are very small for airfoils such as the 65A-010. Of interest is the possibility of laminar flow over the entire surface of the biconvex airfoil due to the pressure pattern falling all the way from leading to trailing edge.

It is interesting to extend our discussion of p. 169 regarding the distribution of lift on a wing at subsonic speeds to that at supersonic speeds. To review, at low subsonic speeds the maximum pressure to be expected from the lower surface is $+1.0q$ (which, by the way, may be obtained over about 90 per cent of the sur-

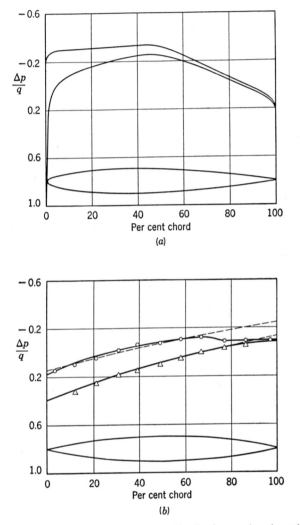

FIG. 12:3. Comparison of airfoil pressure distributions, subsonic and supersonic, for 10 per cent thick airfoils. Figure 12:3a, 65A-010, $\alpha = 0.93°$, $c_l = 0.10$, $c_{d0} = 0.0043$, a.c. at 0.264 chord. Figure 12:3b, 10 per cent thick biconvex airfoil $\alpha = 4°$, $c_l = 0.13$, $c_{d0} = 0.0400$, a.c. $= 0.33$ chord, $M = 2.13$.

face when a flap is down), and perhaps $-2.0q$ on the upper, making a lift coefficient of 3.0. At supersonic speeds, a little more lift is available from the lower surface (of the order of the Mach factor, eq. 11:7), but much less from the upper. It becomes more enlightening to talk in terms of absolute pressures. At a Mach number of 3.0 in standard sea-level air q becomes about 13,000 lb per sq ft, so that something over that amount becomes available as lift on the lower surface. But even a perfect vacuum would yield only 2117 lb per sq ft, so that the upper-surface lift usually runs less than that from the lower surface. This same conclusion holds on down to small angles, a typical diamond-shaped airfoil at 4 degrees angle of attack getting 30 per cent of its lift from the upper surface and 70 per cent from the lower surface.

Extension of this theory to higher speeds leads us to reason that with increasing Mach numbers minimum drag will be obtained by progressively further aft maximum thickness locations until ultimately minimum drag will occur with a simple wedge shape. All this comes about from the fact that the base vacuum can never be greater than 2117 lb per sq ft (at sea level), but the frontal pressure rise may become a substantial fraction of a q ranging upwards of 50,000 lb per sq ft.

12:2. Creation of a Supersonic Stream. The creation of a supersonic stream in a duct has many interesting facets to it, not the least of which is the odd-shaped passage that must be provided. We have already discussed part of this problem, but for completeness we will collect the main conclusions here. In order for air to become supersonic it must first become sonic, and (eq. 11:2) a sonic velocity can occur only at a minimum section in a duct. Thus a supersonic nozzle must first contract and then expand. (See Fig. 12:2.)

In simple words, we are then providing for a marked change in the characteristics of air which occur exactly at the speed of sound. Below $M = 1.0$ the air density decreases more slowly than its velocity increases, so that in order for a subsonic duct to remain filled it must contract as the speed of flow increases. Above the speed of sound, the opposite is true: the density decreases much faster than the velocity increases. The larger volume of air thereby created must have ample room provided.

The relation between area and Mach number has been given in eq. 11:3, but, unfortunately, the simple provision of the proper duct areas will not assure smooth supersonic flow. The added difficulty is introduced by the peculiar fact that a change in Mach number (or pressure) above $M = 1.0$ may *only* be accomplished by *turning* the flow. Thus Mach 2.004, for instance, may be created only by turning a flow at Mach $= 1.0$ through 26.5 degrees.. It may be turned the total amount in one jump, or in a series of little jumps. In a supersonic nozzle we turn it away from the centerline 13.25 degrees and back towards the centerline 13.25 degrees, ending with a flow traveling in the same direction it had when at Mach 1.0. A graphical design method may be made which illustrates that the above procedure results in the area ratio as required by eq. 11:3. Thus a nozzle consists of two sections: the first turns the flow away from the centerline a total of half the angle needed; the second turns the flow back towards it. In practice a number of small angles are faired into a smooth curve (see Ref. 12:1).

The choice of how many small turns to make is left up to the designer, the calculation of a low-Mach-number nozzle using 2-degree turns being a 2-hour job, whereas a higher-speed nozzle using 0.5-degree turns requires perhaps 2 or 3 weeks.

Treatment of the nozzle boundary layer may take one of several paths. First of all, if no allowance is made for it, reasonably good flow at a Mach number lower than design will ensue, and this procedure is advised for classroom-type tunnels or other hurry-up jobs. A second method is to calculate the boundary-layer displacement thickness, including the effect of aerodynamic heating, and widen floor and ceiling to accommodate the boundary-layer growth. The side walls must remain parallel for the schlieren (Sect. 12:11) to work well. This procedure will produce a lateral gradient in Mach number but no vertical gradient. Hence if the model moves vertically in the test section with pitch it will remain in air of a constant average Mach number. The sometimes used procedure of putting a double correction on floor and ceiling (to allow for the side walls) makes little sense theoretically in supersonic flow, as well as making a vertical flow gradient in the test section.

Another approach to the problem is to mount the model with wings vertical and yaw it to simulate pitch. The idea here is that the customary nozzle (floor and ceiling curved) is most likely to make waves that produce vertical inclinations in the flow, and a yawing model with wings vertical would then be least affected.

The answer to the problem is to work on the nozzle until the residual waves are so weak that their effect is negligible. It is relevant to mention that the nozzle design method of Ref. 12:1 will result in a wave in the test section due to the discontinuity in the slope of the nozzle at its inflection point. Another argument for keeping pitch instead of yaw is the ease of checking angles with an inclinometer.

We will now turn to the problem of slowing a supersonic stream to a subsonic value.

12:3. The Return to Subsonic Speed. It is a characteristic of most supersonic flows that they can be slowed only by passing

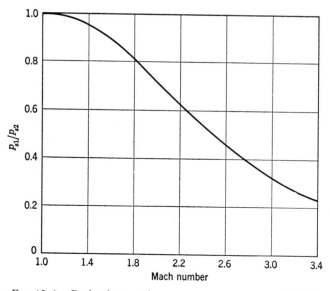

Fig. 12:4.   Ratio of stagnation pressures across a normal shock.

through shock waves. These waves, a few hundredths of an inch thick, under some conditions reduce the speed of the air by as much as 1000 mph. Each time a flow passes through a shock it experiences a loss of total head: its original temperature may be regained, but only at a lower static pressure. In the continuous-type wind tunnel the loss through the shock is added to the other losses to be replaced by the fan.

The loss associated with the return to subsonic speed through a normal shock is plotted in Fig. 12:4. Obviously it is a great waste of power to shock down at operating Mach number instead of reducing the Mach number before the final normal shock. In practice, the added complexity of a second nozzle usually is not justified by the power saved below Mach = 1.6 or even 2.0. For tunnels operating at higher speeds a contracting passage is needed, and a stable location of the normal shock is found just downstream of the diffuser minimum section. A straight passage should be provided downstream of the shock location for general flow evening before the subsonic expanding passage is begun (Fig. 12:5). A general rule for a fixed second throat is to make it such that it just accelerates the flow to Mach = 1.0 when a normal shock is in the test section.

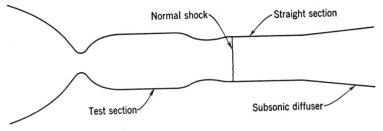

Fig. 12:5.

We will turn now to the types of supersonic wind tunnels, and briefly discuss their advantages and disadvantages.

12:4. Types of Supersonic Tunnels. There are of course many closed-circuit single-return supersonic wind tunnels that the layman would have difficulty distinguishing from sub- or transonic types. In addition, there are a large number of intermittent supersonic wind tunnels, those that store the necessary energy for running in the form of vacuum or high pressure, and run only a fraction of a time that the compressors operate. The continuous tunnels are far preferable, making unnecessary all sorts of special apparatus needed to get quick readings. But when cost is important it is easy to see how the intermittent types come into being.

We may thus classify all supersonic wind tunnels into those that run continuously and those that are intermittent. The intermittent tunnels are either *indraft* (energy stored as vacuum in a large low-pressure tank, and stream total head equal to atmospheric static head) or *blowdown* (energy stored as high-pressure, stream total head equal to reservoir static pressure). The blowdown type has the advantage of remarkably high test

Reynolds numbers in very small tunnels. Frequently high-altitude flight values (see Fig. 12:6) may be duplicated in a test section only a few inches wide.

The continuous tunnels usually are pressure tunnels in the sense that their pressure may be regulated. In a great preponderance of these tunnels, however, the jet static pressure is well below

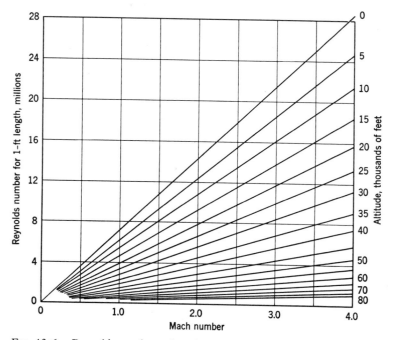

FIG. 12:6.   Reynolds number values for a range of Mach numbers and altitudes, standard atmosphere.

atmospheric. A number of the continuous supersonic tunnels are open-circuit types used for ramjet studies in which recirculating the air is undesirable because of stream contamination; and a few are semi-closed circuit, exchanging enough air so that the stream temperature remains high but not excessively so. This procedure, or any procedure that aids in keeping the stream temperature high, reduces the need for drying apparatus.

12:5. List of Supersonic Wind Tunnels. Table 12:1 gives a partial list of supersonic wind tunnels now operating in this country. It is believed that England currently has four; Australia, one; Italy, China, and Japan none; Russia, unknown.

TABLE 12:1

SUPERSONIC WIND TUNNELS *

National Advisory Committee for Aeronautics

Tunnel	Located	Type	$M_{max.}$	Jet Size	Remarks
NACA 4 x 4 ft	Langley Field, Va.	Closed circuit	2.2	4 x 4 ft	60,000 hp
NACA 9 in.	Langley Field, Va.	Closed circuit	2.5	9 x 7.5 in.	1000 hp
NACA 4 x 4 ft	Langley Field, Va.	Closed circuit	5.0	4 x 4 ft	83,000 hp
NACA 2 x 2 ft	Langley Field, Va.	Closed circuit	4.5	2 x 2 ft	
NACA 24 in.	Langley Field, Va.	Induction	1.8	24 in., variable	
NACA 1 x 3 ft #1	Moffett Field, Cal.	Closed circuit	2.2	1 x 3 ft	10,000 hp
NACA 1 x 3 ft #2	Moffett Field, Cal.	Blowdown	3.4	1 x 3 ft	
NACA 10 x 10 ft	LFPL, Cleveland, Ohio	Continuous blowdown	3.5	10 x 10 ft	250,000 hp
NACA 7 x 8 ft	Moffett Field, Cal.	Closed circuit	3.6	7 x 8 ft	200,000 hp
NACA 6 x 6 ft	Moffett Field, Cal.	Closed circuit	2.0	6 x 6 ft	50,000 hp
NACA 18 in.	LFPL, Cleveland, Ohio	Closed circuit	2.2	18 x 18 in.	
NACA 2 ft.	LFPL, Cleveland, Ohio	Closed circuit	4.5	2 x 2 ft	
NACA 6 x 8 ft	LFPL, Cleveland, Ohio	Continuous blowdown	1.8	6 x 8 ft	100,000 hp

Armed Services

Tunnel	Located	Type	$M_{max.}$	Jet Size	Remarks
AEDC GDF E-1	Tullahoma, Tenn.	Intermittent (2–5 minutes)	5.0	9 x 12 in.	Adjustable nozzle
AEDC GDF "A"	Tullahoma, Tenn.	Continuous	5.0	40 x 40 in.	100,000 hp adjustable nozzle
AEDC PWT Supersonic	Tullahoma, Tenn.	Continuous	5.0	16 x 16 ft	216,000 hp adjustable nozzle
Army Bureau of Ordnance #1	Aberdeen, Md.	Closed circuit	4.4	15 x 20 in.	13,000 hp
Army Bureau of Ordnance #2	Aberdeen, Md.	Closed circuit	2.5	15 x 20 in.	13,000 hp
DTMB 18 x 18 in.	Carderock, Md.	Indraft (8 sec)	2.92	18 x 18 in.	
DTMB 9 x 9 in.	Carderock, Md.	Indraft (40 sec)	2.92	9.5 x 9.5 in.	
DTMB 3 x 5 in.	Carderock, Md.	Continuous	2.92	3 x 5 in.	

* So many supersonic wind tunnels are being both erected and revised that a list of tunnels can be only approximate and transitory. The tunnels listed in the table have been publicly announced.

TABLE 12:1 (*Continued*)

SUPERSONIC WIND TUNNELS

Armed Services (*Continued*)

Tunnel	Located	Type	$M_{max.}$	Jet Size	Remarks
NAMTC	Pt. Mugo, Cal.	Continuous blowdown	3.0	17 x 23 in.	15,400 hp
NAMTC Combustion	Pt. Mugo, Cal.	Continuous blowdown	2.5	22 x 20 in.	
NAMTC Combustion	Pt. Mugo, Cal.	Continuous blowdown	1.4	11 x 11 in.	
Naval Ordnance Laboratory #1	White Oaks, Md.	Indraft	4.3	16 x 16 in.	
Navy Bureau of Ordnance	Daingerfield, Tex.	Closed circuit	2.5	19 x 27½ in.	16,000 hp

Colleges and Industry

Tunnel	Located	Type	$M_{max.}$	Jet Size	Remarks
JPL 12 in.	Pasadena, Cal.	Open circuit	3.0	9 x 12 in.	4000
JPL 20 in.	Pasadena, Cal.	Continuous	4.8	18 x 20 in.	16,000 hp
Cornell Aero. Lab #1	Buffalo, N. Y.	Continuous indraft	1.75	2.25 x 6.60 in.	
Georgia Tech. 4.0 in.	Atlanta, Ga.	Blowdown	2.5	1 x 4 in.	
U. of Maryland	College Park, Md.	Indraft (10 sec)	3.5	6 x 6 in.	3400 cu ft storage
MIT Turbine component	Cambridge, Mass.	Closed circuit	3.0	8 x 8 in.	1350 hp
MIT Naval Tunnel	Cambridge, Mass.	Closed circuit	4.0	18 x 24 in.	10,000 hp
U. of Michigan	Willow Run, Mich.	Indraft	2.0	8 x 13 in.	
U. of Minnesota 6 x 9 in.	Rosemount, Minn.	Blowdown	7.0	6 x 9 in.	
U. of Minnesota 4 x 9 in.	Rosemount, Minn.	Closed circuit	5.0	4 x 9 in.	
U. of Minnesota 12 x 12 in.	Rosemount, Minn.	Blowdown	8.0	12 x 12 in.	
Ohio State free jet	Columbus, Ohio	Blowdown	8.0	12 x 12 in.	1100 hp
Ohio State variable density	Columbus, Ohio	Closed circuit	3.5	3.5 x 5 in.	
Ohio State pressure-vacuum	Columbus, Ohio	Continuous	10.+	3 x 3 in.	
Ohio State Transonic	Columbus, Ohio	Blowdown induction	1.5	3 x 3 ft	
North American	Inglewood, Cal.	Indraft	1.7	16 x 16 in.	
Princeton 4 x 8 in.	Princeton, N. J.	Blowdown (1–5 minutes)	5.0	4 x 8 in.	

TABLE 12:1 (*Continued*)

SUPERSONIC WIND TUNNELS

Colleges and Industry (Continued)

Tunnel	Located	Type	$M_{max.}$	Jet Size	Remarks
U. of Southern California	Fontana, Cal.	Continuous blowdown	2.5	17 x 20 in.	12,000 hp
United Aircraft	East Hartford, Conn.	Continuous indraft	1.7	3.7 x 15.4 in.	600 hp
United Aircraft	East Hartford, Conn.	Continuous indraft	1.8	8 x 9.25 in.	600 hp
United Aircraft	East Hartford, Conn.	Continuous indraft	3.0	4.5 x 5 in.	
WADC 2 ft	Wright Field, Ohio	Closed circuit	2.5	2 x 2 ft.	5000 hp
WADC 6 in.	Wright Field, Ohio	Closed circuit	3.0	6 x 6 in.	1000 hp

Foreign

Tunnel	Located	Type	$M_{max.}$	Jet Size	Remarks
ONERA High-Speed	Chalais-Meudon	Closed circuit	2.5	11.8 x 11.8 in.	880 hp
ONERA #3	Chalais-Meudon	Closed circuit	1.4	3.2 ft, round	3200 hp air exchange
Swiss 15 in.	Zürich	Closed circuit	2.0	15 x 15 in.	900 hp
NPL 11 in.	Teddington	Closed circuit	2.8	11 in., square	1500
NPL 9.5 in.	Teddington	Induction, intermittent, return circuit	1.8	9 ½ in., square	
NPL 9 x 3 in.	Teddington	Induction, intermittent, return circuit	1.8	9 x 3 in., rectangular	
NPL 14 x 18 in.	Teddington	Induction, intermittent, return circuit	1.8	18 x 14 in., rectangular	

12:6. Supersonic-Tunnel Design Features.

The design of a large supersonic wind tunnel is well beyond the scope of this textbook, but it is in order to note a few of the major changes between it and the subsonic-type tunnels. A brief discussion of the small blowdown tunnel is given in the next section.

The need for a contracting-expanding nozzle has been covered in Sect. 12:2, and a photograph of a typical fixed nozzle is shown in Fig. 12:2. Each nozzle gives, of course, a discrete Mach number (subject to small changes caused by Reynolds number variations). Many tunnels have a half dozen fixed nozzles to be used as needed.

After the nozzle is designed there is still the very real problem of its fabrication. Over a period of time practically every material and method that stands a reasonable chance of success has been tried. For the small student tunnel a smooth-grained hardwood or carefully filed aluminum nozzle seems satisfactory. Steel, brass, and aluminum have been used for larger nozzles, as have steel plates over a wood form, and plaster with brass sides. The author is admittedly confused by the wide variation of desirable nozzle accuracies quoted to him by different supersonic-

Official Photograph, National Advisory Committee for Aeronautics.

FIG. 12:7. The terrible complexity of a remotely operated flexible throat is illustrated by this photograph of the nozzle of the Ames 1 by 3 ft supersonic wind tunnel. Note the model mounted with wings vertical as per Sect. 12:2.

nozzle designers. Some desire a calculated control point every 0.05 in. in a block 3 ft long; others are satisfied with a tenth as many points. In view of the doubt surrounding the boundary-layer correction extraordinary accuracy in nozzle design and construction scarcely seems justified. Obviously a variable nozzle would be more satisfactory if the cost can be borne. A simple flexible nozzle that goes a long way towards solving this problem has been advanced by Dhawan and Roshko (Ref. 12:16). Their arrangement is suitable for tunnels up to perhaps 2-ft test section size. Other approaches to the adjustable-nozzle problem have been given by Evvard and Wyatt (Ref. 12:17), who use a variable corner arrangement, and by Allen (Ref. 12:26), who uses a sliding-block arrangement. The complexity of a large, flexible throat nozzle is shown in Fig. 12:7. In addition to its complexity, the flexible nozzle is subject to permanent distortion of the main plates if the jacks are accidentally misoperated.

Besides the conventional fixed and variable nozzles, several special arrangements have been tried with varying degrees of success. One of these is the air nozzle, wherein air is blown into the test section at the end of the entrance cone and removed again a short way downstream. See Fig. 12:8a. This has the

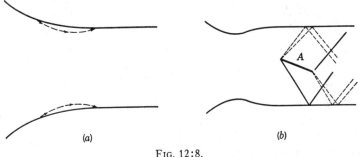

(a)   (b)

FIG. 12:8.

effect of making a minimum section and enables the test section to be at Mach numbers that are slightly supersonic without the added complication of either discrete supersonic Mach numbers or an adjustable nozzle.

A continuously variable range of supersonic Mach numbers in a small area may also be obtained by placing a vane in a supersonic tunnel ahead of the model and varying the angle of attack of the vane. In Fig. 12:8b the Mach number of the flow at A (and the flow direction as well) will change as the angle of attack of the vane is varied.

As the airstream expands through the nozzle there is a tremendous drop in temperature (around 90° F at $M = 1.0$ and 230° F at $M = 2.0$) which may carry all but the driest air well below its dew point, with a resulting condensation of moisture in the tunnel. Since the condensation does not occur in a plane, the flow can become ragged, data not be repeatable, and the Mach number undefined. Actually, since a very short time is involved while the air is traversing the test section, and since there is not an adjacent body of water, condensation does not begin at the dew point, but roughly when the air is four times supersaturated. (See Fig. 12:9)

Even this help is not sufficient for most tunnels, and added efforts must be made to avoid condensation. These take two paths: permitting the tunnel temperature to rise, or drying the air.

Heating is discussed in Sect. 12:15 and may be considered a must for hypersonic wind tunnels using air as a working fluid, but

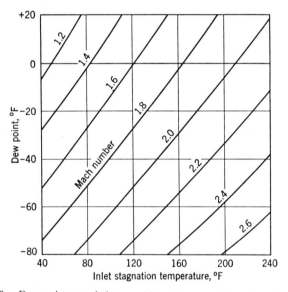

Fig. 12:9.   Dew points needed to avoid moisture condensation shocks, from Fig. 10 of *NACA TN* 2518.

possibly less attractive than drying for lower speed ranges. The design of a drier is discussed in the next section.

As may be inferred by the photograph of the giant compressor for the 8 by 6 ft supersonic tunnel at the Lewis Flight Propulsion Laboratory of the NACA (Fig. 12:10), the theory and design of a multistage axial compressor are very complex and above the level of this book.

Rather than use liners to allow for the large volume of the vertical strut, it is common in supersonic tunnels to bend the tunnel out around the vertical strut so that no change in passage area occurs. This procedure is reasonable since the vertical strut is commonly used for *all* tests instead of being employed

Official Photograph, National Advisory Committee for Aeronautics.

FIG. 12:10.   The huge axial-flow compressor of the 6 by 8 ft supersonic wind
tunnel at the Lewis Flight Propulsion Laboratory.

only part time.   Progressive steps in the wave formation as the
normal shock moves over the model and supersonic flow is
developed are shown in Fig. 12:11.

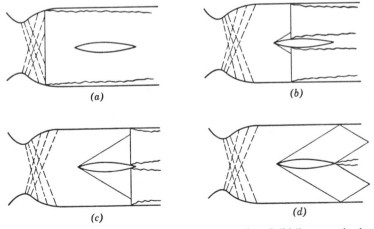

FIG. 12:11.   Flow pattern as tunnel goes supersonic.   Solid lines are shocks;
dashed lines are Mach waves.

We might note at this point that many tunnel engineers feel that the exhaust from a jet engine should be simulated in supersonic flow because shocks form on the exhaust as it expands just aft of the tailpipe and affect the air flow at the tail. Methods for simulating the exhaust are under study.

12:7. Driers. Two desiccants are popular for tunnel drying: silica gel and activated alumina. The gel looks like translucent white pebbles; the alumina is more like ground-up white rock. Both may be treated to harden the surface and reduce dusting, and both may be regenerated (dried) by heating to about 350° F.

The design of driers using silica gel has been discussed by Patterson in Ref. 12:23, and the information contained below may be further extended by reference to his paper and the general discussion of silica gel in Ref. 12:24. Less information seems to be available on activated alumina.

The first step in drier design is of course to determine the amount of water to be removed from the air between regenerations, which usually take about 8 hours. Accordingly the designer normally provides for drying all the air to be used in a day.

Humid air (Washington, D.C., in summer) contains about 0.016 lb of water per lb of dry air. Since the allowable remnant of moisture at a dew point of $-15°$ F amounts to 0.0005 lb per lb of dry air and is negligible, we may reasonably take the local maximum humidity as the weight of moisture to be removed and stored in the silica gel. The weight of this moisture is then divided by 0.08 to obtain the weight of silica gel needed. The figure of 0.08 is about 20 per cent of the maximum amount the gel can hold, but it seems a good operating value, avoiding breakdown of the gel from excessive moisture and affording reasonable regeneration conditions.

The weight of silica gel obtained from the above calculations should be arranged in layers 12 in. thick to avoid blowing free-air paths through the desiccant. From experience this will result in a velocity of about $4\frac{1}{2}$ ft per second through the driers and a pressure loss of about $1\frac{1}{2}$ in. Hg. More gel, keeping the same 12 in. depth, will of course reduce the pressure loss. Other pressure drops may be computed according to

$$\Delta p = 0.0883 \ (1.715 V)^{1.38} \tag{12:6}$$

Δp = pressure drop through 12 in. of gel

V = velocity, ft per sec, through 12 in. of gel.

The silica gel is 3 to 8 mesh and may be retained by a 10-mesh wire and a framework of suitable strength. Silica gel weighs about 43 lb per cu ft.

The cycle of air drying and regeneration may be explained by referring to Fig. 12:12, which shows a drying circuit. For running the tunnel, dampers A, B, and C are put at position 1, and air is drawn through the dust screen and silica gel bed and on into the tunnel or storage tank.

For regeneration, dampers B and C are put at position 2 and the heaters and fan are turned on. Very hot atmospheric air is

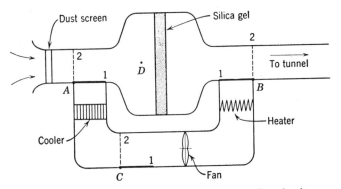

Fig. 12:12. Diagrammatic drier and regeneration circuit.

then blown through the gel, heating it to about 350° F and carrying off the moisture. At first the heat is used up in restoring the water to vapor state and the thermometer at point D rises only slightly. The drying is completed when the reading at D rises to 250° F, indicating that the moisture has been driven off and the silica gel is now hot. At this point in the cycle, damper A is moved to position 2, and C to position 1. The heater is turned off, the cooler is turned on, and the fan is reversed. Reversal of the air flow allows the moisture in the circuit to be removed by the outer face of the silica gel rather than leaving it on the inner face where it would be released by the heating that takes place as the gel removes the moisture from the air. In furtherance of this procedure it should be noted that the performance of the gel may be severely penalized if it is allowed to heat itself excessively during a run. (See Fig. 12:13.) Sometimes the cooling cycle discussed above must be repeated between runs. Normally, return of the gel to 100° F is considered adequate. This permits the use of city water for cooling, the amount varying from 1 to 10 gal per minute for each 5000 lb of silica gel, depending on the cooling time of 7 to 4 hours respectively. About 0.015 kw per lb of silica gel will yield a regeneration heating time

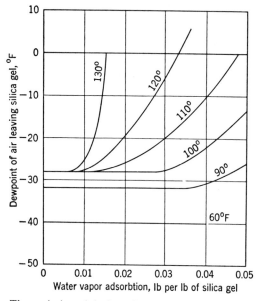

FIG. 12:13.   The variation of drying with silica gel temperature and amount of moisture absorded.

which varies almost linearly with the amount of water vapor absorbed by the gel.   Rough estimates may be obtained from the empirical formula

$$T = 60w + 4.33 \qquad (12:7)$$

where T = regeneration heating time, hours; and w = water absorbed by the gel, lb per lb of gel.

Silica gel should be kept from getting too dusty and, in the continuous or blowdown type of tunnel, should never be subjected to an oil-filled stream.   A commercial precipitron or an oiled cheesecloth can be used as a dust remover if necessary.

The frost point of the tunnel air may be determined by cooling the back of a glass indicator with liquid air or carbon dioxide until the tunnel air on the front starts to condense out.   Such a gadget, available commercially as a "dew-point meter," is accurate to about 1 degree in dew point. A second type takes a sample of tunnel air, compresses it, and allows the compressed air to cool to room temperature when it is suddenly expanded. Again, a condensation on a glass indicates the amount of moisture. Varying the amount of compression until the condensate is noted enables the dew point to be found.

Oil in the tunnel circuit may be eliminated by means of carbon rings on the compressor pistons. Unfortunately they are very expensive.

12:8. The Small Classroom Blowdown Tunnel. A satisfactory small blowdown tunnel is not difficult to build, and a discussion of its main features is in order.

The blowdown type is selected largely because the storage tank is smaller than with the indraft type and thus requires less space, its air may be dried as it is stored with a resulting smaller drier, and the test Reynolds number is high. A moderately serious disadvantage is that the models are so small that their construction is very difficult.

In essence the small blowdown tunnel consists of an air drier, compressor, oil cleaner, storage tank, pressure regulator, gate valve, test section, and diffuser. All these items may be purchased new, but if the usual school economy prevails, most of the parts may be obtained used. Typical local sources are given when relevant.

Dryer: Both silica gel and activated alumina are commercially available and cheap and may be used for drying wind-tunnel air according to Sect. 12:7. The moisture adsorbed may be driven off by electric coil heating. Drying tunnel air may be omitted in many parts of the country as long as the Mach number is kept below 1.6.

Compressor: The customary filling-station type (150 psi) is adequate for most simple supersonic tunnels. Such compressors have a tendency to put considerable oil in the airstream, but it may be removed with a porous filter. The filter will work much better if the compressed air is cooled by passing it through a coil of copper tubing before permitting it to enter the filter.

Tank: Used pressure tanks of the 150 psi range are available in almost all cities for around a few hundred dollars for a 160 cu ft capacity. (This size will permit a 15-second run in a tunnel with a 4 sq in. test section.) According to code requirements the tank must have a safety valve and must be hydrostatically tested to

1½ times the working pressure. Pressure tanks are always a potential source of danger and should be treated accordingly.

Pressure regulator: Frequently a satisfactory pressure regulator may be borrowed from the local gas company. Such a regulator must be selected to withstand the maximum pressure, of course. It has been the author's happy experience that regulators in general work well under much wider limits of volume and pressure than their rated values. Many regulators stabilize in 1 second.

Gate valve: A quick-acting gate valve is needed to save precious time in getting the tunnel up to operating Mach number. Gate valves are available at very reasonable cost.

Test section: The test section must be designed for ease in getting to the model and making changes. Usually the test section will be small so that doors on both sides may be easily designed. The low pressure usually found in the test section of supersonic tunnels and the consequent large pressure difference from the test section to the room should be kept in mind and care taken that leaks do not occur. When they do the test-section Mach number is changed.

Although clear plastic may be used in a very small installation on a temporary basis, it scratches easily, and glass is a must for a permanent set-up. If a schlieren is to be used, good glass is necessary, and either a lot of money must be spent on optical glass or a lot of time in hunting through plate-glass specimens for some coincidentally good. Since deflections of even the best glass would interfere with the schlieren system, a factor of safety of 10 is used in selecting its thickness.

The installation of the glass is a problem too. Glass is difficult to machine to close tolerances, yet it must fit the internal surface of the test section with extraordinary smoothness. One solution of this problem is to put the inside face of glass on a flat plate and set its mounting frame around it, filling the gap between with Wood's metal or other low-melting-point alloy.

Diffuser: In a small installation the benefits resulting from the ease of getting to the test section without a diffuser usually outweigh the increase of running time with one. Diffusers do, however, reduce the noise. This may be an important point in some installations.

A blowdown tunnel may be designed by the method of Sect. 2:11 plus the charts of Ref. 12:19. The procedure is to start at the downstream end of the tunnel and work upstream, adding in the losses as they occur and computing local conditions according to the continuity equation and the gas law. A small amount of iteration is normally necessary. About 10 psi must be added for loss in the pressure regulator, and the final cut-off pressure with the starting pressure and temperature, tank volume, and throat size may be used to get the run time.

Instrumentation of a small classroom blowdown tunnel may start in a very elementary manner with measurement of settling-chamber static pressure and temperature, and rows of static orifices in nozzle and test-section floor and ceiling. (The orifices may well influence the flow until they bleed out enough air to become equalized.) Experiments may embrace comparing theory of area ratio and Mach numbers actually attained; measurements of shock angles off various bodies and comparison with shock expansion theory; schlieren studies of wave reflection and flow from a free nozzle; elementary diffuser studies; and comparison of test-section size, Mach number, and running time.

Much less run time for good supersonic testing is required than one would normally guess. Thirty seconds is ample time for obtaining data with even the crudest instrumentation, and with good equipment it suffices for obtaining a whole polar. Pressure read electrically can be measured in 5 seconds; with simple pressure tubes, 7 to 10 seconds. If sufficient time is not available, a guillotine cut-off on the pressure tubes will permit two runs to be used to get one set of pressures.

12:9. Calibration of the Test Section. Just as with low Mach number operation, the tunnel engineer using a supersonic wind tunnel must know in advance what the testing conditions will be. This includes the variation of Mach number, static pressure, total head, temperature, and flow direction in the useful part of the test section and whether condensation shocks may occur. Turbulence has not received a great deal of attention, although indications are that it soon may.

The distribution of Mach number in the test section may be found in a number of ways:

1. By photographing the wave angles off a wedge and determining the Mach number through the use of the charts of Dailey and Wood (Ref. 12:3).

2. By measuring the local static pressure p and the local pitot pressure * p_{sp} and using the Rayleigh formula

$$\frac{p}{p_{sp}} = \left[\frac{2\gamma M^2}{\gamma + 1} - \frac{\gamma - 1}{\gamma + 1}\right]^{1/(\gamma-1)} \left[\frac{2}{(\gamma + 1)M^2}\right]^{\gamma/(\gamma-1)} \quad (12:8)$$

3. By measuring the settling-chamber stagnation pressure p_{ss} and the local pitot pressure p_{sp} and using the following shock loss equation

$$\frac{p_{sp}}{p_{ss}} = \left[\frac{\gamma + 1}{2\gamma M^2 - \gamma + 1}\right]^{1/(\gamma-1)} \left[\frac{(\gamma + 1)M^2}{2 + (\gamma - 1)M^2}\right]^{\gamma/(\gamma-1)} \quad (12:9)$$

4. By measuring the static pressure on the face of a wedge and the settling-chamber stagnation pressure, and using the shock expansion theory or charts from Ref. 12:3.

5. By measuring the settling chamber total head and the test-section static pressure and using eq. 12:2.

A few comments on the above may be helpful. Method 1 (measuring shock angles off a cone or wedge) is widely used for preliminary work, or rough checks of the other methods. It suffers from difficulties associated with measuring the wave angles to a high degree of accuracy, and to uncertainties of adding in the boundary-layer displacement thickness as an increment of wedge or cone angle. Wedges are normally to be preferred over cones since they make stronger shocks, but in the low supersonic range, Mach 1.05 to 1.2, wedges thin enough to have attached shocks may suffer from leading-edge bending due to being struck by particles in the airstream. They may hence not be as satisfactory as cones.

The Rayleigh formula is widely used and is satisfactory when the static pressure can be accurately determined, as, for instance, when a static pipe is mounted along the tunnel centerline. For obtaining local Mach numbers, however, the ratio of pitot to stagnation pressures seems to be best, although at low Mach numbers it requires extraordinary accuracy in pressure reading—perhaps to 0.005 cm Hg. The accuracy of pitot pressure can best be assured by using a blunt total-head tube with a small hole at its center, a hole 0.02 in. in diameter being reasonable for a $\frac{1}{8}$-in. O.D. tube. (This construction insures a reading made behind a normal shock.)

* See footnote, p. 493.

A typical centerline calibration and a method of presenting tunnel Mach number calibration data are shown in Fig. 12:14. Determining the Mach number by measuring the velocity V and the temperature in order to get the speed of sound is an entirely different matter, and profoundly more difficult. Although V could be found with a device that measured the stream velocity by its particle speed, such as the ultramicroscope, the author is unaware of any device that can measure the stream temperature

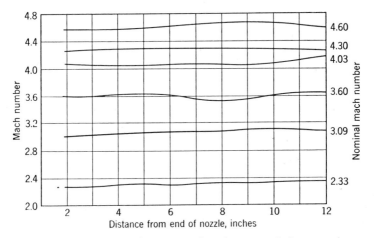

FIG. 12:14.   Variation of Mach number along a typical test section.

to the needed accuracy. The problem is that any device immersed in the stream will be subject to at least part of the stream's stagnation temperature rise, and would read something between freestream temperature and full stagnation temperature. Some interesting experiments involving measuring the speed of sound in the stream, and thence determining its temperature, are now going on and may lead to important gains in knowledge.

The *stagnation* temperature of the airstream may be read to within a few per cent by means of a stagnation thermometer as shown in Fig. 12:15. Basically it consists of a device to slow the air to a low Mach number so that its temperature is essentially the actual stagnation value plus a shielding such that radiation losses will not be large.

The flow angle in the test section may be found to a few hundredths of a degree by means of a wedge yawhead. This instrument is simply a wedge having pressure orifices on both faces.

When the two orifices read the same pressure, the axis of the yawhead is facing the undisturbed stream direction. Under some circumstances (low supersonic Mach numbers) a cone is preferable to a wedge. A 3-degree included angle cone will yield $0.006q$ per degree of inclination to the airstream.

Variations of less than 0.05 degree in flow direction are tolerable in all but the most exacting equipment. It should be noted in passing that variations in flow direction in a supersonic stream

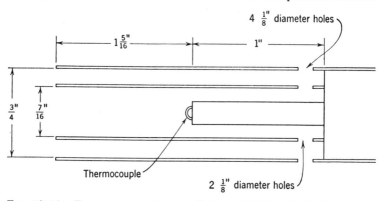

FIG. 12:15. Temperature probe described by McLellan in Ref. 12:5. It reads stagnation temperature within a few per cent. The light-weight construction reduces temperature lag, an especially important item with intermittent tunnels.

are inextricably linked with changes in pressure, or in other words they both exist because a wave does, not having been canceled out in the wave-canceling section of the nozzle.

As pointed out by Puckett in Ref. 12:22 the relations between static pressure, dynamic pressure, and Mach number are such that, if it is desired to hold force accuracy to 1 per cent, the Mach number will have to be held to within 0.007 for the range up to $M = 4.0$.

The static pressure across the test section may be determined by a rake such as the one shown in Fig. 12:16. The principle of the rake design is to reduce the shock-pressure rise through the nose shock by means of a slim body and sharp nose, and then to reduce the afterbody effect (which can extend forward through the boundary layer from 20 to 40 boundary-layer thicknesses) by keeping well ahead of the rake body. Static pressure measurements taken close to a wall may suffer from the reflected bow wave striking near or at the pressure orifices.

McLellan in Ref. 12:6 found that the static-pressure rake shown in Fig. 12:16 read freestream pressure within measurable accuracy. Variation from this design may be made according to the following: (1) changing the cone angle from 10 degrees to 40

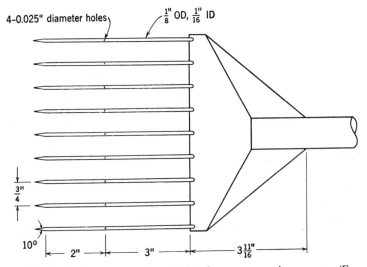

4-0.025" diameter holes $\frac{1}{8}$" OD, $\frac{1}{16}$" ID

$\frac{3"}{4}$

10°   ⟵ 2" ⟶   ⟵ 3" ⟶   ⟵ 3$\frac{11}{16}$" ⟶

FIG. 12:16.   Static-pressure rake suitable for a supersonic stream.   (From Ref. 12·6.)

degrees produced no change 16 diameters back; (2) with a 10-degree angle the static pressure is unchanged from 20 to 40 diameters back; (3) at least 16 diameters are needed from orifices to supports.

These conclusions were from high-Mach-number tests.

Special multiple manometers are needed in many supersonic wind tunnels where the changes in static pressure from point to point may be very small. In many cases the most suitable reference is vacuum, and fluids employed must not boil off, nor usually should they be heavy. This double requirement is met through the use of silicone oils such as DC 200 (specific gravity 0.90) whose viscosity and boiling point are extremely low. With the vacuum reference a guillotine cut-off should be provided so that an excessively long run (36 ft) will not be needed when the tunnel is stopped. The fluid should be placed under vacuum conditions at least a day before use to draw off entrained air.

Sometimes mercury is useful as a fluid, and it too has a low boiling point. Normally, of course, it is most satisfactory with high-pressure set-ups. Some engineers hang a glass shield in front of their multiple manometers to avoid personnel injury due to a tube break during a high-pressure run. With any manometer a trough along the bottom may save considerable clean-up time by catching the fluid when a break occurs. Figure 12:17 gives the variation of the specific gravity of mercury and tetrabrome ethane with temperature.

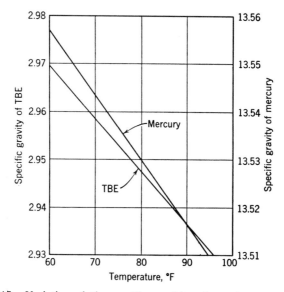

FIG. 12:17. Variation of the specific gravities of tetrabrome ethane and mercury with temperature.

The question whether condensation shocks are or are not occurring in a supersonic tunnel is difficult to answer unless rather more than usual apparatus is available. In the event that it is possible to vary the inlet stagnation temperature (by heating the storage tank or by varying the amount of cooling) a series of runs can be made during which the static pressure can be measured at some point in the test section. If no condensation shocks are occurring, the static head at the point should remain constant as long as the inlet stagnation pressure is held constant. When the inlet temperature reaches a low enough value that condensation takes place, there will be a rise in static pressure. A far simpler approach is to dry the air until its dew point is below the limits given in Fig. 12:9.

12:10. Model Design. A glance at test-section dynamic pressures, which may run as high as 20,000 lb per sq ft, coupled with considerations of the effect of dust particles at high speed usually suffices to illustrate the importance of using metal for models to be tested in supersonic wind tunnels. Indeed, the metal usually employed is high-strength steel, sometimes chromium plated to reduce surface erosion.

If strength had not dictated the use of steel for models, their size probably would. The supersonic wind tunnels commercially available have test-section widths of less than 1.5 ft, and tunnels at the various schools are only a fraction of that. Thus the finest workmanship becomes necessary for supersonic models, accuracy to perhaps 0.0003 in., and design and construction capable of withstanding high loadings.

Many supersonic models do not have control surfaces adjustable by the tunnel engineer. Instead, detachable parts with permanently deflected surfaces are provided for each setting, and the inevitable error arising from errors in the "fixed" surface has to be tolerated.

In this country models are invariably mounted on stings with the internal strain-gage balance for force reading. It comes as a surprise to learn that in Europe wire balances are frequently used in supersonic tunnels.

Since a body supported by a sting is essentially in the zone of silence of the sting, no appreciable interference from the sting is obtained except on the body base pressure. This effect may be minimized by using the smallest possible sting diameter and a fairly long sting. At Mach = 1.5 a body with a boattail is unaffected by the sting if its diameter is less than 0.4 body diameter and at least 1.7 body diameters long. At the same Mach number, a body of revolution without boattailing was much more critical, needing a sting length of 5.2 body diameters and a sting diameter of 0.35 body diameter for negligible interference. The method of sting evaluation given by Perkins in Ref. 12:13 should be used as a check.

12:11. Optical Systems. The density gradients due to the flow pattern become strong enough in supersonic flow (and in transonic flow as well) so that they may be made visible through the use of fairly simple apparatus. Viewing the flow enables the Mach number to be obtained by measuring the wave angles and results in a better understanding of the entire flow action.

The cost of optical systems can range from a relatively few dollars up to several thousands, according to their size and accuracy. It seems in order to discuss the principle of operation and briefly outline one of the inexpensive types, called a schlieren system.

Consider Fig. 12:18. A source of monochromatic light at A is shielded so that only a rectangular opening emits light. A lens C is placed at its focal distance from B so that the light is bent into a parallel beam. A second lens E collects the parallel beam into an image of the first slit at F, and an inverted image appears

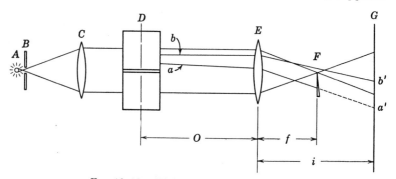

FIG. 12:18. Diagrammatic schlieren set-up.

on the screen at G.* Now, if a knife-edge is moved into the light stream at F, the image on the screen darkens uniformly. Consider the system described above to be oriented so that the parallel light beam crosses a wind-tunnel test section D. A light ray a, bent down by appropriate density gradients in the test section, cannot be brought to focus at F, being to low, and is interrupted by the knife-edge so that a dark spot occurs at a' on the screen. Ray b, bent up by an opposite type of gradient, escapes the knife-edge and appears as a light spot at b' on the screen. Thus a picture of the density gradients appears on the screen and may be interpreted macroscopically. Sometimes intensity charts can be correlated with numerical values of the density gradients.

In more elaborate set-ups mirrors are used instead of lenses. Turning the slit and knife-edge vertical shows up gradients along the flow rather than perpendicular to it.

With each set of schlieren photographs presented, it is invaluable to present a schlieren photograph of the test section with no

* For an image the same size as the object, $i = 2f$.

air flowing through it. This identifies the inevitable scratches and glass imperfections and may save the reader hours of puzzlement.

Another method, useful in the higher-speed range where good flow is indicated by the lack of large density changes in the air,

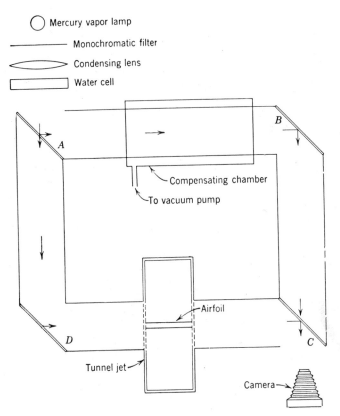

○ Mercury vapor lamp

—————— Monochromatic filter

⬦ Condensing lens

▭ Water cell

Compensating chamber

To vacuum pump

Airfoil

Tunnel jet

Camera

Fig. 12:19. Diagrammatic set-up for striae system.

is called the "striae" system and makes use of an apparatus called the "interferometer." This was developed by the Germans during World War II. The arrangement is as follows:

Monochromatic light (see Fig. 12:19) from a mercury-vapor lamp is separated at A by a half-silvered mirror. Part of the light continues around a free-air space, and part passes across a two-dimensional model in a test section. The two light beams are brought together again by the half-silvered mirror at C. The minute differences in the two paths produce striae at the viewing lens of the camera, and any changes in density due to the air-density changes over the model appear as deformations of the even striae field.

12:12. Tunnel Operation. The operation of the intermittent and continuous tunnels differs somewhat, and we will consider them separately, noting, however, that with both types considerable preliminary procedure must be finished before the run starts.

The intermittent tunnels must be pumped up or down to be ready for use, and in addition, since their running times are quite limited, assumed pressure readings may be preset and held with guillotine cut-offs to reduce fluid stabilization times to a minimum. In both the indraft and blowdown types operation is pretty well beyond the control of the operator, and the only control is a start-stop button which opens the valves and lets the air flow through the tunnel. There is usually a noise like a great sneeze as the valve is activated and the shock moves on down the tunnel. Then, a steady rumbling goes on as flow is maintained. In the blowdown tunnel without a diffuser the noise level may be quite objectionable.

The continuous-pressure-type tunnel is a little different from the above. Normally the first step after an extended shutdown is to charge the tunnel with dry air from the dry-air storage tank. This is accomplished by pumping down the tunnel and bleeding in some dry air until the pressure is up to atmospheric. Then the cycle is repeated until the required dryness is obtained. Four cycles suffice in a typical case. The adjustable nozzle is set for a low Mach number * to reduce starting power and shock buffet, and the compressor is then brought up to speed. During the time that the nozzle is subsonic, large amounts of detached flow are visible in the schlieren until finally the normal shock passes and the test section is at supersonic speed. Customarily the compressor rpm is then increased a small amount to assure that the normal shock is where it belongs and that adequate power is being provided for a higher Mach number. The nozzle is then moved to the proper position for the desired supersonic Mach number, and the test proceeds through the model angle-of-attack range.

---

* If the model is excessively large and ample power is available, it is possible to start the tunnel at a higher-than-test Mach number and avoid choking, later throttling back to a lower speed by a nozzle change.

The passage of the shock is particularly spectacular when the moisture content of the tunnel air is high. Under this condition, as the shock passes the model disappears in dense white fog. Then, as the tunnel warms up, the fog gradually thins. Measurements should be withheld until clear air exists, as until this time the Mach number is not defined. In many tunnels this may take from 5 to 30 minutes. Previous drying of the air is of course greatly preferable.

The continuous tunnels may well need to have their compressor speeds brought up to their maximum values very gradually on account of heating and expansion loads and shaft sag. On the larger installations sag becomes so serious that the compressors are *never* shut off, being very slowly turned by auxiliary motors night and day after once being installed, the cold turning being protection against permanent set in shafts under high bending loads. Warm-up times for compressors may run as high as a half hour.

In addition to special procedure for the equipment, fixed-nozzle supersonic tunnels suffer from requiring much greater power to start than to run. This springs from the fact that, the higher the Mach number at which a normal shock occurs, the greater the head loss through it, and, as the shock initially passes down the test section before being swallowed by the diffuser, it is at a maximum Mach number and maximum loss. The tunnel engineer may use the short period overload rating of the power supply during this starting cycle, reduce the tunnel static pressure to a minimum before starting, or provide extra energy in the form of an air storage tank and an ejector in the diffuser.* The low-pressure procedure has the advantage of reducing the loads on the model while the normal shock passes over it, a period of great anxiety. During this time the model bucks and rears as though being clubbed with a mighty hammer, and many models indeed have succumbed. Here the intermittent tunnels have a slight advantage since their starting time is a fraction of a second, and model hammering is over in the minimum time. A second starting procedure employed at one tunnel uses a test section by-pass during compressor warm-up so that the tunnel crew can work on the model while the compressor warms up, and

---

* Some experiments seem to indicate that about 20 per cent of the tunnel air should be continuously applied as an ejector.

when the time comes to pass supersonic air over the model it can be done in a split second by cutting out the by-pass.

Steady running of a supersonic tunnel requires less monitoring than is needed by the lower-Mach-number types. Unless the static pressure changes over wide limits the boundary layer in the test section will not be affected enough to result in a serious change of Mach number. As the runs proceed the angle changes of the model produce very small and usually negligible changes in test-section static pressure. These may immediately be brought back up to value either by bleeding in a little more dry air from the dry-air reservoir or by increasing compressor output directly by increasing propeller pitch or rpm. At all times the test-section static pressure or the pitot pressure should be monitored in order to have q for the data reduction. Possibly the most accurate is to read the pitot pressure at a reference point and use a reference curve (obtained with a static pipe) to find the test-section Mach number.

As the model drag is increased the normal shock will move upstream towards the model, and its progress should be monitored during testing, either by watching a multiple manometer connected to wall pressure orifices, or visually with the high-intensity lights turned on. A word of caution: At low supersonic Mach numbers the sting support may make the normal shock balloon upstream and wall pressures are then not a good indicator of the shock's location. Orifices on the sting may be used to keep informed of the whereabouts of the shock.

The combination of pressure rise required and typical compressor capacity usually results in a drop of Reynolds number with increased Mach number rather than a steady increase as shown by subsonic tunnels. See Fig. 12:20.

All pressure tunnels leak to some degree, and a surprisingly small amount of wet air leaking in can raise the dew point of the tunnel air to an objectionable figure. Accordingly the tunnel operator keeps close watch of the dew point on a dew-point meter, and of the pressure to assure constant Reynolds number. (The Mach number is held constant by the nozzle-area ratio.) When the dew point reaches undesirable values the tunnel may be recharged while running, or it may be shut down for recharging. The obvious procedure of pumping up the tunnel so that leaks are only outward may not be compatible with the desired Reynolds number range, or with the cooling capacity of the tunnel coolers for the extra tunnel power thereby incurred.

The problem of maintenance of a laminar-type boundary layer rather than a turbulent one is just as important supersonically as it is subsonically. In supersonic flow the possibility of laminar

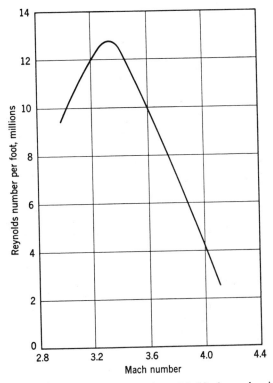

Fig. 12:20.   Variation of Reynolds number with Mach number in one wind tunnel.

flow is greatly helped by the falling pressure gradients possible over the entire surface of a wing, by a cooling effect of the metal surfaces on the boundary layer, and under some conditions by lower flight Reynolds numbers gained through high altitudes.

There are no simple limits for the existence of laminar flow, but if the engineer feels that he wants to be assured of transition there are several approaches he can easily take. The usual No. 280 Carborundum sprinkled on a 0.5-in. strip of freshly lacquered surface along the leading edge of a wing or around the nose of a missile body will produce transition as it will in subsonic flow. In the pressure tunnels the Reynolds number can be progressively increased by increasing the static pressure until the drag *coefficient* completes its rise.

Model size limitations apply to supersonic as well as nearsonic tests according to the Mach number-area relation (eq. 11:3), but there is one marked difference: in supersonic tunnels, the faster one goes, the *larger* the permissible model size. This comes about from the bow wave reflection, as follows:

To a first approximation the bow wave from a body in a supersonic stream is at the Mach angle * to the flow, and to the

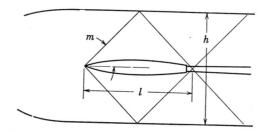

Fig. 12:21.   The test rhombus.   Trailing-edge wave not shown.

same approximation the bow wave reflects from the tunnel floor and ceiling at the same angle incidence as the original wave. Thus if the model length l is greater than h cot m, where h = the tunnel height, the reflection will strike the model and confuse the simulation of free-air conditions. In fact, since pressure impulses can carry forward in the subsonic wake, and since the bow wave is actually steeper than the Mach angle, it is good practice to keep l below $0.7h$ cot m. Thus (see Fig. 12:21) there is a "test rhombus" length which limits the permissible model length, and the rhombus grows with increasing Mach number. Suggested limits are in Fig. 12:22.

The supersonic tunnel will also choke if the model frontal area is excessively large. For the choked condition, sonic speed occurs at the model maximum cross-sectional area, and the front of the model never gets into supersonic flow. An exception to the choking effect may arise if the tunnel in question has a variable nozzle and plenty of power. Then the tunnel may be started at

* The Mach angle is an angle whose sine is $1/M$, where M is the Mach number.

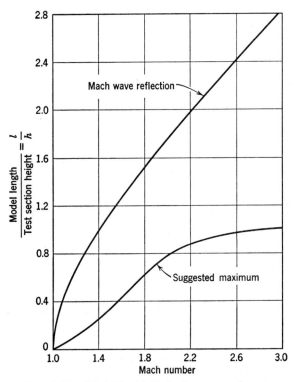

FIG. 12:22. Model-length limits for supersonic tests.

a high Mach number which is reduced after the normal shock has passed the model.

12:13. Work-up of the Data. Data obtained at supersonic speeds are reduced to coefficient form in the same manner as low-speed data by dividing forces by a characteristic area and the dynamic pressure, and moments by the above plus a characteristic length. However, $(\rho/2)V^2$ is rarely used for the dynamic pressure since its alternative form $(\gamma/2)pM^2$ is more convenient. Thus:

$$C_L = \frac{\text{Lift}}{(\gamma/2)pM^2S}$$

$$C_D = \frac{\text{Drag}}{(\gamma/2)pM^2S}$$

$$C_m = \frac{\text{Moment}}{(\gamma/2)pM^2Sc}$$

Presentation of the data may follow the usual lift, drag, and moment coefficient plots or, as the occasion demands, may include variations of the coefficients with Mach number.

12:14. Wall Corrections. Since pressure impulses cannot travel laterally across a supersonic stream, the walls of the tunnel (provided the model is not too big) have *no* effect on the models, and neither boundary corrections nor blocking exist. However, the customary non-uniformities in the tunnel have more significance in a supersonic stream than in a subsonic one since each change of pressure signifies a change in Mach number *and* in direction of flow. The net result can be a very complex situation indeed. A study of the effects of reasonably sized variations in a supersonic stream upon a model immersed in that stream has been made by Ludloff and Friedman and reported in Ref. 12:25. The basic buoyancy correction remains the most important, but other effects can become important too. If use of a tunnel having large gradients is contemplated, Ref. 12:25 should be consulted.

12:15. Hypersonic Wind Tunnels. The difficulties of supersonic-wind-tunnel testing are multiplied many fold when the Mach number reaches the hypersonic (greater than 5.0) range. The most pronounced change is that due to the pressure and temperature change with Mach number, which results in liquefaction of unheated air. The power requirements, large for supersonic

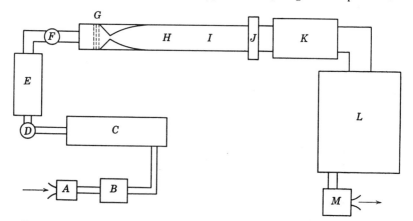

Fig. 12:23. Diagrammatic layout of hypersonic wind tunnel A, compressor. B, oil cleaner and drier. C, high-pressure tank. D, high-pressure cut-off valve. E, heater. F, test section cut-off valve. G, turbulence screens. H, nozzle and test section. I, variable diffuser. J, low-pressure cut-off. K, cooler. L, low-pressure storage tank. M, vacuum pump.

tunnels, become so enormous in the hypersonic range that so far no large tunnels have been built.

The set-up employed at the NACA 11-in. hypersonic tunnel is shown in Fig. 12:23. It consists of a high-pressure (50 atmospheres) tank which bleeds through a pressure regulator and a heater into the test section. The flow, controlled by quick-acting

Official Photograph, National Advisory Committee for Aeronautics.

FIG. 12:24. Photograph of hypersonic wind tunnel illustrating the tiny throat and great area ratio necessary in this Mach number range.

gate valves,* then proceeds through a variable diffuser into a vacuum tank roughly thirty times larger than the high-pressure tank.

The new problems associated with a test set-up such as this embrace (1) those due to air liquefaction; (2) those due to tunnel expansions associated with the high temperature needed to avoid trouble (1) above; (3) those due to operating an optical viewing system with extremely low air densities; and (4) those associated with measuring extremely low pressures. The problem list is indeed imposing.

* The gate valves shown in Fig. 12:23 are necessary even with a continuous-type tunnel in order to seal off the jet during model changes so that a minimum of wet air can enter.

Air cooled sufficiently under proper conditions of pressure and temperature will of course liquefy. Such conditions are found in a hypersonic wind tunnel where small droplets of already con-

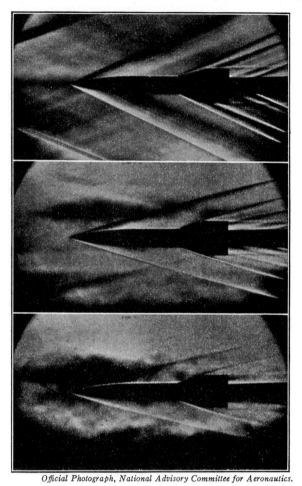

Official Photograph, National Advisory Committee for Aeronautics.

FIG. 12:25.   Schlieren photographs made over a wide range of Mach numbers. Reading from top to bottom, the test Mach numbers are 2.8, 4.6, and 6.3.

densed moisture (even though the air is previously dried to a dew point of $-50°$ F or more) furnish nuclei upon which the air itself may condense quite readily. The result of such condensation is a flow condition unlike nature, and unsuited for research that is to be extrapolated to free-air conditions.

Checking for the presence of liquefaction in a hypersonic wind tunnel parallels looking for moisture condensation in a supersonic wind tunnel: the inlet temperature is raised until no further change in some significant parameter takes place. In this instance, we may use measured shock angles for a thin (11-degree) wedge. The shock angle increases when liquefaction takes place, and the consequent air heating reduces the Mach number of the flow. In Fig. 12:26 (from Ref. 12:11) a temperature of above

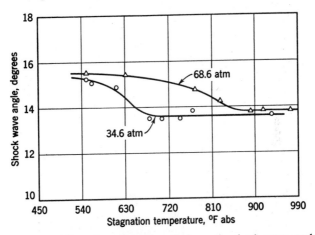

FIG. 12:26. The effect of condensation of air on the shock wave made by a 5.5-degree semi-angle wedge at $M = 6.8$. (From Ref. 12:11.)

500° K would assure a flow free of condensation. It might be added that liquefaction produces no loss in pitot pressure * since the temperature rise through the shock wave of the total-head tube permits a return to fully evaporated conditions.

Since the static conditions at which liquefaction will take place are known, it is of interest to discover whether they differ from the rapidly changing conditions in the tunnel stream. Apparently, there is some time lag in the process, but from a tunnel standpoint the most important factor is that a small amount of condensation does not seem to produce serious errors in the data. Wegener (Ref. 12:8) demonstrated that failing to reach the stagnation temperature indicated for static liquefaction by 180° F produced

* *Pitot pressure* could be called measured total head, it being the total head measured behind the normal shock caused by the instrument itself. At hypersonic speeds pitot pressures reduce to *a few per cent* of the freestream total head due to the great shock loss.

no serious error in data taken in the NOL hypersonic tunnels. This was under somewhat specific conditions.

Avoiding condensation by heating the air (to around 800° F or more) is probably a must for hypersonic operation, but heating brings with it a number of annoying consequences. First the customary copper tube heaters scale badly, and it may be necessary to get rather expensive stainless-steel ones. Second, as the high temperature reaches the test section the walls expand and, changing the area ratio of the nozzle, also change the Mach number of the stream during the run. The windows (some 2 in. thick) * are distorted with a resulting reduction in the accuracy of the schlieren system, already badly overstrained by the low density of the air. A solution of the nozzle distortion is to measure the area ratio carefully before and immediately after a run and assume that the Mach number has varied linearly during the run, or (better) to bleed a little hot air through the test section before the run to get all parts up to maximum temperature. Since such temperatures reduce the strength of most materials, it is in order to heat the air without heating the primary structure. One way to do this is to feed the high-pressure air into the center of the settling chamber through a pipe that is itself a heating element. In this way the air is heated, but a minimum of heat is given to the tunnel walls.

It is of interest in connection with the problem of great dryness to note that copper has water-holding and -releasing qualities and cannot be used in the hypersonic tunnel proper. Nickel steel is a satisfactory substitute.

Also, paints, constructional materials, and tubing that is not hurt by high temperatures must be used. The previously mentioned schlieren troubles are compounded by heated currents of air in the room around the test section. Heating to 1300° F seems satisfactory at least to $M = 8.0$, but above a Mach number of about 10, gases other than air are needed. In this temperature range, values of the coefficient of viscosity according to Fig. 12:27 are better than the linear approximation.

When planning a heater, incidentally, the designer makes use of its storage capacity rather than assuming that it must heat the mass per second that travels down the tunnel. Monitoring the downstream end of the heater will assure that the proper stagnation temperature is being held.

---

* Others have found ¾-in. glass satisfactory to 2700 psi and 1500° F.

The low density and temperature of the airstream leads to low Reynolds numbers, and thus to very thick boundary layers in the test section.* A pitot pressure survey (from Ref. 12:8) made in the NOL 12-cm tunnel is shown in Fig. 12:28. This thick boundary layer confuses the proper nozzle design, since a correction for it is unknown. We are therefore justified in taking

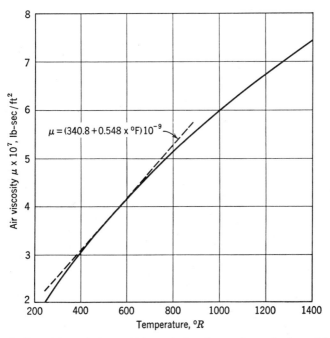

Fig. 12:27. Values of the coefficient of viscosity as determined empirically and the linear approximation which is quite satisfactory in the atmospheric temperature range.

less care in hypersonic nozzle design than when more exact methods are available. In some installations simple divergent cones are used for the supersonic nozzle while in the subsonic part everything from flats to quarter circles have been used as profiles. The lack of rigor becomes more reasonable when one considers the enormous contraction ratio that is realized when the nozzle is only a few hundredths of an inch wide, and the wide effects of varying boundary layers in the throat.

* The thickness due to Reynolds number is greatly augmented by the aerodynamic heating. Boundary layers at Mach $M = 7.0$ are approximately ten times as thick as those at the same Reynolds number but at $M = 1.0$.

To get a rough idea of the correction needed for the boundary layer it may be noted that 0.5 degree between floor and ceiling proved too little in one tunnel. A nozzle that expanded horizontally and then vertically in order to "even" out the expansion has been tried and found very poor.

On the brighter side, the very low density of the air in the test section results in corresponding low values of dynamic pressure

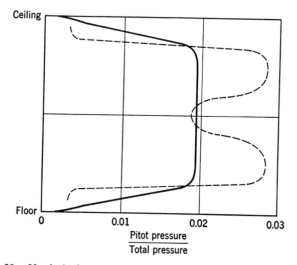

FIG. 12:28. Vertical pitot pressure surveys taken at $RN = 838,000$ (solid line) and 365,000 (dotted line) in a hypersonic wind tunnel.

so that little difficulty is experienced in obtaining adequate strength of models, rakes, etc.

Actually the low test Reynolds numbers (of around 1,000,000) are not so bad from a practical standpoint since aircraft or missiles using Mach numbers of around 7.0 will undoubtedly fly pretty high. At 120,000 ft, for instance, a 4-ft wing chord at Mach 7.0 corresponds to a Reynolds number of 1,000,000.

Table 12:2 lists a number of hypersonic tunnels now being operated in this country. No information is available about similar tunnels in other countries.

In closing this very brief outline of hypersonic tunnels it is in order to note that the determination of the Mach number in a hypersonic tunnel is not the relatively simple procedure it is in the supersonic tunnel. The use of wave angles and shock theory

TABLE 12:2

HYPERSONIC WIND TUNNELS

Tunnel	Location	$M_{max.}$	$T_{stag.,}$ °F	Dew Point, °F	$P_{stag.,}$ psi	Run Time	Test Section	Remarks
AEDC GDF 40 in.	Tullahoma, Tenn.	10.0	2000	−60	....	Continuous	40 x 40 in.	100,000 hp
APL	Silver Spring, Md.	10–16	1240	..	....	Blowdown 30 sec.	....	Nitrogen or helium
Caltech 5 in.	Pasadena, Cal.	10	900	−55	....	Continuous	5 x 5 in.	
MIT	Cambridge, Mass.	7.0	550	..	3000	Blowdown	2.25 x 2.75 in.	
NACA 11 in.	Langley Field, Va.	6.9	700	−50	750	Blowdown-indraft	11 in. x 11 in.	
NACA 10 x 14 in.	Moffett Field, Cal.	12.0	....	..	....	....	10 x 14 in.	
NOL 12 cm	White Oaks, Md.	8.25	1010	−60	3000	Blowdown	4.7 x 4.7 in.	
NOL 40 cm.	White Oaks, Md.	6.5	70	..	15	Indraft	15.7 x 15.7 in.	
Princeton 4 x 4	Princeton, N. J.	15	80	..	1500	Blowdown	4 x 4 in.	Uses helium

charts suffers from the previously mentioned inexactitudes of computing the boundary-layer displacement thickness and adding it to the wedge or cone angle, and of measuring the wave angles themselves to sufficient accuracy. The tunnel area ratio is confused by the thick boundary layer, and the relations between pitot total pressure and static pressure are complicated by the change in γ associated with the great changes in temperature. However, if proper allowance for these defections is made, the Mach numbers computed by all methods can be made to agree.

12:16. Superaerodynamics. We have so far classed wind tunnels as subsonic, nearsonic, transonic, supersonic, and hypersonic, thus basing the classification on the test section Mach number. Allied with this classification is the Reynolds number attainable in a given tunnel. Another parameter of testing similitude is the ratio of the mean free path of the molecules l to a significant dimension L of the test model. "Superaerodynamics" is the name given to the region of conditions when this parameter is not negligible. Since the mean free path is about 0.000002 in. at ordinary room conditions, 1 in. at 50-mile altitude, and 1 mile at 100-mile altitude, it is seen that above about 90 miles the conditions of superaerodynamics are encountered. As this region is used by rockets of the V-2 and Viking type it is of interest to the aerodynamicist and hence to the tunnel engineer as regards drag and stability data. The possibility of sustentation by lifting surfaces in this region is remote since the dynamic pressure at $M = 20$ and 90 miles altitude is only about 0.04 lb per sq ft, far less than the weight of the surface itself.

To get a feel for the superaerodynamic conditions, we note that at a constant Mach number the Reynolds number of a body decreases as the pressure decreases and the mean free path becomes greater. In the low-altitude range of normal flight the ratio of body size to mean free path yields values of perhaps a hundred million. Under this flow condition it is well known that the velocity at the body surface is zero. As the altitude increases, the mean free path increases until it approaches the body length. The molecules then slip along the surface so that surface velocity is not zero. This regime, lasting from $l = L/100$ to $l = L$ is called the "slip flow" regime of superaerodynamics. Still further reduction in pressure results in a "free molecule" regime in which collisions between molecules are negligible compared to collisions between air molecules and the body in question. Free molecule flow covers the values of $l = 10L$ to ∞, the region between slip flow and free molecule flow being a mixed condition. The above regions are subject to the low-Reynolds-number assumption that the boundary-layer thickness δ is of about the same order as the body length.

Tsien in Refs. 12:28 and 12:29 has discussed both the mechanics of rarefied gases and the difficulties of wind-tunnel work using them. Some of his interesting conclusions are reviewed below.

As we have seen in discussing supersonic wind tunnels very great losses are associated with the return to subsonic velocity, and indeed these losses are so large that the viscous losses can almost be ignored when computing the power requirements for the system. In the nozzle, also, the compressibility effects are first taken care of and then small allowance is added for the boundary layer.

To illustrate the difference for the superaerodynamic case, Tsien computed that the boundary layer would fill the test section when the mean free path was 5.6 per cent of the boundary-layer thickness. Since such a relation is possible in superaerodynamics it is easy to see that extraordinary allowances for the boundary layer will have to be made if a predetermined Mach number is to be realized. In fact, in an example given by Tsien, a nozzle with an area ratio that would yield $M = 4.0$ with no boundary layer actually developed $M = 2.5$ at a pressure of 0.0948 in. H_2O and 1.30 at a pressure of 0.0368 in. H_2O.

To compare the shock and friction losses, and from the previously quoted very low dynamic pressure under superaerodynamic conditions one may conclude that only supersonic superaerodynamics will interest the tunnel engineer, calculations based on laminar skin friction and the pressure drop through a normal shock at $M = 2.0$, tunnel length/breadth $= 2.0$, and a mean free path of 5.6 per cent of the boundary-layer thickness show the friction loss to be 63 per cent of the shock loss. Clearly viscosity cannot be neglected here.

Measurement difficulties are even more formidable in superaerodynamics than in hypersonics. Tsien mentions that the change in temperature of a wire heated by constant energy may be a means of measuring pressure; that a schlieren probably will not have sufficient sensitivity; and that excessive shock-wave thickness prevents the use of the Rayleigh formula for determining a supersonic Mach number. It would appear that a hot-wire anemometer will remain a useful tool.

As a final summary of superaerodynamic-wind-tunnel difficulties Tsien points out that it appears that for the model flow to be similar to full-scale flow one must duplicate surface material, Reynolds number, Mach number, and freestream temperature and radiation conditions. Experience will determine which if any of these criteria may be relaxed.

PROBLEMS

12:1. A model having a maximum frontal area of 4 sq in. is to be tested in a supersonic tunnel having a test section of 1.0 sq ft. What is the minimum permissible starting Mach number?

12:2. If the above test section is 12 in. high, and $M = 2.0$, what is the suggested maximum model length?

12:3. A Mach $= 2.6$ indraft tunnel takes in standard air. What will be the temperature, pressure, density, dynamic pressure, and Reynolds number per foot in the test section?

12:4. A Mach $= 2.6$ blowdown tunnel runs off a 200 psi (gage) tank at $59°$ F. Calculate the temperature, pressure, density, dynamic pressure, and Reynolds number per foot in the test section. Assume isentropic flow.

12:5. Calculate the Reynolds number per foot and the dynamic pressure for the tunnel of problem 12:3 if $M = 5.0$.

12:6. A $M = 10.0$ wind tunnel has a square test section with a 1.0 sq ft area. Calculate the height of the throat, neglecting any allowance for the boundary layer.

REFERENCES

12:1. Alan Pope, *Aerodynamics of Supersonic Flight*, Pitman and Co., 1951.

12:2. A. E. Puckett, Supersonic Nozzle Design, *JAM*, December, 1946.

12:3. C. L. Dailey and F. C. Wood, *Computation Curves for Compressible Fluid Problems*, John Wiley & Sons, New York, 1949.

12:4. J. V. Becker, Results of Recent Hypersonic and Unsteady Flow Research at the Langley Aeronautical Laboratory, *Physics Review*, Vol. 76, 2nd Series, No. 6, September, 1949.

12:5. C. H. McLellan, T. W. Williams, and M. H. Bertram, Investigation of a Two-step Nozzle in the Langley 11-In. Hypersonic Tunnel, NACA *TN* 2171, 1950.

12:6. C. H. McLellan, T. W. Williams, and I. E. Beckwith, Investigation of the Flow through a Single-Stage Two-Dimensional Nozzle in the Langley 11-In. Hypersonic Tunnel, NACA *TN* 2223, 1950.

12:7. C. H. McLellan, Exploratory Wind-Tunnel Investigation of Wings and Bodies at $M = 6.9$, *JAS*, October, 1951.

12:8. Peter P. Wegener, Summary of Recent Experimental Investigations in the NOL Hyperballistic Wind Tunnel, *JAS*, October, 1951.

12:9. Warren C. Burgess, Jr., and Ferris L. Seashore, Criterions for Condensation-Free Flow in Supersonic Wind Tunnels, *TN* 2518, 1951.

12:10. F. A. Friswold, R. D. Lewis, and R. C. Wheeler, Jr., An Improved Continuous Indicating Dew Point Meter, *TN* 1215, 1947.

12:11. H. Guyford Stever and Kenneth C. Rathbun, Theoretical and Experimental Investigation of Condensation in Hypersonic Wind Tunnels, *TN*, 2559, 1951.

12:12. E. P. Neumann and F. Lustwerk, Supersonic Diffusers for Wind Tunnels, *JAM*, Vol. 16, No. 2, June, 1949, pp. 195–202.

12:13. Edward W. Perkins, Experimental Investigation of the Effects of Support Interference on the Drag of Bodies of Revolution at a Mach Number of 1.5, *TN* 2292, 1951.

12:14. R. W. Fish and K. Parnham, Focusing Schlieren Systems, RME *TN* IAP 999.

12:15. A. Kantrowitz and R. L. Trimpi, A Sharp Focussing Schlieren System, *JAS*, May, 1950.

12:16. Satish Dhawan and Anatol Roshko, A Flexible Nozzle for a Small Supersonic Wind Tunnel, *JAS*, April, 1951.

12:17. John C. Evvard and DeMarquis D. Wyatt, Investigation of a Variable Mach Number Supersonic Tunnel with Nonintersecting Characteristics, NACA *RM* E8J13.

12:18. C. Frederick Hansen and George J. Nothwang, Condensations of Air in Supersonic Wind Tunnels and Its Effect on Flow about Models, *TN* 2690, 1952.

12:19. W. F. Lindsey and W. L. Chewn, The Development and Performance of Two Small Tunnels Capable of Intermittent Operation at Mach Numbers between 0.4 and 4.0, *TN* 2189, 1950.

12:20. R. Betchov, Nonlinear Theory of a Hot-Wire Anemometer, *TM* 1346, 1952.

12:21. R. Betchov and W. Welling, Some Experiences Regarding the Nonlinearity of Hot Wires, *TM* 1223, 1952.

12:22. Allen Puckett, Design and Operation of a 12-In. Supersonic Wind Tunnel, *IAS* Preprint 160, 1948.

12:23. R. T. Patterson, The Design and Performance of an Air Drying System for a Supersonic Wind Tunnel, *DTMB Aero Rept.* 80, 1951.

12:24. Frank C. Dehler, *Silica Gel, Its Use as a Dehydrating Agent*, The Davison Chemical Corporation, Baltimore, Md.

12:25. H. F. Ludloff and M. B. Friedman, Corrections for Lift, Drag, and Moment of an Airfoil in a Supersonic Tunnel Having a Given Static Pressure Gradient, *TN* 2849, 1952.

12:26. H. Julian Allen, The Asymmetric Adjustable Supersonic Nozzle for Wind-Tunnel Application, *TN* 2919, 1953.

12:27. Clarence A. Syvertson and Raymond C. Savin, The Design of Variable Mach Number Asymmetric Supersonic Nozzles by Two Procedures Employing Inclined and Curved Sonic Lines, *TN* 2922, 1953.

12:28. H. S. Tsien, Superaerodynamics, Mechanics of Rarefied Gases, *JAS*, December, 1946.

12:29. H. S. Tsien, Wind Tunnel Testing Problems in Superaerodynamics, *JAS*, October, 1948.

ANSWERS TO PROBLEMS

2:10. 30,000 hp.

2:14. $q = 100$ lb per sq ft; $p = 2100$ lb per sq ft.

3:1. 5.2% water, sp. gr. = 0.796 at 26° C.

3:2. ——

3:3. $TF = 1.64$.

3:4. $ER_f = 2.68$.

3:7. 1.21.

5:1. ——

5:2. $e = 0.962$.

5:3. $dC_D/dC_L = 0.0893$ and 0.0876.

5:4. 0.218, $CP = 0.468$.

5:5. ——

5:6. 0.998.

6:1. 0.191 lb.

6:2. 0.141 lb.

6:3. 0.0039.

6:4. $\Delta\alpha_i = 0.91°$.

6:5. ——

6:6. (a) −0.134, (b) +0.134, (c) 0.085, (d) 0.160, (e) 0.110.

6:7. $V' = 102.4$.

11:1. 0.900.

11:2. 3700, 3697, 3395 lb per sq ft.

11:3. 0.70.

11:4. $M_u = 0.8962$.

12:1. 1.194.

12:2. 9.4 in.

12:3. 220° R, 106.8 lb per sq ft, 0.00028 slug per cu ft, 505 lb per sq ft, 2,800,000 per ft.

12:4. 220° R, 1549 lb per sq ft, 0.0041 slug per cu ft, 7330 lb per sq ft, 41,800,000 per ft.

12:5. 70 lb per sq ft.

12:6. 0.0224 in.

APPENDIX

Numerical Constants and Conversion of Units

1. Speed of Sound, V_c.

$$V_c = 49.1\sqrt{°R} = 65.9\sqrt{°K}, \text{ ft/sec.}$$
$$°R = °\text{Fahrenheit} + 459.6.$$
$$°K = °\text{Centigrade} + 273.0.$$

2. Standard Sea-Level Conditions.

Pressure p_0 = 14.7 lb/sq in. = 29.92 in. Hg.
Density ρ_0 = 0.002378 slug/cu ft.
Viscosity μ_0 = 3.73 × 10^{-7}.
Speed of sound V_{c0} = 762 mph.
Temperature t_0 = 59° F.

3. Standard Atmosphere.

Temperature decreases 1° F for each 280 ft of altitude until 35,332 ft. Above 35,332 ft temperature is constant at −67° F.

Pressure decreases according to

$$p = (1.910 - 0.01315Z)^{5.256}$$

up to 35,332 ft, and according to

$$p = 6.94e^{(1.69 - 0.0478Z)}$$

above 35,332 ft. In both formulas above, Z is in thousands of feet, and p is in inches of mercury. Density decreases according to

$$\rho = \rho_0 \frac{p}{p_0} \frac{T_0}{T}$$

Viscosity decreases * according to

$$\mu = (358.3 + 0.987 \times °C)10^{-9}$$

or

$$\mu = (340.8 + 0.548 \times °F)10^{-9}$$

4. Conversion Factors

A. LENGTH

Multiply	by	to obtain
Inches	2.54	centimeters
Feet	30.48	centimeters
	0.3048	meters
Miles	5280	feet
	1.609	kilometers
	0.8684	nautical miles

* These values are within 1 per cent from −20° F to +180° F.   See Fig. 12:26.

Multiply	by	to obtain
Centimeters	0.3937	inches
Meters	39.37	inches
	3.281	feet
	1.094	yards
Kilometers	3281	feet
	0.6214	miles
	1094	yards

B. AREA

Multiply	by	to obtain
Square inches	6.452	square centimeters
Square feet	929.0	square centimeters
	144	square inches
Square centimeters	0.1550	square inches
Square meters	10.76	square feet

C. VOLUME

Multiply	by	to obtain
Cubic feet	1728	cubic inches
	0.02832	cubic meters
	7.4805	U. S. gallons
U. S. gallons, dry	1.164	U. S. gallons, liquid
	0.83267	imperial gallons
Imperial gallons	0.03531	cubic feet
	4.546	liters
	277.4	cubic inches
U. S. gallons, liquid	0.1337	cubic feet
	231	cubic inches
	4	U. S. quarts
Cubic meters	35.31	cubic feet
	1.308	cubic yards
	264.2	U. S. gallons

D. VELOCITY

Multiply	by	to obtain
Feet/minute	0.01667	feet/second
	0.01136	miles/hour
Feet/second	1.097	kilometers/hour
	0.5921	knots
	0.6818	miles/hour
Miles/hour	0.447	meters/second
	1.467	feet/second
	1.609	kilometers/hour
	0.8684	knots
Kilometers/hour	0.9113	feet/second
	0.5396	knots
	0.6214	miles/hour
	0.2778	meters/second
Meters/second	3.281	feet/second
	3.6	kilometers/hour
	2.237	miles/hour

E. Weight

Multiply	by	to obtain
Ounces (avoirdupois)	0.0625	pounds (avoirdupois)
Pounds (avoirdupois)	16.0	ounces (avoirdupois)
Tons (short)	2000	pounds (avoirdupois)
	907.18	kilograms
	0.90718	tons (metric)
Tons (long)	2240	pounds (avoirdupois)
	1016	kilograms
Tons (metric)	1000	kilograms
	2205	pounds
	1.1025	tons (short)
Kilograms	2.2046	pounds

F. Pressure

Pounds/square inch	0.06804	atmospheres
	2.036	inches of mercury
	703.1	kilograms/square meter
Pounds/square foot	0.19242	inches of water
	4.883	kilograms/square meter
Atmospheres	76.0	centimeters of mercury
	29.92	inches of mercury
	1.033	kilograms/square centimeters
	14.7	pounds/square inch
	2116	pounds/square foot
Inches of water	5.198	pounds/square foot
	25.38	kilograms/square meter
	0.07349	inches of mercury
Kilograms/square meter	0.2048	pounds/square foot

G. Temperature

To change Fahrenheit to Centigrade
1. Add 40.
2. Multiply by ⅝
3. Subtract 40.

To change Centigrade to Fahrenheit
1. Add 40.
2. Multiply by ⅑.
3. Subtract 40.

To change Fahrenheit to Rankine, add 459.6.
To change Centigrade to Kelvin, add 273.0.

Index